EMBRACING THE DRAGON

One Mother's Relentless Search for Healing and Hope

Lindsay Beane

Lindsay

Published by Zerflin, Baltimore, MD in 2020.
First published by Opus Self Publishing, Washington D.C. in 2019.
Edition: 2.
Version: Lindsay Beane Embracing the Dragon 5.25x8 Book 3.
Modified: February 24, 2020 11:36 PM.
Printed by Black Classic Press, Baltimore, MD.

Words by Lindsay Beane
Cover design by Gareth Bentall of Opus Publishing

Made in the United States of America

LINDSAY BEANE

Zerflin.com
Books@Zerflin.com
931.305.0883

LindsayBeane.com
@LindsayBeane1

This book is dedicated to the late Dr. Robert Fulford (1905-1997) who, without making it seem like a big deal, gave me the key.

And to my sweet Russell – may you never stop making me laugh!

Impossible is just a big word thrown around by small men who find it easier to live in the world they've been given than to explore the power they have to change it. Impossible is not a fact. It's an opinion. Impossible is not a declaration. It's a dare. Impossible is potential. Impossible is temporary. Impossible is nothing.

Muhammad Ali (1942-2016)

Table of Contents

Foreword

When I was an infant, I was diagnosed with cystic fibrosis (CF). It's considered a fatal disease, and the prognosis was hard on both my parents and my older brother. I am a fairly private person, but I felt comfortable with my mother's sharing some of our experience, because this book is not really about me. This book is about my disease and my mother's experience with health care professionals of all kinds. The reason I agreed to write this Foreword is to tell you, the readers of the book, that I am indeed healthy. I have a cough sometimes, typically when I'm not on antibiotics. But I am generally very hale and have never had to limit myself because of my CF. To this day, no one I meet even knows I have CF unless I tell them. I take it for granted that I will live a long life and will continue to be a reasonably healthy person, and I'm indebted to my mother for my positive outlook on CF.

I don't think anyone should base important health decisions on the anecdotal experiences of someone else, no matter how convincing. What I hope is that you will allow yourself the possibility of being convinced by the evidence shared in this book. I hope you will consider new healing options, even ones you may have previously dismissed. My mother and I both hope that hearing our story will be helpful to people in a similar situation. If it is, then I'm glad the story has been shared.

Russell

Fall 2019

Preface

I first met Lindsay and her son Russell as acupuncture clients over twelve years ago. Since that time, I have been fortunate to know them as friends as well. *Embracing the Dragon* is a brave telling of the journey Lindsay and her son Russell began at his birth. Lindsay shares the trials and blessings of this very personal path. It is a story of motherhood, healing, and transformation.

When Lindsay's youngest child, Russell, was born with spina bifida, she was quickly initiated into a medical system that took on a life of its own. With little information, immediate urgency, and fierce love, Lindsay eventually found her own voice as an advocate for her son. After months of trusting the professionals without question, and witnessing both the positive and negative impact these interventions were having on her son, she became dismayed at the lack of compassion shown for her son and for her as his mother. When Russell was diagnosed with cystic fibrosis, Lindsay could no longer be a passive witness in his care and treatment. This was a turning point in both of their lives, as Lindsay became proactive in the health, healing, and wellness of her son.

In the face of a medical system that is too often callous and fear-based, we forget that we can say no. As consumers, as patients, it is so important to actively question the diagnosis, the treatment, and the endless testing. We can be empowered in the process of asking questions, but it takes courage. Lindsay's telling of her experiences highlights the importance of being an active participant in the process of our own health and recovery from dis-ease, and the importance of learning to advocate for ourselves within the standard western medical system and to seek alternative treatments.

Russell's care and wellness was paramount to Lindsay as she sought out practitioners and treatments outside of the western medical paradigm. She found acupuncturists, homeopaths, nutritionists, and other alternative practitioners to support her son in his health and vitality. Through her descriptions of the various modalities, she gives us a glimpse into diverse systems of medicine that honor the entirety of a person, systems that have faith in the body's ability to heal and to flourish.

Modern medicine has its place and, as Lindsay so eloquently reminds us, it also has its limits. When we educate ourselves, we are better equipped to navigate our path towards health and healing. Personal responsibility is critical, our voice is critical, and our intuition is critical. When we yield our power of inquiry and of decision-making to others, even those who are "professionals," we do a disservice to the integrity of our own health. More and more conventional physicians have come to understand the impact that our thoughts and emotions have on the health of the body, and the truth that we cannot disengage from our own process and expect to become well. A truly holistic view summons all of who we are, and allows us to be intimately engaged in the journey before us—a journey toward healing, health, and wellness.

This story of catharsis is a guide to alternative medicine options that Lindsay learned through trial by fire. She shares the science and some brief history of five holistic modalities that support healing and wholeness. Healing is a call for us to return back to ourselves. The body is the vessel we live through, and healing is always possible. We need not be limited to symptomatic treatment, but instead we can tend to the body's core. In addition to supporting Russell's journey back to health, Lindsay found her own path toward healing. It is said in Chinese medicine that in order to treat the child, you must also treat the parent... roots and branches.

Lindsay has demonstrated her courage and spirit of inquiry into the unknown. Her journey has been a gift to Russell, and this book is a beautiful sharing with other parents who are navigating the health concerns of their own children.

It has been an honor to be a part of this inspirational journey to reclaim hope.

Melanie Birch, L.Ac., M.Ac.

EMBRACING THE DRAGON

Chapter 1

Our Journey Begins

Everything will be okay in the end. If it's not okay, it's not the end.

John Lennon (1940-1980)

MY SECOND CHILD RUSSELL WAS BORN ON A HOT SUMMER'S EVE in August of 1992, the day after I turned 40. This birth was *much* easier than the three days of labor and Pitocin-epidural cocktail required to coax my first baby out of the womb. Labor lasted a mere 18 hours and, unlike his brother's birth, which involved a transfer to the hospital, Russell was born at the midwife-staffed Maternity Center in Bethesda, Maryland, without any medical intervention.

Despite the shorter labor, I was still relieved that I had once again survived the ordeal of childbirth. I've never been able to fathom stories of an easy birth during which a woman labors calmly (and quietly!) to a backdrop of candlelight and soft music. I was quite sure that I would die of exertion both times, and if I had been armed, I would have happily put a gun to my husband's head during "transition," the phase in which labor turns the no-backing-down-now corner-from-hell. The concept of relaxing between contractions was also lost on me, but I tried anyway with each labor, not wanting to be judged a weakling by Richard, my strong and stoic husband. For years afterwards, whenever I heard a woman describing a quick and easy labor, I suspected that the re-telling was an extravagant distortion of what really happened—no doubt a simple case of jealousy on my part.

As soon as Russell exited the birth canal, he started yelling at the top of his lungs. His big-barreled chest made him look robust and masculine, even as a newborn. As he lay on my belly continuing his noisy complaint, our midwife, Michelle, helped my husband cut the umbilical cord. Michelle jokingly chastised me to quiet the baby down as she began stitching up my torn perineum.

"Go ahead and yell, babe!" I told him instead, flinching at her needle sticks. "You've got a great set of lungs and your mum's a little fatigued at the moment."

Once she had finished her repair, Michelle weighed and measured the baby. "Nine and a half pounds, Lindsay!" she announced gleefully.

Oh my God, I thought, *no wonder* I'm so tired! I struggled to sit up while my husband stuffed pillows behind my back to give me support. Once I was upright, Michelle placed my little newborn into my arms, and I offered him the greatest pacifier known to man (or rather babies). He eagerly latched onto my nipple and quieted down.

A short time later, my friend Roberta ushered our older son into the room. Four-year-old Gus hesitated at the doorway and then bounded across the room, handing me a lovely bouquet of lavender roses before reaching up to touch his new baby brother. His eyes grew wide as he marveled at the baby's tiny fingers and toes, his little boy's naked awe bringing tears to my eyes.

For one merciful moment, my husband, our two sons, and I remained blissfully unaware of what was to come—ordeals caused by as yet undiagnosed medical conditions that would threaten this new baby's life. Despite the August heat, we snuggled in close on a big double bed in the Maternity Center's little house, surrounded by loving friends. We were flooded with relief and great joy.

Our joy was short-lived. An hour or so after the birth, the midwife shared her concern that our baby's respiratory rate was faster than it should have been. She wasn't terribly alarmed, she said, adding that this sometimes happens with newborns. But once a second hour had passed and his breathing still hadn't normalized, she told us that we would need to take him to the hospital until his breathing calmed down rather than take him straight home. Richard and I thought we had avoided any hospitalization with this second birth, and we were very disappointed. The midwife assured us that I would be allowed to spend the night with my baby, and that it was likely that he would be discharged first thing in the morning. When Richard and I told Gus that he would have to go back with our friend Roberta and spend another night at her house, he became very upset that he wasn't going home with his parents and new baby brother.

As soon as Richard and I arrived at the hospital, the baby was whisked out of my arms and placed in an incubator. I stood to the side and watched anxiously as a nurse fastened a hard plastic identification bracelet around his tiny, soft, wrinkled wrist and then put one on my wrist to match. She wheeled him away without even telling us where she was taking him. I was shocked at the complete loss of control over my own child and upset by the nurse's technically-oriented focus—themes that would become all too familiar in the days ahead. After several hours of waiting, we were reunited. Once the baby and I were settled into a private room, Richard went home to get some sleep.

Russell's incubator was stationed at the foot of my twin-sized bed, which felt very far away. I finally asked the night nurse if I could bring him into my bed instead.

"I'm sure that would be okay," she said, helping me.

Even with Russell back in my arms, that first night was grueling. I barely slept. One of my son's alarms kept going off over and over, scaring me repeatedly that he was in danger. Each time, a nurse would pop in, glance briefly at the monitor, push a reset button (which also stopped the noise), and then disappear. With the shift change in the early morning, the new nurse explained that if my newborn even wiggled his toe where the oxygen monitoring device was attached, an alarm would sound. I wondered grumpily why someone didn't explain this to me *hours* ago, affording me at least a little undisturbed sleep.

Later that morning, the hospital's chief of neonatology came by during rounds to assess Russell's breathing and oxygen level. He pronounced Russell "fully recovered and fit to go home," rattling off a list of possible causes for his respiratory rate to have been temporarily elevated. I found it curious that the doctor wasn't compelled to pinpoint the precise cause in my baby's case, but I took what appeared to be his casual attitude as a sure sign that there was nothing more to worry about. As the doctor gave Russell's medical chart a final rundown, he hesitated and said, "Before you go, let's take a quick look at the marking on your baby's back." This quick look changed our whole world.

The midwife had been confident that the translucent patch of skin on Russell's lower back (about the size of a nickel) indicated *occulta* or "false" spina bifida—at most a minor and typically asymptomatic defect of the spinal column. I had almost forgotten it was there. As the doctor gently turned Russell over onto his stomach, I anticipated more reassurance that my newborn was just fine. Much to my amazement (I think I was too shocked to feel anything else), the doctor took one look at Russell's back, blurted out "Oh, my God!" and rushed from the room. I stood rooted in place with my jaw hanging open, looking back and forth between Russell and the doorway, trying to make sense of the doctor's reaction and sudden disappearance. I tried to stem the panic I felt brewing and had a sudden urge to grab Russell and rush from the room myself. Something was obviously very wrong, and part of me didn't want to hang around to find out what it was.

Within minutes, the doctor reappeared with a nurse and announced tersely, "I've arranged for your son to be emergency transported to Children's National Medical Center in D.C."

"Emergency *whaat*...?" I stammered.

He explained that the patch on my son's back was most certainly not false but, instead, true spina bifida, and that this patch of semi-skin was open to the world, inviting all sorts of deadly germs to invade my son's spinal fluid. The growing panic in my gut quickly transformed into dread.

He turned to the nurse and ordered her to put a sterile bandage over the patch. "Now!" he said crossly. The nurse recoiled at his tone and quickly did as she was told.

"This should have been done when he was admitted last night!" the doctor muttered angrily under his breath as he hurried from the room a second time. As soon as the nurse left, I phoned my husband.

I figured that, between the two of us, we would be able to somehow make this nightmare go away.

"Wow," he said when I described the doctor dashing out of the room, "that's weird. I'll be there as quickly as I can!" I heard the growing concern in his voice.

Richard's uncharacteristic anxiety didn't help my own frenetic state. I hung up the phone and stared out the window, tense with worry. I knew very little about spina bifida, except that when the defect is severe, it can mean a lifetime confined to a wheelchair. I lay back down on the bed with my newborn cradled in my arms and began to cry, my body still aching from childbirth, wondering what awful challenges lay ahead.

Minutes later, an emergency transport team swooped into the room with a huge portable incubator on wheels. As soon as I got up from the bed, one of them snatched Russell from my arms. They paid no attention to my running list of questions as I stood there in a nightgown still wet with postpartum bloodstains and colostrum. In fact, the transport team completely ignored me as they briskly hooked the baby up to EKG monitors and an oxygen mask, with him protesting loudly all the while. I stood out of their way in shock as they methodically went about their business. When one of them started to close the lid of the incubator, I suddenly had a flashback of the heart-wrenching scene in the movie *ET*, in which scientists strap a dying alien into an incubator despite the pleadings of the little boy who has come to know and love the extraterrestrial.

This was no movie, though. Complete strangers had strapped my screaming newborn into a coffin-like box and were getting ready to take him away. At the last minute, I instinctively thrust my arm in the way of the closing lid and asserted, "Wait a minute! I need to give my baby a quick hug and reassure him that I'll be with him the whole time!"

I reached in and tried to console Russell. I wanted so badly to pick him up and rescue him, but I could tell that I was no longer in charge. When I stepped back, they closed the lid and started to wheel the incubator out of the room.

"Wait!" I shouted. "Where are you taking him? I don't have my clothes on! My husband hasn't arrived yet! Where are you going? *Wait for me!*" The team stopped and looked back at me with blank expressions.

"We're taking him to Children's Hospital," one of them said.

"I know, I know," I said impatiently, looking around the room for my sweat pants. "Just give me a second; I need to throw some clothes on."

One of the women reached over and gently touched my arm. "I'm sorry but you can't go with him in the ambulance," she said.

"You can't be serious!" I protested, "No, no. I'm staying with him!"

"There are liability constraints…" she started, her mouth firm.

I didn't hear the rest of her sentence; it was becoming clear that I would not be able to ride in the ambulance with my newborn. I was dumbfounded. How was it possible that I, the baby's mother, had so little say in anything?

In desperation, I mustered up as much of a pretense of authority as I could and declared to the room-at-large, "Okay, well, you are not to do anything to my son until I get there and am able to give my explicit permission." Someone on the transport team seemed to mutter an assurance in response.

Just as the team was leaving the room, my husband arrived. Richard glanced down at Russell inside the closed incubator and then looked up at me with a shocked expression on his face. When I complained that they wouldn't let us ride in the ambulance, he too asked them why not. But, in the end, the team was not to be dissuaded, and they made a hasty exit. I whipped off my nightgown and fumbled into my clothes, paying no attention as to who might be around to see me undress.

"We have to hurry," I said to my husband. "We need to follow the ambulance to make sure that it doesn't go too fast. Or get into an accident!" If I had been in anything close to a rational state, I would have realized that we could hardly prevent such things from happening, but I was in the throes of total anxiety.

Richard and I hustled our way down the hallway to the elevator and out the hospital's front door. We didn't even stop to check out of the hospital. My mind whirled with questions. What did "emergency transport" mean? Was this really an emergency? Would the ambulance speed through the streets with sirens blaring? Was the damned incubator secured to the ambulance floor? Would someone at least sit in the back with him? What if he needed something—how could anyone even hear his cries through that awful plastic box?

Once outside, we quickly realized that the ambulance had already left. We hurried to our car in the hospital parking lot. Richard drove well above the speed limit as we made the harrowing 30-minute trip from the local hospital in Maryland to Children's National Medical

Center (hereafter referred to as "Children's Hospital") located in the heart of Washington, D.C. I counted on my husband's impeccable knowledge of the layout of the nation's capital, his hometown, to get us to the hospital ahead of the ambulance—a ludicrous notion, but I was impatient to regain control over my newborn. I wanted him back in my arms where he belonged.

By the time we arrived at the hospital in D.C., Russell had long since been admitted and was already receiving a barrage of x-rays, blood tests, and who knows what else. Nobody had even bothered to ask our permission.[1] Richard and I suddenly found ourselves in a medical environment that was completely foreign, and neither of us had any idea how things were supposed to work. Here our baby was less than 24 hours old and all these tests were happening without even consulting us? It was beginning to feel as if he had been kidnapped! I was furious.

The registrar calmly instructed my husband to fill out a pile of forms as I sat next to him, fuming. After the paperwork was finished, we were told to take the elevator up to the hospital's Neonatal Intensive Care Unit [NICU]. Once there, someone handed us blue paper gowns to put on over our clothes and instructed us to scrub our hands thoroughly at the sink located just outside the unit. Only then were we allowed to enter the NICU. Once inside, we were confronted with a sea of incubators containing tiny premature and sickly-looking babies hooked up to all sorts of tubes and noisy monitors. Nurses in white uniforms bustled about the babies like bees in a hive. None of them seemed to notice that we were there, let alone lost. We finally located Russell in his assigned crib, but before I even had a chance to touch him, Dr. Catherine Shaer,[2] the pediatrician in charge of the hospital's Spina Bifida Clinic, took us away for consultation.

From the moment we met, I was struck by Dr. Shaer's tact and the bright pink blouse and flowered skirt that peeked out from beneath her standard-issue white coat. She exuded both compassion and confidence. Once the three of us were seated in a private consultation room, Dr. Shaer started off with a description of the possible consequences of our baby's birth defect. Listening to her long list of serious disabilities that might afflict our son was terrifying. Spina bifida is a general term, she explained, that is used to describe defects of the "neural tube" that occur *in utero* at the very beginning of a pregnancy. Around four weeks following conception, an evolving embryo's neural plate wraps around to meet itself and close. The top part of this plate (now more like a tube) becomes the brain, and the rest of it forms the spinal cord. If spina bifida occurs, this all-important transformation is interrupted—the plate does not fully close and the neural tube does not take its proper form. In other words, some portion of the brain, spinal cord, and *meninges* (protective tissue surrounding the brain and spinal cord) may not fully develop.[3]

Richard and I hung in there with the doctor, trying to take in as much as we could in our first medical tutorial. Occasionally, one of us asked Dr. Shaer to repeat herself or clarify the meaning of a four-syllable term. Our induction into the realm of medical science was intense. I felt as if I'd suddenly been transported into an advanced classroom at medical school, without any underpinning of basic anatomy or biology. The scant Latin I'd gleaned in high school wasn't doing me much good either.

Even in my emotional state, I tried to size the doctor up professionally. I liked her, and I reassured myself that we were in one of the best pediatric hospitals in the country. If anyone could help our son, I decided, she could. I soon found myself turning over all authority to Dr. Shaer (and, by proxy, to the other doctors as well) to make whatever medical decisions needed to be made.

Because the doctors didn't yet know precisely what they were dealing with in terms of Russell's exact defect, Dr. Shaer felt compelled to cover the full landscape of potential outcomes with us. The most severe and, unfortunately, also the most common form of spina bifida, she explained, is called *myelomeningocele*. This defect causes nerves from the spinal cord to bulge through an opening in the spinal column, forming a visible and sometimes open sac on the baby's back. Even the sophisticated corrective surgery now performed on fetuses and newborns does not fully reverse the impact of this severe form of spina bifida, which can include compression of the spinal cord, paralysis, cognitive impairment, and hydrocephalus or fluid on the brain that commonly requires the implantation of a shunt into the brain cavity to drain off the excess fluid.

Although Russell had no visible sign of the severe *myelomeningocele* defect, Dr. Shaer cautioned that the seriousness of his condition was still unclear. Even when spina bifida is mild, nerves that spread out from the spinal cord at the site of the defect are often unable to properly communicate with the organs or appendages that they connect to. This lack of communication can then compromise the functioning of these organs and the child's control over his appendages.

According to the Spina Bifida Association, "Spina bifida is the most common permanently disabling birth defect in the United States, occurring in one out of every 800 births."[4] While babies can still die from the defect, today most survive and live well into adulthood. There are some 160,000 Americans currently living with spina bifida. Typical symptoms include hydrocephalus, compromised mobility, compromised bladder and bowel control, and learning disabilities. Fortunately, ongoing advances in corrective surgery make it increasingly possible to reduce both the occurrence and severity of these outcomes.

Though the cause of spina bifida has not yet been pinpointed, the working list of suspects includes the mother's nutritional deficiencies, either parent's exposure to radiation or other environmental toxins (such as Agent Orange), unknown viruses, and genetics. Recent studies have shown that a mother's prenatal supplementation with folic acid (vitamin B9 or pteroylglutamic acid) can reduce the risk of spina bifida by as much as 50%.

Russell's particular defect was mild when compared with the severest form. There was no bulging mass of nerves outside his body, and Dr. Shaer told us that the neurologist suspected that his defect would prove to be a relatively simple "tethering" of his spinal cord. She described this tethering as the presence of extraneous (abnormal) fatty tissue that connected his filum, or the "tail" of his spinal cord, through the opening between his vertebrae to the skin on his lower back, where it then manifested as a small patch of translucent tissue instead of normal skin.[5]

In some babies with a mild defect, this tissue does not completely cover the opening on the back, allowing extremely dangerous bacteria, such as bacteria that cause meningitis, to enter directly into the spinal fluid (the neonatologist's fear). Dr. Shaer reassured us that the tissue on Russell's back was not open and that he was not at risk of infection. Because the doctors didn't yet have a clear picture of our baby's particular defect, however, they couldn't be sure what its impact would be. She cautioned that the multitude of problems that accompany severe spina bifida can sometimes occur even when the defect appears to be mild, as in Russell's case. Thus, the same threats of crippling, lack of bladder and bowel control, the need for shunts to his brain, and even the risk of death would have to be ruled out.

"Do you have any questions?" Dr. Shaer asked, once she had finished.

I could barely breathe and felt totally inadequate. I didn't want to ask a question and risk having her repeat her description of the possible future problems. The scenarios that she had laid out for us were shocking, and all I wanted to do was leave the consultation room as quickly as possible. I could barely understand what she was telling us, let alone contribute anything intelligent to my son's situation. Despite the obvious threat to my baby's well-being, I didn't want to learn anything more. I chose instead to trust that these good and smart doctors would somehow save Russell and protect him from anything too terrible. Richard and I thanked Dr. Shaer and limped back to our son's side as we tried to fathom our family's abrupt departure from life as we knew it.

At 9½ pounds and just over 21 inches long, Russell filled out his NICU incubator in a way that was totally incongruous with the one to two pound preemies all around him. I kept thinking: He doesn't belong here! He's not ill! There's nothing wrong with him! I yearned to take my newborn home and tenderly place him in our king-sized bed, where he would be safe, swaddled in the love and protection of his mother, father, and big brother. It was painful to realize that I could not in fact protect him from the onslaught of medical procedures. I felt utterly powerless.

Unfortunately, the hospital had no accommodations for parents with babies in the NICU. After spending the day at Russell's side, we decided to drive home that evening to be with our older son, Gus, rather than check into a nearby motel. At the tender age of four, Gus was being shuttled back and forth between playmates' homes, not understanding what was going on and receiving scant reassurance from his mother or father when he needed it badly. I was painfully aware that I was neglecting him but felt helpless to do more. Every time I thought about Russell, I began to cry, and I didn't want to start crying in the middle of trying to reassure Gus. But it seemed to me that everything was *not* going to be okay, and I couldn't find the strength to fake it, even for my young son's sake.

For three days, Richard and I commuted back and forth between the farm in Maryland where we lived and the hospital in D.C. I was exhausted and should have been in bed resting, given the recent childbirth. Richard miraculously found an adult-sized wheelchair on our second day in the pediatric hospital, and from then on, he wheeled me around so that I wouldn't have to walk. Each day, I fretted about leaving Gus behind and, each night, I worried about leaving Russell all alone in the NICU.

On top of everything else, a year earlier we had been given a puppy who had since grown into a beautiful, close to 100-pound, out-of-control Malamute who could not stand to be cooped up. Because Max could not be trusted around any of the farm animals, we had to keep him locked in the house each day while we went to the hospital in D.C. Returning home exhausted from the city each evening, we were confronted with shredded pillows, torn screen doors, scratched table legs, and other remnants of his mania during our absence. Half the time, we didn't even clean up Max's mess before putting Gus to bed and then falling into bed ourselves. We had to let most everything and everyone go during this time. All that mattered was our precious little second born, who could end up paralyzed or crippled, or might even die.

Every morning before being allowed into the NICU, we had to cover our street clothes with sterile gowns and scrub our hands and forearms with a disposable plastic brush and soap for three full minutes. The huge metal sink just outside the unit had floor pedals to operate the water faucets and timers to make sure we didn't shirk our cleansing duty. Richard and I were both very eager to see Russell each morning, and three minutes of scrubbing felt like an eternity. We were usually alone while washing our hands at the sink, and we took that opportunity to curse the hospital colorfully for its obsession with hand hygiene. The cursing often led to morbid giggling and a rare flicker of relief in what was turning into an unrelenting ordeal.

There were many sources of stress in those early days. Getting into a healthy breastfeeding pattern with Russell, for example, was nearly impossible. I was only allowed to nurse him according to the hospital's feeding schedule. I notified the NICU nurses on day one that I was breastfeeding my baby and would be at the hospital each day for the whole day. I shared my concern that he might reject the breast with only intermittent nursing and was pleasantly surprised when the nurses told me that Children's Hospital had a strong pro-breastfeeding policy. They even directed me to a pumping "lounge" where I could prepare bottles of my own milk, which Russell would then be given while I wasn't there during the night.

I immediately went to find the lounge. Having had no prior experience with breast pumps, I casually settled into position with the suction end on my nipple and flicked the switch on a massive electric pump. *Ouch!* It was less than 24 hours since Russell's birth and, despite the strong and rather painful sucking of the pump, all I had to offer were a few trickles of colostrum. It was immediately clear that pumping before my milk came in would be pointless, and I decided to scrap the idea. Besides, I naïvely counted on being able to take my baby home very soon, where I could nurse him whenever he wanted.

In the meantime, I implored the nurses not to give Russell a bottle of formula or a pacifier. Getting milk out of the big hole in artificial nipples is easier for a baby than sucking milk through the tiny milk duct openings in a mother's nipple. It had taken me weeks to get Gus into a healthy nursing habit after he was born, and I became so discouraged that I had almost given up nursing altogether. This time, I was doubly concerned that Russell might reject the breast, given our separation at night and the hospital's inflexible feeding schedule during the day. The nurses reassured me that he would be fine.

When I arrived back at the NICU the next morning, I found

Russell sucking happily on a pacifier. I took him out of his incubator to nurse him but found with alarm that he didn't want to nurse. It dawned on me that, in addition to the pacifier, he had been given a morning bottle of formula, despite my explicit requests to the contrary. I wanted to complain, but could not justify Russell's lying there crying hour after hour in my absence just because of some purist desire I had to breastfeed. Of course, as a newborn, he needed to be fed every few hours and couldn't have gone without for an entire night. I also saw that the nurses were constantly on the run, tending babies who were a good deal needier than my son was, and that they were doing their best to keep these babies (and their anxious mothers) calm. Because I wasn't nursing around-the-clock or pumping, once my milk supply came in on day two of the NICU stay, I spent the evening at home leaning over a huge bowl filled with hot water in a futile attempt to ease the pain caused by overfull breasts. They were calling out for my baby and relief!

During Russell's three days in the NICU, we were obliged to consult with doctor after doctor: neurosurgeons, orthopedists, urologists, geneticists, and pediatricians. These interactions were often intimidating, especially if the doctor was cold and clinical, which many of them were. Children's Hospital is a teaching and research hospital, so every doctor on the ward was followed around by a little entourage of five or six nameless medical residents in white coats.[6] At times, they would all close in around Russell's incubator, completely blocking our view. None of the doctors spoke (or cooed) to Russell or even said his name out loud; nor did they express any sympathy to us as his parents, despite the agony that was plainly visible on our faces.

It felt as if Richard and I were part of some bizarre public audience rather than at the private side of our own baby who was perhaps desperately ill.

The neurology team in charge of Russell's care came every day to examine him, performing a battery of tests each time. I found one test that was routinely performed to be particularly odious. A doctor would take a long wooden Q-tip, break it in half to create a nice sharp point, and poke Russell in his testicles. Each time, it made him startle and then wail. I suspected that his strong reaction was a positive sign, but I found it unbearable to witness his distress over and over. When I finally got up the nerve to question one of the doctors about the need to repeat this particular exam so often, I was told that it tested Russell's nerve function and was a necessary part of his reflex inventory. When I quipped that the test seemed a bit medieval in nature, I was given a quick look of surprise and then ignored.

When the doctors ignored me, I became incensed. I started to wonder how and when I had been demoted from protective and loving mother to the role of passive observer who was excluded from the inner circle of the all-powerful doctors. Their casual brush-offs of my lame attempts to protect my son did not help. Each time I was ignored, bile slowly crept up my throat, threatening to escape in fits of anger. I often had to deliberately clamp my mouth shut. Years before, my father had taught me how to swear like a sailor but, in this hospital setting where the doctors were trying to help my son, as tempting as it would have been to let hot words fly, I made every attempt to mind my manners.

I didn't tolerate the hospital's medical residents well either. When they came with their preceptor (supervising staff physician), most of them remained respectfully quiet, merely observing examinations and listening to our answers if the preceptor asked us any questions. But when they returned later without their preceptor to ask their own questions and conduct their own examinations, I found their insensitivity toward Russell—and their arrogant rebuffs when I expressed concern about their poking and prodding—intolerable. I quickly grew tired of the residents repeating the same examinations that a more senior doctor had only just completed, and I hated it when they spoke to each other too quietly to overhear or in technical language that was impossible to follow.

It didn't take long before my initial inclination to give over power to the doctors was replaced by strong urges to protect my son from the doctors. I stopped having reservations about my ability to follow along in medical conversations and started asking questions, even if that meant interrupting doctors' examinations. I yearned to understand everything that was going on. I wanted to be informed about my son's condition and be an active participant in discussions about his treatment. I didn't have a medical background, but I was no dummy and had unlimited motivation to learn anything I needed to in order to overcome this threat to Russell's well-being. But the residents were clearly not focused on us as Russell's parents and seemed to resent any questions we posed as an intrusion and extraneous interruption of their exam. The whole experience was supremely frustrating.

By the third day, I was compelled to openly object. Two female residents, who to my middle-aged eyes looked just barely beyond adolescence, came to examine Russell. Along with the requisite Q-tip torture, there were other pokes and prods that made him miserable. Unfortunately for these young women, their visit was a tipping point and they fell victim to a volcano of pent-up frustration.

I stopped them in the middle of their examination. “My son is very tired from all of your poking and prodding,” I said. “Please—I think it’s time for him to rest.”

They looked at me oddly for a moment without saying anything and then returned to their task. I could not believe they were ignoring my request to stop. Sharpening my claws, I deliberately goaded them: “Perhaps you can tell me why it’s so necessary for you students to repeat every single examination that the doctors have already completed?”

My calling them “students” did not go over well—admittedly, just the response that the exhausted misbehaving mother in me was hoping for. One of them puffed up like a cobra preparing to spit: “I am a full-fledged medical doctor, thank-you-very-much, and the *chief* of pediatric residents at Children’s Hospital,” she said, jutting her chin out like a petulant child.

Like the resident, I too was spitting mad, and this interaction could have deteriorated even further. But as the older adult in the mix, I felt compelled to curb my tongue as best as I could. “How nice,” I retorted sarcastically. “Now please leave.” Amazingly, they did.

I knew that I was overreacting; the residents were simply following orders and learning their trade. My behavior called to mind my mother’s rudeness that she had dished out to undeserving shopkeepers and waitresses throughout my childhood—something that had especially mortified me as a teenager. I didn’t want to be disrespectful, but it was very irksome to watch the residents repeat every exam and every test, not because it was medically necessary for my son, but because it was necessary for them as part of their learning process. Each time I saw someone reach for a long wooden Q-tip, my muscles tensed, and I would catch myself start to make a low growl. The instinct to protect my baby was slowly overshadowing any sense of propriety.

After the two residents left, I made a silent vow to Russell to stay by his side in the NICU around the clock, no matter how many more days we were there and regardless of the limited visiting hours. As if someone had heard me and feared that I might make good on my pledge, within minutes, the geneticist came to interview us and announced that we would be allowed to take Russell home as soon as she was through asking us a few questions. Unfortunately, however, just as she was wrapping up, she received a phone call and informed us that instead of being able to leave right away, we would have to wait for the urologist to examine Russell and give his permission to leave as well. We waited two hours for the urologist to arrive. The moment he completed his exam and told us we could leave, my husband and I eagerly grabbed our baby and fled. Our three very long days in the NICU were finally over.

Late in the afternoon on the day that Russell was discharged, Dr. William Chadduck, the chief of neurosurgery at the hospital, called us at home. Dr. Chadduck was an older doctor whose quiet voice and patience with my endless questions and concerns had inspired my faith in his abilities. As soon as we met, I liked and trusted him. His understated but self-assured manner suggested years of experience and lots of know-how. In the phone call, Dr. Chadduck confirmed that Russell's back was not open, which ruled out the serious risk of an infection, such as meningitis. But, he said, the tests so far had failed to give him a clear picture of our son's exact neural tube defect.

"I'm confident that there is some sort of internal involvement; I just can't tell what it is without getting an interior view. So I've ordered a screening for your baby with a Magnetic Resonance Imaging machine to help pinpoint the defect," he said.

Dr. Chadduck went on to explain that Children's Hospital shared one of these very expensive MRI machines with the veterans' hospital next door. Although most patients had to wait for months, he said that he had been able to schedule Russell's screening for Thursday, the very next day. I was relieved that we would finally learn about Russell's exact defect but, at the same time, wondered why there was enough cause to bump him ahead of an apparently long list of other patients waiting for an MRI. What was the rush?

The next morning, as we drove back into D.C. to have Russell undergo an MRI, Richard and I lamented the fact that we both knew so little about medicine. Neither of us had had much prior exposure to doctors or hospitals, and we didn't know anything about MRIs, a screening method that was nowhere near as commonplace then (in 1992) as it is now. Dr. Chadduck had also cautioned us that, if awake, babies and children were likely to flinch inside an MRI tunnel because of the machine's very loud clunking that comes at unpredictable intervals. Any movement on the part of the patient, however, will blur the picture. Thus, Russell would need to be sedated in order to remain very still while the screening took place.

After we registered at the MRI site, a technician inserted an IV into Russell's tiny arm and started the flow of the sedative. I grew increasingly anxious as I watched my baby succumb to the drug that would ensure that he remain completely still during this bizarre screening. Even though he was obviously still breathing, his artificial slumber made my three-day-old baby look uncannily dead, and it terrified me.

My husband noticed tears welling up in my eyes and said impatiently, "He's going to be fine!"

I flinched. Fine? *Fine?* It didn't take a genius to see that *nothing* was fine, and in my state of utter exhaustion coupled with hormones and my current panic, it definitely felt as if nothing would ever be *fine* again. "I'm having a little trouble bucking up," I snapped back at him.

I assume that Richard was experiencing the same parental emotions that I was, though quite possibly not as strongly, given my postnatal hormonal see-saw. He had been taught during his childhood, and especially during adolescence when his father died unexpectedly of a heart attack, to take it on the chin. He usually kept his emotions in check or at least hidden from view. I knew I needed to somehow pace myself, but I was a mess and had no idea how to take Russell's medical nightmare in stride. Both my husband and I suffered from frayed nerves, and neither of us knew how to cope with the emotional quicksand caused by our interactions with an intimidating and coldly formal medical world. Unfortunately, as scared as we were, we often picked on each other rather than finding solace in our shared worries.

After the MRI was completed and Russell began to come around, we asked the person at the front desk if we could speak with someone about our baby's test results. He told us that protocol prohibited patients (or parents) from speaking directly with the technicians involved in conducting the screening, but we kept pleading with him to please talk with someone, *anyone.* He finally got up and walked back into the screening area. A few minutes later, we were pleasantly surprised when the radiologist himself walked down the hall toward us with a big smile on his face.

"Your baby is absolutely fine," he stated firmly. "There is nothing amiss!"

I made him repeat himself at least three or four times. Each time, he smilingly repeated that Russell had no defect whatsoever. Yielding to the effects of battle fatigue and the rarity of good news, Richard and I were positively giddy on the ride home. After collecting Gus from the neighbor's house, we walked across the driveway to our cozy milk barn, broke open a bottle of champagne, and proceeded to get very drunk. We were on the phone a lot throughout the weekend with our respective mothers and siblings and the close friends that we had kept at bay during the three days that Russell was in the NICU. I felt positively victorious sharing the good news that the worst was over. Everyone was thrilled and very relieved.

Monday morning, the phone rang. I picked it up and said a cheerful "Hi!" when Dr. Chadduck identified himself. I was about to launch into a happy tirade about how relieved we were and what a great weekend we had had, when he began to speak.

"Just as I suspected," he said quietly, "Russell's MRI revealed a tethering of his spinal cord. This is something that we can correct with surgery."

He waited for me to say something in response, but I couldn't speak. I felt as if I had entered the Twilight Zone. Finally, I squeaked out, "You must be mistaken, Dr. Chadduck. We spoke with the radiologist right after the MRI on Thursday, and he told us there was nothing there. And then we came home and celebrated with champagne, and... Oh, please," I begged, "you *must* be mistaken."

"No, no," he said gently. "The radiologist was mistaken, and he was sorely misguided to even speak with you."

Dr. Chadduck said that we would need to bring our baby back to the hospital that very afternoon. After we hung up, I wandered toward the barn and wondered how on earth to break this awful news to Richard.

Back at the hospital later that afternoon, with a little guidance from Dr. Chadduck, Richard and I could easily make out the tethered cord on Russell's MRI films. I asked the doctor how the radiologist could possibly have missed what we laypeople could plainly see. He shrugged his shoulders without saying anything, but I could tell that he was sympathetic with how terribly betrayed we felt.

Dr. Chadduck went on to explain that Russell's tethered cord was considered a mild defect, as spina bifida goes, but that this did not mean that the impact was guaranteed to be negligible. His defect was located just below the waist, between Lumbars 3 and 4, potentially compromising his future ability to control his bladder and bowels as well as his ability to walk. Dr. Chadduck said that corrective would entail making a horizontal incision in Russell's lower back several inches long, cutting away a portion of two or three vertebrae in order to easily access the spinal cord, and delicate microscopic neurosurgery to snip off the unnecessary tissue. Every time he used words like "cutting" or "snipping" I shuddered.

"He'll be okay," Dr. Chadduck said quietly, looking at me intently over the top of his glasses and gently placing his warm hand on my shoulder. "We'll wait to operate until Russell reaches five weeks of age and is strong enough to endure the surgery."

"Now, go home," he said, "and love your baby." Never again would I be so eager to follow a doctor's orders.

Waiting for Russell's surgery brought little relief. It had only been a few weeks since his birth, and our lives were already consumed with doctors, diagnoses, tests, hospitals, and highly technical conversations about scary threats to our baby's well-being. Plus, we had to revise the happy declaration to our family and friends that Russell was okay and had no defect (per the radiologist's reassurance), and share with them that Russell was, in fact, *not* okay and that surgery would be required on his spinal cord. Every phone conversation was an exhausting ordeal in which Richard or I had to relive the trauma again and again. Our mothers and siblings and their spouses were all shocked by the turn of events, and everyone was crying by the end of each call. Their own misery made it very difficult for any of our relatives to comfort or reassure us.

Normal life had stopped as soon as Russell's spina bifida was discovered. I had stopped working about a month prior to his birth, and neither Richard nor I had gone back to work since the birth. Finances were tight even when we were both working. But now that no one was earning any money, the pile of unpaid bills mounted. We simply ignored them while we attended to the more important matter of our baby's life or death. We were in another time and space, often crying, barely able to articulate thoughts or questions. Some days it took effort just to breathe. We ate when we remembered to, and we often argued over the broken washing machine or some other stupid thing that didn't matter, just so we wouldn't have to vocalize our true fears. We were both a mess, but I found it exasperating to try and share the thoughts and emotions that overwhelmed me with a husband who was hell-bent on keeping his (and my) worries and emotions in check. Because of this, we were each mostly alone with our pain. Our marital partnership was not strong to begin with, but even a strong partnership would have been challenged by the emotions we felt as a result of our child's life being in danger. I was not surprised when I learned much later that three-fourths of all marriages with a special-needs child end in divorce.

Richard often found reason to be outside working on the farm during the weeks of waiting before Russell's surgery, while I nursed and cradled my baby inside our home and held on tight to Gus whenever my little boy came within arm's length. Gus was a bundle of nerves, frightened by his parents' palpable fear and the growing tension between us. It caused me great pain to admit that the four years of unfettered delight with my beloved firstborn were over. It was a loss that would dog us, especially Gus, for many years to come.

Gus's best friend, Aidan, lived next door to us on the 50-acre farm where we lived. Their close friendship and the generous open invitation that our neighbors offered Gus enabled him on most days to escape the emotional tension in our home. Aidan's parents owned the farm and, at the time that I met Richard in 1986, he was the farm's caretaker. Aidan's parents, Rob and Mary, were originally friends of Richard's, but once I moved from Boston to live with him in the milk barn that he had converted into a living space, they became my friends as well.

The farm was nothing like my family's working farm on the coast of Massachusetts, where I grew up taking care of animals that would eventually end up on someone's dinner plate. Instead, it was a *Fund For Animals* rescue site with quite an eclectic array of animals in need of permanent shelter. There was a huge herd of goats that had originally been brought over by Spanish conquistadors but were now impeding practice bombing by the U.S. military on an island off southern California. There were donkeys (also originally brought over by Europeans) culled from a herd that was overpopulating Death Valley. There were retired race horses that would otherwise have been turned into dog food, and a completely untamed mule who was a cross between a wild Mustang and a donkey. The mule's extraordinary muscle tone and high energy level reminded me more of the wild zebras I had photographed years before in East Africa than a domesticated horse. "Muley" was a handful! Richard had grown up in the city, but somehow had the instincts of a farmer and competently handled all of the animals. He finally found it necessary, however, to draw the line when Rob and Mary contemplated bringing rescue elephants into the mix!

Life on the farm with a little boy and a new baby was demanding for both of us, and the five weeks of "go home and love your baby" prescribed by Dr. Chadduck passed by quickly. The night before

Russell's surgery, I took Gus next door where he would stay with Aidan's family until the surgery was over. I then went home and attempted to prepare myself psychologically. I had never experienced surgery myself or with anyone close, and I had no idea what to expect. My fundamental response was intense fear: fear that the operation would go awry, fear of what else they might find hidden in Russell's spinal column and, ultimately, the fear that I could even lose my child.

The pre-op nurses had instructed me that Russell should not have anything to eat or drink for a full 12 hours prior to surgery. He was nursing avidly now—surely, he could nurse. No, I was told, he could not. His surgery was scheduled for 8:00 a.m., which meant he couldn't eat or drink anything beginning at 8:00 p.m. the night before. It didn't seem conceivable to me that a five-week-old baby could hold out that long. After some pleading and conferring with midwives, doctors, and surgical nurses, I finally received permission to nurse him one last time at midnight. Somehow this one feeding got him (and me) through the night. My husband and I awoke at 5:30 a.m., got dressed, and prepared a bag of clothes and baby supplies without waking Russell. At 6:00 a.m., we bundled him up and left for the hospital. Once awake in the car, he wanted badly to nurse. On a whim, sitting next to him in the backseat, I offered him my thumb, which he sucked with vigor for the hour-long ride. My thumb ended up incredibly sore, but I was relieved to be able to distract him and, given my own anxious state, grateful not to have to endure his screams the whole way there.

When we arrived at the hospital, we were asked to complete a thick folder of pre-surgical paperwork. Richard offered to hold Russell while I took care of the insurance forms since the policy was in my name, but I was reluctant to let go of my baby. So Richard filled out the forms instead. When the time came to sign them, however, I had to relent. My signature is pretty illegible anyway but, on this day, my hands were shaking so badly that it more than resembled a toddler's scrawl. We were sent to several more stations before finally landing in the pre-surgical waiting area.

While we waited for someone from surgery to come collect Russell, a young doctor that I recognized from Russell's stay in the NICU asked me to bring my baby into a small private examining cubicle at one end of the waiting area. This doctor was a very quiet young man who had previously shared with me that, after more than 10 years of school and subsequent advanced training in pediatric neurosurgery, he had decided to go into research rather than practice medicine. It puzzled me that he would choose to squirrel himself away in some laboratory after such a big investment of time and effort. The young doctor asked me to lie Russell down on the table and undo his diapers. The doctor then drew a long wooden Q-tip out of his jacket pocket and broke it in half. I looked up at him in horror. This was surely a major turning point for me. Five weeks after giving birth, the protective mother in me was finally on full alert. I couldn't believe that he wanted to do a test that would inflict pain on my baby just before surgery, and I was done allowing anyone to hurt Russell.

"What on earth are you doing?" I protested.

"Testing his reflexes," he responded.

"Oh no, you're not!" I countered.

Scooping Russell up diaper-less, I ran back into the waiting area with the doctor staring after me in confusion. I was disgusted, both at this last attempt to torture my son and at my own weakness for not stopping him—*all* of them—weeks before. Reflex inventories be damned.

After what felt like interminable waiting, the anesthesiologist finally came out of the operating room to collect Russell. Tears were streaming down my face. I did not want to let him go. I suddenly remembered how I had comforted Russell with my thumb on the drive to the hospital and suggested to the anesthesiologist that she might offer him her thumb if he didn't stop crying. It didn't even occur to me how silly this suggestion might sound to her, given the context; I simply did not want him to endure pain or cry anymore.

I was so tense I could barely speak. "Please," I whispered haltingly as I handed him over, "don't let my baby die."

She looked at me with enormous sympathy and then carried Russell back into the operating suite, the double doors closing behind them. I knew even at the time that expressing my fear out loud that my baby could die would only add to the tremendous pressure that a surgical team about to operate on a newborn presumably already feels, but it was all I could do not to try to extract some sort of blood covenant out of her to guarantee my son's safety. Giving him up like that, placing him at the mercy of a stranger's skill and non-maternal motivation, felt monstrously risky.

Richard led me to yet another waiting area with armchairs and a television, obviously designed with the ludicrous notion that parents are able to distract themselves while waiting to hear of their child's fate. We had been told that the operation would take around two hours. Richard kept opening and closing the Tony Hillerman mystery he had brought with him. I was sleep-deprived from nursing around the clock and still plagued by hormonal ups and downs. I kept having to unstick my legs from the fake leather chair and found it hard to get comfortable. I tried reading magazines, and when that didn't work, I tried watching television. Eventually, I tried to seek solace on my husband's shoulder, but nothing helped. Every minute of the wait was agonizing.

At 10:15, Dr. Chadduck finally appeared, still wearing his surgical garb. "Your baby's surgery went very well," he reassured us. "It was a simple matter of a tethered cord."

"Where is he?" I asked.

"He's still in recovery," the doctor said.

"When will you take us to him? Can we go right now?" I asked impatiently.

"He'll need to remain in the recovery area for a couple of hours, but feel free to go ahead and wait for him in his assigned room on the ward," he said.

"Huh?" I said, incredulous that I couldn't see Russell right away. I asked Dr. Chadduck again and again why I couldn't see my baby right away. My husband grew frustrated. What he and the doctor didn't understand was that I had spent all of my time and effort preparing for Russell's actual surgery—no one had bothered to prepare me for what recovery would be like. In my complete ignorance, I had counted on being reunited with him as soon as his surgery was over. That's all I wanted—to have my baby back in my arms where I could protect him from this endless parade of doctors and sharp wooden Q-tips and whatever horrendously sharp and cold metal tools the surgeon had used to cut into his body during surgery. I resented my husband's lack of understanding and started to sulk.

A nurse directed us upstairs to Russell's assigned room in the inpatient unit to wait for him. Sometime later, the same doctor who had taken Russell into the surgical suite that morning wheeled him into the room in a mobile crib. I took one look at my baby and shrank back in horror. His skin was terribly mottled, with huge red and white splotches everywhere, and he was croaking loudly like some horrible frog. For a moment, I became completely disoriented.

"Where is my son?" I demanded. "This is not my son!"

"This isn't your son?" the doctor asked in confusion, checking Russell's identification bracelet against mine.

It certainly didn't look like him! But then I realized that, of course, it was him.

"Oh my God," I cried softly. "What have they done to you?"

A nurse helped the doctor transfer Russell into a regular crib, both of them taking extreme care to keep him flat on his back. I sat down next to his crib and reached in to brush his cheek. "I'm here, little one," I said tearfully, "Mummy's here."

I didn't notice if there were other parents nearby in the same tortuous state, but there must have been. I was so focused on my baby that I noticed little else that was going on around me. Frankly, I have only a blurred memory of the rest of the day. Richard left at some point to go home to Gus, but I didn't leave Russell's side for a second, completely unaware of any urge to eat or relieve myself. Despite my devotion, I felt utterly useless as he lay there crying and crying and crying, until finally he became so hoarse that no sound came out at all.

I was forbidden to pick him up or even move him. All I could do was caress him gently on his face or arm and coo to him in between my own sobs. There was nothing that I could do to help relieve his pain. His IV carried a modicum of pain medication, but it obviously wasn't enough. When I complained to the nurses, one of them told me that not so long ago, doctors didn't give infants *any* pain medication, somehow convinced that they didn't actually feel pain.

That was before surgeons were mothers, I thought to myself, horrified at the thought of the pain that Russell would have had to endure if he had been given no pain medicine at all. The nurse checked Russell's IV and confirmed that he was getting as much medication as he was allowed to have.

Later that evening, the night nurse offered to move him from the crib into my bed, so that we both might sleep. I was grateful to finally be next to my sweet little suffering baby, skin to skin. Off and on throughout the night, I tried repeatedly to nurse Russell, thinking it would comfort him through his horrible agony. But every time he took a suck of milk, he gagged, and I worried that he was choking. I pushed the button for the nurse every 10 minutes for hours. She came running with each ensuing ring, offering words of comfort and a warm smile. Each time, I apologized for disturbing her again, for my ignorance about what to do, for my total ineptitude. I am quite certain that I was blessed with an angel disguised as a nurse that night. Not once did she complain or shirk her commitment to my son and me. She probably saved my life, I was such a mess of nerves.

After several more failed attempts to nurse Russell, I remembered my thumb. He took it readily. We spent the rest of the night lying next to each other, him sucking hard on my right thumb, all the while gripping my left thumb tightly in his tiny clenched fist. We both slept in fits and starts. When I awoke in the morning, I discovered that both of my thumbs were visibly bruised. I giggled at the image of him gripping my thumbs all night long and was impressed by his strength. I was also reassured that he must have at least known I was there. Later that morning, Russell was finally able to nurse without gagging. Nursing stimulated his bowels, however, which caused him more pain. His first post-surgical stool reminded me of a bird's—dark green and stark white in color. It struck me as very odd and, when I asked for her opinion, the nurse said she also thought it was quite unusual. Indeed, it was a sign of what was to come, if any of us had known what to look for.

On the second day following surgery, we both turned a corner—Russell from his intolerable pain and me from my constant panic—and I finally started to take in our surroundings. I became acutely aware that a young child in the room next to us had been crying incessantly for hours. I called the nurses' station.

"He never has any visitors," said one of the nurses, "but comforting him doesn't do any good. Besides, we're seriously short-staffed."

"I'm sorry." she added apologetically.

I believed that she was genuinely sorry, but I was shocked at the inhumanity of the situation. Whether or not holding this child would have stopped his constant crying, I couldn't help but believe that it would alleviate some of his misery. For a brief moment, I was sorely tempted to rock him myself while Russell slept, but I knew that I would be crossing a line.

My brother, Geoff, came down from his home in Boston to stay with Richard and Gus for a few days following Russell's surgery. His show of support was meaningful for all of us, but especially for Gus, as Geoff and Gus had always been very close. The three of them came to the hospital to visit Russell. As soon as Gus entered the room and saw Russell's face, which was still somewhat mottled, he scuttled off to a corner of the room, shrinking down until he sat on the floor. His uncensored reaction was hard to witness as it mirrored my own distress. Geoff immediately went to join him, sliding his own back down the wall to sit on the floor next to Gus. It was an incredibly touching gesture of love and protection, and I was so grateful that Gus had Geoff there to support him.

The day following their visit, Russell was discharged. He was nursing well and passing stools without pain, and the large incision on his back was beginning to heal without any sign of infection. Richard came alone to take us home and held Russell while the nurse helped me pack up our things. As we left the room and said our good-byes, one of the nurses slipped Russell's hospital wrist band into my hand "as a memento." It was a kind gesture, and I thanked her. Once far enough down the hall to be out of sight, however, I chucked the wrist band into the nearest trashcan. This was not a memory I wanted to hold onto; I felt tremendous relief to be leaving the hospital behind.

In the car, we loosely fastened Russell face up on a makeshift padded board that Richard had prepared with a blanket, papoose style. I got into the backseat, and Richard gently set the board with Russell onto my lap. It felt ridiculous to wear a seatbelt when my vulnerable post-surgical infant was lying totally unprotected on my knees. But we had been instructed to keep Russell flat on his back for two weeks, as any other position would risk a pooling of blood and resultant migraine-level headaches. There simply was no way to position him in a car seat lying flat.

Once home, the dictate to keep Russell still and on his back was hardest on Gus, who was desperate to get physically close and cuddle with his new baby brother. I alternated between sternly ordering him off the bed lest he jostle Russell and cause him further pain, and letting Gus cuddle Russell so that they could relish each other. Even though just an infant, Russell was clearly as eager to interact with Gus as Gus was to play with him. Despite the doctor's firm instructions, I suspected that the personal contact and exchange of love between all of us was far more vital to Russell's recuperation than following any doctor's orders. Besides, we all needed to recuperate.

Somehow we muddled through the weeks that followed. Russell's back healed, though his enormous stitches left quite a dramatic scar. His smiles and giggles increased with each passing day; his newfound happiness was balm to my soul. I started to relax again, and often noticed myself taking in deep breaths and letting them out with an enormous sigh. It was such a relief to have the surgery behind us, to be all finished with the medical world. I was confident that his surgery had fixed everything and that there would be no more issues or scares related to his birth defect. I was amazed by my little baby's resilience and sunny personality, and I began to suspect that my child might prove to be the stronger of us in the long run. He was the one who had endured all of the poking and prodding, not to mention major surgery and the painful aftermath; and yet, I was the one who had practically fallen apart from the emotional load that I carried as his mother. Despite how unfair it would be to burden him with my needs, I wondered if someday I might find myself relying on his strength. Little did I know just how true this hunch would prove to be.

Dr. Shaer had mentioned at one of our clinic visits that Russell's type of neural tube birth defect, less serious than the more commonplace severe form of spina bifida, was occurring with increasing frequency and that a whole new classification for this defect was being considered. In addition, there has been a heightened focus on nutritional deficiencies as a cause of spina bifida. Women in their reproductive years are now routinely advised to take prenatal vitamins that include folic acid—a precaution that was announced to the public just before Russell was born, sadly too late for us to benefit from the new recommendation.[7]

Several weeks after Russell's surgery, Dr. Shaer, the pediatrician from the hospital's spina bifida clinic, called to check in on us.

"How's everyone doing?" she asked.

"Russell's healing really well," I said. "And the rest of us are doing okay too!" I added, chuckling.

"So glad to hear it," she said warmly.

"I thought you might like to know," she continued, "that, last night, another baby was born with a 'signature mark' on his back similar to Russell's. But instead of ordering an emergency transport to Children's Hospital in the middle of the night, similar to what you went through with Russell, I dragged my husband and sleeping child down to the maternity hospital in northern Virginia so that I could examine the newborn and see if it even needed to be hospitalized."

She didn't explain why her family had to go with her, but it was a detail that emphasized her commitment to go to great personal lengths to do something differently with this other newborn, and it cemented my positive initial impression of her.

"The mark on that baby's back was closed just as Russell's had been," she said. "Since there was no risk of infection, I told the parents to take their newborn home and call the next day to schedule a follow-up outpatient appointment with the spina bifida clinic at Children's. They were able to avoid any hospitalization."

She was essentially acknowledging that Russell's stay in the NICU and separation from his family for the first three days of his life had been unnecessary.

"Thank you so much for sharing this with me," I said, hanging up the phone.

I found this conversation astonishing. In one fell swoop, Dr. Shaer personified the "first, do no harm" promise in the Hippocratic Oath: she admitted that she and the other doctors had made an error in judgment about Russell's need to spend any time in the NICU; she recognized that our son's hospitalization had been an unnecessary hardship for our family; and she changed her protocol with subsequent newborns as a result of learning from our experience. Maybe even more striking, she had made the effort (as well as taken a risk) to tell me about her revelations, which didn't change our own personal experience but meant a great deal to me nonetheless. In this brief call, she had not only shown herself to be a rare doctor, she had proven herself to be a rare human being.

It was not just spinal cord surgery that Russell had to recover from.

With the possibility that he might need to self-catheterize later on should the spina bifida compromise his bladder control, the urologist on the spina bifida team had advised us to have him circumcised at the same time as he had his back surgery. We had not circumcised our older son, and the idea of forcing Russell to recover from two gaping wounds at the same time (one on each side!) horrified me, but I was assured that circumcision would be a whole lot easier for him at five weeks than at four or five years, and Richard and I had succumbed.

In complete contrast to Dr. Shaer's willingness to reconsider past judgments, not to mention reconsidering them out loud to me, several years later when I pointed out to the urologist who recommended Russell's circumcision that, in hindsight, the procedure had been unnecessary given my son's successful potty training and obviously healthy bladder control, he simply said that it was "better to be safe than sorry." I am continually perplexed at doctors' facile willingness to cut away at the body as if we do not need our tonsils, appendix, uterus, ovaries, gallbladder, spleen, or foreskin. I view the human body as a most amazingly perfect machine of cosmic engineering, and I am not sure that we should be so casual about taking out organs or lopping things off. I hoped that my feedback would be "food for thought" for the urologist in terms of future decisions with other babies who had similarly mild manifestations of spina bifida. Instead, he was firm that there had been no mistaken judgment on his part.

The exact location where the spina bifida defect occurs along the length of the spinal cord is critically important. Not only are the nerves at the site of the defect impacted, but so are the rest of the nerves from that location on down the rest of the spinal cord. Thus, the higher up a defect is located on an embryo's neural tube (which eventually develops into the spinal cord), the more involved and more damaging the consequences. Fortunately, Russell's spinal cord defect was quite low down, just below his waist. But the potential damage that he still might experience, despite his corrective surgery, was significant. Even after he had completely recovered from back surgery, we were cautioned to prepare for the possibility of crippling nerve damage to the organs and appendages associated with the nerves in the lower portion of his spinal cord. Nerve damage might impede his ability to walk, compromise bladder and bowel control, and make it difficult for him to have an erection after the onset of puberty. A re-tethering of his spinal cord might also happen as he grew, which would require more surgery.

Richard and I desperately wanted to hear that the worst was over, but the doctors made it clear that, while Russell's surgery had been deemed "successful," we still had years of watching and waiting ahead.

Chapter 2

The Crueler Threat

Remember that hope is a powerful weapon even when all else is lost.

Nelson Rolihlahla Mandela (1918-2013)

Robbin Island, 1969

AS THE WEEKS AND MONTHS PASSED, AND RUSSELL'S corrective surgery was behind us, an array of new symptoms surfaced, seemingly unrelated to either the spina bifida defect or the surgery. Russell was ravenous with hunger all the time, waking three and four times during the night to nurse in addition to nursing constantly throughout the day. Even on short car rides, I had to pull off the road to nurse him and quell his screams. His stools were also very odd—green, foamy, smelly, and so voluminous they spilled out the side of his diapers—unlike anything I remembered with my first child. His hair color changed almost daily, from tints of brown to blond to red. When red, the color reminded me of the artificial copper tint of the hair on my "Ginny" doll from childhood. And where my older son's cheeks had always been bright pink, to the point where friends and strangers alike joked that I must have applied rouge, Russell's skin was so pale it looked bleached.

Photographs of him from this time show huge dark eyes offset by pasty white skin.

Throughout the fall and into the winter, Russell was constantly sick with ear and sinus infections and a croupy cough. I grew exhausted with little sleep and a colicky baby who was demanding to nurse two to three times the normal amount. During the hot months, Russell had been unusually susceptible to the heat, suffering from heat rash and constant sweating. But even now in the cold months, he left huge circles of residual sweat on the bed after nursing. His sweat tasted peculiarly salty to me, with kisses to his forehead causing my chapped lips to sting.

I raised concerns with our pediatrician, the doctors on the spina bifida team, the La Leche consultant I conferred with about repeated bouts of mastitis (infections of the milk ducts in my breast), family members, fellow mothers—anyone who would listen. I knew that something was terribly wrong with my baby but everyone chose to give me reassurance that the worst was over rather than entertain new fears. My reports even failed to raise an alarm bell with our pediatrician, who tried instead to calm the anxious mother with an overactive imagination.

At the time that I became pregnant with Russell, I had a full-time job in Baltimore that enabled us to finally pay off a number of past due bills. The work was enjoyable, but my stress level increased as my pregnancy advanced, and I became more and more sleep-deprived from insomnia as I got closer to my due date. Despite music and books-on-tape to help keep me alert during the hour-long commute from the farm to my office, from time to time I caught myself nodding off while driving. Given our desperate need for money, my husband and I had hoped that I would continue to collect paychecks right up until the birth. But in the end, I was compelled to start maternity leave a month earlier than intended, scared that I would hurt both myself and my unborn child on the highway. My terms of employment permitted three months of unpaid maternity leave, during which my health insurance would continue. My husband was self-employed, and our only health insurance was through my job. The loss of salary was hard for us, but the continuation of family health insurance turned out to be crucial.

Just before my three months of maternity leave ended, I decided to quit my job. I planned to go into consulting instead, which would allow me to work from home and be available to my children—especially important to me given Russell's challenges. After I resigned, we were permitted to continue my health insurance policy (due to the federal COBRA law) at a cost of $750 per month for up to 18 months.[1] I began to shop around for a less expensive policy right away, but it was hard to find another insurance carrier that would accept us since both my husband and I were now self-employed, and one of our children had a serious pre-existing condition. This was before the Patient Protection and Affordable Care Act (or ACA) protected families like us from insurance companies' discrimination against patients with pre-existing conditions. BlueCross BlueShield initially accepted our application, only to turn around and suddenly reject us. When I questioned the rejection over the phone, the salesperson said, "When you stated on your application that Russell had undergone surgery to correct a tethered cord, I thought you meant umbilical cord not spinal cord." Having to interact with mindless paper-pushers at insurance companies that so blatantly prioritized profit over my son's well-being was a constant source of irritation.

In January, we were finally able to obtain a new but expensive policy through the George Washington University Health System, a local HMO that accepted us despite our son's condition.[2] Because the HMO policy required us to use their physicians, we were obliged to change pediatricians. Russell was just shy of five months old. We got to know our new pediatrician, Dr. Barbara Brynelson, during a long winter of Russell's non-stop ear infections.

Dr. Brynelson was a tall, slim, pretty blond who wore cheery flowered dresses—a nice contrast to the doctors' sterile white coats at the hospital. She had a gentle manner, but exuded confidence that I found reassuring. Though a bit younger than I was, she was a seasoned physician who got along well with both children and parents. I immediately liked her manner with my sons, and loved her constant references to children's books in her discussions with my older son, Gus. Though he had only just turned five years old, he was already an avid reader.

Every time we saw Dr. Brynelson, I complained about Russell's symptoms: his insatiable hunger, his odd stools, his colicky behavior, his skin pallor, his changeable hair color, his salty sweat. Each time she reassured me that he seemed fine, but eventually brought up the "old saw" that salty sweat might indicate cystic fibrosis. I knew very little about cystic fibrosis except that it was a deadly disease, and I became increasingly eager to dismiss the possibility.

In early April, after hearing me complain about Russell's troubles for several months, Dr. Brynelson conducted a routine physical examination. Along with the symptoms I had reported, her exam supported her growing suspicion. She worried out loud, "In eight months, he's gone from being above the 90th percentile for both weight and height [at birth] to below the 5th percentile."

She sat down and showed me Russell's growth chart. Her notations from that day's exam practically placed him off the bottom of the chart. He had been a big newborn and had continued to be well-proportioned, even chubby, as a baby. I hadn't noticed that he was small for his age. I had been so focused on his recovery from surgery that I failed to take note of the sorts of things that mothers might normally notice, such as his need to move up a clothing size taking a lot longer than his brother before him.

Russell's clinical failure to thrive, ear and sinus infections, salty sweat, and steatorrhea (bulky, loose, and smelly stools) indicated a fairly classic profile of cystic fibrosis. Dr. Brynelson looked down at her hands folded in her lap and said quietly without making eye contact, "Lindsay, I think it's possible that Russell has cystic fibrosis." She then looked up at me and said,

"You need to take him to Children's National Medical Center for a diagnostic test."

I sat frozen to my seat. Dr. Brynelson was the only person who had taken my observations seriously, but suddenly her concerns ramped up my own fears. Even though I was quite sure something was terribly wrong, it was frightening to have that fear confirmed. When I came around, I turned on her with a fierceness that only a parent whose child has been unreasonably threatened can muster.

"I know you mean well, Dr. Brynelson," I said icily, "but we can't just go down a long list of serious medical conditions with my son, checking them off one by one. Surely his birth defect was enough bad luck! There must be another explanation for all these symptoms." To her credit, Dr. Brynelson tolerated my venom quietly. She knew that I was in pain and quietly reiterated the need for the test, generously offering me her forbearance.

As I got up to leave, she tried to console me, "I certainly hope that my diagnosis proves to be wrong."

I went home furious and overwrought. With some reluctance, I called the hospital and scheduled an appointment for the diagnostic test later that week. When I woke up the next morning, the doctor's concerns from the previous day seemed ludicrous. I called the hospital back and canceled the test. My denial persisted throughout the weekend. By Monday, however, my son's odd symptoms seemed to be even more pronounced, and I couldn't pretend that everything was okay—I just couldn't believe it was something as serious as cystic fibrosis. That afternoon, I called Dr. Shaer at the Spina Bifida Clinic seeking sympathy and conspiracy with my denial. She was shocked at the mention of cystic fibrosis (commonly referred to as "CF"), but was nonetheless concerned with the odd configuration of symptoms, seeming to hear them for the first time. When I complained about going down a checklist of serious medical conditions with my son, she likened his chances of having both spina bifida *and* CF to the odds of winning the lottery.

Sure, maybe the devil's lottery, I muttered to myself. Dr. Shaer rattled off a long list of conditions that could cause an excess of salt in his sweat, using big Latin words that meant nothing to me except possible salvation from this chilling scenario.

"You know, Lindsay," she said, continuing to reassure me, "it's just not possible that he has CF." She suddenly went quiet and then offered, "But if it were my child, I would want to do the test, just to be sure." This honest statement from her as a mother, not a doctor, helped me to turn the corner. As soon as we hung up, I called the hospital back and rescheduled the test.

On the morning of Russell's test, I sent Gus over to the neighbors' house to play with his friend Aidan. I appreciated how lucky we were to have supportive friends living right next door. Richard wanted to catch up with his farm work, so he stayed home. I bundled Russell and an overflowing diaper bag into the car to make our way to Children's Hospital—a route that was by now all too familiar. Once we arrived at the hospital's parking garage, for a brief moment I found myself tempted to flee, to go back home where our ignorance could continue to be bliss. I dreaded the outcome of this test, but I also knew that we had to rule out CF for certain.

We took the elevator up to the lab. After I signed us in, we were escorted to a little room where I sat down, holding eight-month-old Russell in my lap. He sat contentedly, gripping his favorite stuffed blue Hippo as he watched the technician's movements. Even as a baby, Russell was a trooper with all these visits to the hospital. The technician rolled up a cart with an odd assortment of supplies that didn't look at all medical. He sat down next to us, and began taping electrodes covered in gel onto one of Russell's arms.

"How does this test work?" I asked the technician.

"Once I connect the ends of each wire to a battery, these electrodes will conduct positive and negative charges to Russell's forearm. His arm will heat up from the battery charge and stimulate a sweating response."

The test seemed oddly primitive and more suitable to jump-starting a car.

"Will it hurt him?" I asked.

"No," he said. "His arm will get very warm, but it won't be painful." The technician then taped a small container and wick to Russell's forearm, and placed a plastic bag around his whole arm, taping it in place.

"The wick will soak up a sample of his sweat," he continued, "and we will then analyze the level of salts or electrolytes [predominantly sodium chloride] in the sample." I knew from my conversation with Dr. Brynelson that a high concentration of salt—typically, anywhere from two to five times the normal amount—would indicate cystic fibrosis.[3] Once sweat started to appear on his skin, the technician disconnected Russell from the battery. He told me that as long as I kept Russell from tearing the bag off of his arm, we could move about the lab or sit in the waiting area to pass the time while the wick collected an adequate sample of sweat. "It'll take about 30 minutes," he said.

As soon as the test was finished, I drove us home and waited for the results that the lab would forward to Dr. Brynelson's office. Russell and I lounged on the back deck in the warm spring sun. He cooed at "Sluggo," our double-pawed yellow tiger cat, as the cat rubbed up against his legs, purring loudly. I then nursed Russell and put him down for his nap. Shortly after he fell asleep, Dr. Brynelson called.

"I'm so sorry," she said quietly. "The sweat test confirmed my suspicion of cystic fibrosis."

My knees grew weak.

"I need you and Richard to come to my office this evening so that we can talk about what you'll need to do to get started with his treatment."

I croaked out a feeble "okay," hung up the phone, and crumpled to the floor. I began wailing and cursing the gods with a primal vehemence I had never experienced. I yelled until the weeping closed my throat and I could no longer make a sound. Somehow Russell slept through my uncontrolled ranting.

Richard was in the horse barn, and thankfully, my older son, Gus, was out of earshot as well, still playing next door. What I felt most at this second attempt on my son's life was pure, unadulterated rage.

Later that evening, Richard and I left the boys with a babysitter and drove the 30 minutes to Dr. Brynelson's private practice in stony silence. I was still enraged and, though I wasn't mad at *him*, Richard could sense that I was only just barely containing my emotions. He chose not to open the floodgates. When we arrived at her office, Dr. Brynelson asked if we would mind if one of her medical residents sat in on our discussion. I glanced at my husband who shrugged his shoulders and left the decision up to me. It was bad enough to be discussing our baby's demise in an impersonal clinical environment; I was reluctant to include any non-essential bystanders, particularly residents who, given my prior experience in the hospital's NICU, were not apt to inspire any warmth.

"I'd prefer it just be the three of us," I told her.

"That's fine," she said.

Dr. Brynelson led us into her office and invited us to sit down as she closed the door. She sat at her desk. Richard and I listened numbly as she proceeded to describe the horrors of this deadly disease. She told us that cystic fibrosis impacts a number of major organs and systems throughout the body. She explained that it was impeding his digestion, resulting in his diarrhea and constant need to nurse as well as poor growth ("failure to thrive"), and that eventually the disease would lead to chronic lung infections, irreversible lung damage, and premature death. After an hour or so, we got up to leave. I felt completely empty, sapped of all my strength, and devoid of any emotion.

"You should call tomorrow to make an appointment with the Cystic Fibrosis Center at Children's Hospital," she urged, "so that you can get started with his treatment right away."

She gave each of us a gentle hug before re-emphasizing the urgency of our situation.

"Please call the hospital first thing in the morning," she repeated.

We drove home, again in silence, but this time with tears streaming down both our faces. Once home, I went to place a gentle kiss on each of my sleeping sons' foreheads and crawled into bed, pulling the covers over my head to keep what was starting to feel like a monstrous fire-breathing dragon at bay. Richard crawled in beside me and held me close. He tried to soothe my crying, but I kept whispering unanswerable questions that only made both of us more miserable. Eventually, exhaustion got the better of us, and we fell asleep.

As we walked through the doors of the hospital several days later, with Russell in Richard's arms, I felt physically weighed down by this second diagnosis. I am walking down a gangplank, I thought grimly, realizing that we were about to become acquainted with yet another wing of the hospital, another team of doctors, another dreadful disease. Even though I still knew little about the particulars of CF, I understood from our conversation with Dr. Brynelson that the disease was both incurable and fatal. It didn't seem possible that this was happening. I was almost outside of my body, watching myself as I moved in slow motion along the hospital's escalator ramp, passing by the other parents with sick children who were coming and going, each of us trapped in our own private hell.

At our first encounter with the Children's Hospital CF team, we were told that Dr. Sean Sullivan, the chief of pulmonology and director of the hospital's CF Center, was busy with patients and would be unable to sit with us during our "orientation." At one point, he stuck his head in the doorway to give us a brief greeting. He was wearing a bright red bowtie and Mickey Mouse socks—an outfit I found oddly comforting in the context of our awful situation.

When he asked if we had any questions, I suddenly blurted out, "Have you ever heard of acupuncture or homeopathy being used to treat cystic fibrosis?"

My question wasn't planned, it had simply popped into my head on the spur of the moment. I genuinely wanted his opinion but, at this point in my learning curve, I was also extremely naïve as to how the topic of alternative healing might be received by a conventionally trained doctor in a traditional medical institution. His eyes widened a bit as he chuckled out loud. Rather than interpreting his laughter as malicious, I understood it to be a spontaneous expression of utter disbelief. The doctor obviously thought (correctly) that I was grasping at straws.

"I suppose they'd be harmless enough, but probably a huge waste of effort and money," he said, implying that we would need a great deal of both in the times ahead.

He went on to say, "CF is an unpredictable disease, both in terms of severity and life span."

"What are the factors that determine a child's prognosis?" I asked.

"It depends on three things," he said, still standing in the doorway, "the child's general inherited constitution, luck, and parental compliance."

Without yet realizing how casually the term "compliance" was tossed about in medical settings, it stuck in my craw, and I thought it likely that I would end up despising this man. Actually, in spite of some fundamental differences of opinion, I eventually grew rather fond of Dr. Sullivan, won over by his gentleness with Russell and his patience with my endless questions.

Shortly after Dr. Sullivan left the room, Dr. Shaer from the spina bifida clinic joined us. Everyone was surprised to see her, including me. She introduced herself to the CF team and briefly summarized her history with treating Russell's spina bifida. She then went on to state the conditions under which the team would work with Russell.

"Here's what we will do…" she began, leaving little room for negotiation.

Her authoritative posture was very impressive. I suspected that I was witnessing a rare event, i.e., a doctor advocating for a patient outside her own department.

"I want to make it very clear that you will hear from me personally if Russell is given any unnecessary tests or treatments," she warned.

She shared with complete candor that he had been hospitalized unnecessarily for the first three days of his life.

"This kind of mistake is not to happen again," she stated firmly in conclusion.

I was very impressed both by Dr. Shaer's honesty and by her courage, and I silently thanked her for taking on the role of Russell's guardian angel. After she finished giving her directive, she abruptly stood up and left. The team exchanged a few glances and then continued on, explaining to us that CF patients are normally hospitalized for three to four days upon diagnosis to help the parents learn about the necessary treatments.

"Is there anything we need to learn that cannot be accomplished on an outpatient basis?" I asked.

"No," someone responded.

"Fine, then," I said. "We will make the necessary outpatient appointments."

On the tail of Dr. Shaer's rather dramatic ultimatum, it was easy for me to feel cocky and difficult for them to put up a fight.

Two weeks after Russell's diagnosis with CF, I was to experience one of the most difficult days of my life. The CF specialist told us that a number of CF patients had been diagnosed following a *younger* sibling's diagnosis. Some of these older siblings had previously appeared to be completely symptom-free. We had, in fact, met several families that had experienced this awful surprise. The doctor thus cautioned us that, although apparently healthy, Gus, too, might have the disease.

On the specified day, Richard took Gus, age five, in for a diagnostic sweat test at Children's Hospital, planning a visit to the National Zoo before they came home. I was relieved that Richard had the courage to withstand such a mental ordeal, and I knew that his calmer attitude was likely to convey security to Gus who, after all, had no idea what was going on. As soon as they were gone, I put Russell down for a nap and began to clean the house with a fury, even washing the painted concrete block walls of our little milk barn. My frenzied cleaning alternated with periods of sitting absolutely frozen to the couch, staring out the window. At one point, I exploded, cursing the gods in a loud voice, *"You will not take both my sons!"* I was sure that if my firstborn were also burdened with this horrifying disease, I would crack; I knew it would be more than I could possibly bear. During a phone call with my mother in the days leading up to Gus's test, I had made a morbid "joke" about driving off a cliff with both boys should Gus's test result be positive.

As I continued cleaning the house, I thought back to Russell's sweat test in the hospital and the brief conversation I had had with the woman sitting opposite me, holding her own newborn. I sat next to her in the lab with tears streaming down my face, not knowing what to say, but wanting badly to connect with this other mother. She gently asked me, "Is this child your first?" "No," I said, "he's my second." She smiled down at the baby in her arms. "This is my fifth child," she said, "and my *third* with CF." I was stunned. I could not fathom having a child with CF and then going on to have another, and *another.*

She reassured me, "Life with CF is OK. You'll get used to the routine; it won't do you in." I figured she ought to know and held on to her words, however strange.

Waiting around all morning for the call from our pediatrician, Dr. Brynelson, that would reveal Gus's test results was torture. (Dr. Brynelson told me later that she too had been waiting on tenterhooks at her office, checking the fax machine every two minutes for the hospital's lab report.) I switched back and forth between the manic cleaning and utter paralysis for over an hour until the tension became too great. As soon as Russell woke up from his nap, I packed him off to the grocery store, hoping that a shopping excursion might distract me. It would at least use up some of the deadly time.

Arriving back home, as I drove up the long curved hill that led to the farm's milk barn where we lived, I saw that someone was standing by a car just outside our front door. I wondered who it could be. As I got closer, I realized with astonishment that it was my mother.

For years, my mother and I had endured a tense relationship, fraught with deep-rooted anger and pain. We both suffered through difficult childhoods, which might have brought us together, except that I held her responsible for mine. During my twenties, whole years went by during which I refused to have any contact with her. In later years, visits were unbearably tense for both of us, even with the buffer of my older siblings. My mother was not always a welcome guest, and she knew it. I never expected her to show up uninvited.

The unexpected arrival of my mother caught me totally off guard. I stepped out of the car in wonderment, only to collapse into her open arms. While I would resent the suggestion that anything positive could come from my child's illness, a reconciliation with my mother probably would not have occurred without it. This was to be a major turning point in our relationship. I cried, she cried, and Russell wailed until I finally realized that he was still in the car.

My mother was extremely nervous that she had hopped on a plane to come visit me without asking first. I was surprised to find that I wasn't at all resentful. To the contrary, I was flooded with relief that she was there. I reassured her over and over that she had done the right thing—at no other time in my life had I been in such dire need of a mother.

This rash move of hers, prompted by my wisecrack in an earlier phone call about driving off a cliff with the boys should Gus too have CF, literally transformed what had been an extremely thorny relationship. After her impromptu visit, we began to spend hours upon hours on the phone with her patiently "by my side," listening to my endless renditions of medical encounters, emotional traumas, and scientific theories. No one else has even come close to her incredible staying power.

She had been given a second chance to mother, and it allowed me to acknowledge that part of me was weak and vulnerable. Until her death from lung cancer six years later, she filled a crucial void in my life, making everything more bearable.

Shortly after my mother arrived, I received a call from Dr. Brynelson—Gus's CF test result was negative. I let out a gigantic sigh, and my mother burst into relieved tears. The universe has a funny way of previewing a worse hell to convince you that the current one is tolerable. Thank you, I thought, *this* I can do. My mother stayed only one night, since her need to prevent cliff-jumping had been averted.

In the weeks and months that followed, I started up a steep learning curve, reading everything I could get my hands on to better understand Russell's new diagnosis. I learned that CF is the most commonly inherited childhood disease in the U.S., affecting some 30,000 children and young adults.[4] Contrary to its reputation as a respiratory disease, CF is a mutation that impacts the much broader exocrine system, a system that includes every organ or gland in the body that manufactures and then secretes fluids through a duct to another part of the body. As a system, it represents a group of unrelated organs that all manufacture fluids that are then distributed to other parts of the body, rather than a group of organs that work together collectively such as with the digestive or cardiovascular systems. In fact, many of the organs and glands included in the exocrine system are also considered part of another system in the body. And all of these organs and glands—including the pancreas, stomach, liver, gall bladder, small intestine, sweat glands, salivary glands, testes (or ovaries), and lungs—are affected by the CF mutation.[5]

In 1938, pediatrician and pathologist Dr. Dorothy Andersen realized that the cysts in the pancreas and the fibrosis in the lungs were related during autopsies she performed on children. Until that time, the malabsorption and malnutrition common to CF had been diagnosed as solely a pancreatic condition, with any concurrent respiratory complications receiving a completely separate diagnosis.[6]

On a cellular level, where the genetic mutation of CF manifests, the mechanism that transports chloride (a component of salt) in and out of the cell is defective. The mutation manifests differently depending on the organ. In the case of the sweat glands, for example, chloride can exit the cells but cannot be continuously re-absorbed, as it normally is in a healthy person without the disease. (This explains the salty taste of Russell's sweaty forehead and the crusty salt crystals that were left behind after his sweat dried.) In addition, people with CF often sweat more than normal. Thus a person with CF experiences an abnormally high loss of salt and resultant imbalance of electrolytes. Electrolytes are minerals (including calcium, potassium, magnesium, sodium, chloride, and phosphorous) that carry an electrical charge, and circulate in the blood and other bodily fluids. Proper electrolyte balance is crucial to the health of muscles and, because the heart is a muscle, maintaining a proper heart rhythm.

On the other hand, in the case of the lungs, the chloride cannot *exit* the cell, essentially becoming trapped. This causes normally occurring healthy mucus in the lungs to become abnormally thick and viscous, and creates a perfect environment for bacterial growth. Over-colonization of bacteria causes chronic bacterial infections that, over time, lead to irreversible damage to the lungs, such as enlarged airways and scarring. In the pancreas, the thick CF mucus literally forms a plug in the tiny duct that connects the pancreas to the duodenum—the first section of the small intestine. This plug prevents essential digestive enzymes that are produced in the pancreas from entering the duodenum and catalyzing the digestive process when a person eats food. The lack of sufficient enzymes impedes the individual's metabolism and absorption of nutrients, and eventually leads to malnutrition, even when he or she eats large quantities of food. In males, the *vas deferens*—the duct through which sperm must travel from the testes—becomes obstructed by mucus plugs as well, causing sterility in males. Females tend to experience more severe CF symptoms and a shorter lifespan than males; researchers suspect that the hormone "estrogen" may play a role.[7]

The cellular-level transport mechanism that causes so much trouble is a defective protein called the "cystic fibrosis transmembrane regulator" or CFTR. Though the defective CF gene was identified in 1985, it took researchers another decade (around the time that Russell was diagnosed) to discover that this protein has another critical role to play in addition to chloride transport—that of combating infection. In the lungs, where the thick warm mucus facilitates colonization of dangerous levels of bacteria, this double whammy of trapped chloride plus a compromised ability to fight infections is lethal. People with CF typically suffer from chronic lung infections which eventually lead to pneumonia and other long-term bacterial infestations, some of which (such as *Burkholderia cepacia*) are impervious to treatment with antibiotics. The lungs are relatively fragile organs and cannot withstand these endless battles with bacteria. Over time, the infections cause more and more airways to be blocked with mucus plugs, reducing a person's ability to breathe deeply. Chronic inflammation permanently enlarges the airways and the scarring reduces elasticity, which impedes the ability to cough up mucus. The irreversible damage to the lungs eventually leads to lung failure and death. Both the CFTR protein's inability to serve as a bacterial combatant and the damaging role of chronic inflammation are major discoveries that have helped to shed further light on the respiratory complication of CF and led to the development of promising medications, such as *Pulmozyme*.

My previous knowledge of anatomy was limited to an eighth grade physical science class in which we dissected frogs. (Actually, if memory serves me, my lab partner wimped out at the last minute, and I ended up doing most of the dissecting myself.) As far as I knew, the pancreas was a close cousin to the appendix and not all that important. As it turns out, the pancreas is one of our more crucial organs, and the pancreatic malfunction caused by CF is as life threatening as the disease's eventual impact on the respiratory system. The nutrients contained in food that are critical to growth and sustained health are not adequately absorbed unless pancreatic enzymes are available to break down food matter. In the case of CF, because mucus plugs in the pancreatic duct prevent enzymes from getting through to the small intestine, most of the food's nutrients end up being discharged from the body along with waste matter. Unless artificial enzyme replacement is instituted to support the digestive process and absorption of nutrients, a person with CF will soon become malnourished. This explained Russell's insatiable hunger and voluminous stools during the months leading up to his diagnosis as well as the stark white that appeared in his post-surgical stool at five weeks, representing perhaps unprocessed fat or a lack of bile—both of which are symptoms of CF. This impediment to his digestion is what slowed his growth and ultimately led to Dr. Brynelson's "failure to thrive" diagnosis.

Following his CF diagnosis, we received instruction from hospital staff on the two basic therapies that conventional medicine had to offer children with CF: pancreatic enzyme supplementation to enhance the digestive process, and chest physiotherapy to help clear the lungs of mucus. The enzymes come in the form of small hard globes packed in a gel capsule that must be swallowed whole. If a child is too young to swallow a pill, as Russell was at eight months, the capsule can be opened and the little globes inside mixed into applesauce or baby food—something that does not require chewing. If chewed, the enzymes taste quite repugnant but, more importantly, they begin to activate in the mouth instead of waiting to activate until they reach the duodenum (or first part of the small intestine). Enteric coating of enzymes was a critical invention in the early 1960's that exponentially increased the lifespan of children with CF. The coating seals enzymes and prevents them from activating in the mouth or in the acidic environment of the stomach (as long as they are swallowed intact and not chewed), preserving them for activation in the alkaline environment of the duodenum where they are needed (and where they would normally be deposited directly from the pancreas in a person without CF).

Getting Russell to swallow the little enzyme particles at eight months was no easy task. I had only recently (and half-heartedly) introduced solids into his diet, and these little globes with flat surfaces like a soccer ball made him gag. He gagged rather consistently with every type of food (read: differently flavored mush) that I tried, and he was unable to swallow more than a few globes at a time. He was supposed to take enzymes every time he nursed as well as with the new solid food I was giving him. Mealtime became an excruciating ordeal for both of us. I would place him in his high chair, ready to introduce a new flavor of mushy baby food, such as plums or apricots, girded each time with renewed patience and optimism that this time he would conquer the task at hand, only to soon find myself loudly insisting to an eight-month-old baby that he control a completely involuntary gag reflex. I became increasingly worried about him not being able to swallow these enzymes. If I hadn't been able to nurse him non-stop during that period, he probably would have lost quite a bit of weight.

After several months of sharing our enzyme travails with the nurse at the CF clinic, the doctor finally changed Russell's prescription (*Pancrease*) to a higher strength brand (*Zymase*) with the hope that the few little globes he was able to get down would do the job.[8] In addition to being higher strength, the new brand of enzymes happened to contain smaller and smoother pieces. After struggling to swallow the larger "soccer balls," Russell was able to swallow these new smoother enzymes with ease. The nurse expressed surprise when I told her that the size and shape of these different enzymes made all the difference in his ability to swallow them. His meals became a much more pleasant experience (for both of us), and his diarrhea finally began to lessen.

The other essential CF treatment is lung clearance, which involves a daily regimen of thumping the individual with CF on the front and back of his or her chest. This thumping causes the lungs to vibrate which, in turn, loosens the build-up of thick CF mucus on the lung surface. Thumping is usually followed by an urge to cough, which brings the mucus up and out of the lungs. At one of our first CF outpatient visits, Richard and I received instruction in chest physiotherapy (commonly called "chest PT") from one of the hospital's physical therapists, a short stocky woman who spoke with a thick foreign accent.

The therapist whipped through a rapid-fire demonstration: "Cup your hand like this, place it here, thump like this for three minutes, then do the same thing here, and here, and here."

I had a hard time following her and remained pretty much in the dark as to how it was done. The therapist handed us an instructional hand-out as she prepared to leave. Not wanting to appear stupid, I thanked her and pretended to have understood her cursory pointers; for some reason, I felt that it was my fault that I couldn't seem to get the knack.

Before I learned how to decipher articles in peer-reviewed journals in graduate school, and well before the Internet was in full swing with today's search capacity, I was totally dependent on the doctors and other clinical staff for all of my information. It was absurd to expect that I could garner even a cursory education in the context of our brief ten to fifteen minute interactions with clinical staff, but I persisted. Once I learned enough to engage moderately well in clinical conversations with the CF specialist, my confidence grew and I started to view my endless questions as proof of my commitment to learn, rather than an indication of ignorance. I also came to view any confusion on my part as the clinician's burden. If I had trouble understanding their responses, instead of worrying about how stupid a follow-up question might make me look (or how much time I was taking, disrupting a doctor's busy line-up of appointments), I learned to ask the doctors and other clinical staff to repeat themselves as many times as I needed them to in order to understand their instructions or the reasoning behind their recommendation to try this or that treatment, glibly ignoring any impatience on their part. The urgency of our situation overcame any worries I had about being well-behaved.

This appointment with the physical therapist was early on, however, and I hadn't yet learned how to flex that particular muscle. Russell's CF diagnosis was painfully fresh, and all I wanted to do was finish up the therapy session so that we could leave the hospital and go home. I didn't absorb much of her demonstration but was hopeful that Richard and I could teach ourselves the "chest PT" using the written instructions and diagrams she had given us once we were back home. At the end of the session, when I sat Russell up to put his clothes back on, the therapist suddenly noticed the horizontal scar across his lower back.

"What happened here?" she asked as she gathered up her paperwork.

I quickly summarized the spina bifida story. She frowned thoughtfully and set her papers back down. She lay Russell down and moved his legs all around, bending them up and down, crossing and uncrossing them. She then abruptly announced in a matter-of-fact tone, "He'll never walk."

My jaw dropped open.

"I'm sorry that I don't have time to go into more detail," she apologized after noting the shocked look on my face, "but given his limited range of motion, I'm certain that he will never walk." At a time when we were still raw with his days-old diagnosis with CF, this reminder of the spina bifida nightmare was paralyzing.

These moments tested Richard and me dearly in terms of our ability to cope, both as individuals and as a couple and Russell's parents. We were dumbstruck at the physical therapist's authoritative prediction, and it rekindled an involuntary flow of tears on my part, which continued all the way home. Richard's face took on a steely expression, but I knew he too was in pain. When we arrived home, he went straight to the horse barn without even speaking. As I lifted Russell out of his car seat, I looked down at my little baby and wondered why this was happening, why he was being tested like this. He was just an innocent baby who deserved a life, a full life, without this endless stream of threats. I didn't know if he would be able to cope with all of this. Heck, I didn't know how any of us were going to cope.

I didn't dare call my sister or my mother—I didn't want to repeat what the therapist had said and give this latest threat any more weight than it already had. For the rest of the day, I used the pressing tasks of daily life to distract me: changing diapers, preparing the boys' meals, washing clothes, feeding the dogs, putting toys away, reading bedtime stories. I yearned to ward off these damned medical intrusions and be left alone to enjoy my children. From time to time, I fretted about what the therapist had said. What had the doctors missed? Could the therapist possibly be right? Would he never walk? With each question, tears would well up all over again.

After a few days, I began to doubt the validity of the

therapist's quick conclusion and was desperate for another opinion even though I was fearful that her judgment might be seconded. I finally called the hospital and asked to speak with Dr. Laura Tosi, the orthopedist on the spina bifida team.

When she returned my call later that afternoon, Dr. Tosi firmly reassured me, "That therapist was *way* off the mark."

I wanted to believe her, but I was skeptical and reminded myself how often the lowly staff person in the field knows more than the head honcho back at headquarters. I wasn't deliberately trying to exacerbate my torment, but I was worried that the therapist had noticed something that the orthopedist might have missed during her whirlwind examinations.

Several weeks later, we were back at the spina bifida clinic for Russell's routine check-up with the usual line-up of specialists. When it was Dr. Tosi's turn, she came to the doorway of the exam room and hesitated for a moment. Standing there in a rumpled white coat, with glasses askew and her arms chock full of charts, she looked like an absent-minded professor. She somehow managed to extract Russell's chart out of her pile and open it without dropping the rest of them.

"Now, what's this about his not being able to walk?" she asked, leaning casually against the doorframe as she looked through the notes in his chart, "and what were you doing with a physical therapist anyway?"

I answered that we had been obliged to learn chest therapy.

"Why?" she asked, glancing up at me over the top of her glasses.

"Because of his cystic fibrosis," I answered.

At that, the normally composed Dr. Tosi dropped her entire armload of charts, scattering them all over the floor. She slumped against the doorframe with a look of shock on her face that validated my own disbelief.

"But he doesn't look like he has CF," she gasped. She, too, associated CF with skinny children who are visibly malnourished. Despite his odd skin and hair color, Russell's chubby cheeks and big belly served as decoys.

My husband helped Dr. Tosi pick up the charts as she regained her composure. She then walked over to the examination table, said a quick "Hi there" to Russell, and started to examine his hips and legs, taking considerably more time than she normally did. She reassured us repeatedly throughout her exam that his reflexes, x-rays, sonograms, and physical development all contradicted the therapist's prediction.

"He will certainly walk," she said firmly. "I'm quite sure of it!"

As we left the hospital, Richard and I realized that we had been given completely conflicting professional opinions and, without so much as a moment's hesitation, we chose to believe hers.

Russell's daily regimen of chest PT soon began in earnest. Until I looked them up, I had no idea what lung lobes were (sections of the lungs) or what cilia did (tiny hair-like "organelles" on the interior of the lungs whose coordinated waving action helps move particles up and out of the lungs). We had been instructed to do the thumping for three minutes on each of 16 different places on Russell's chest, back, and sides. I couldn't imagine how two tiny balloons in his little chest could possibly have so many different surfaces. We both found it tricky to adequately cup our big hands and thump in more than one place on Russell's tiny torso.

The job of Russell's daily chest PT soon fell to me. I was so terrified of his prognosis that I followed the written instructions to the letter twice a day, thumping him for several minutes on each of ten locations in the morning and thumping him again on six more in the evening. I usually did this while sitting on our double bed using several pillows to prop me up, with Russell lying on a pillow across my lap. I kept track of the three minutes per location using the clock on the bedside table. In the beginning, Russell wailed pitifully during his therapy as if he were being tortured—and not just with the onset, but throughout the entire 40-minute ordeal. Tears streamed down my face as he struggled futilely to get off my lap. I felt awful and tried to console him with stories; I even tried intimidating him crossly into cooperating, which of course made both of us feel even worse. Finally one night I began to sing Shawn Colvin's recently released song, "I Don't Know Why." I was in competition with a screaming baby, and my serenade was hardly delivered as a peaceful lullaby, so I was shocked to discover that it actually worked—Russell fell asleep. Whether my singing was so unbearable or the competition for volume too stiff, his sleep was a boon to us both. It struck me as outlandish that Russell could tolerate such violence to his body without waking. I recalled the unemotional musing of the (same) physical therapist back at the hospital, "Don't worry if he screams. It helps to open up the child's lungs and makes the therapy more productive." Whether a valid point or not, I felt pity for the babies on the ward who were obliged to endure therapy performed by someone who offhandedly rationalized their screaming as more productive.

When Russell caught a cold, he hated the chest PT even more than on regular days. His ribs and lungs must have been sore from the excess mucus and coughing, and his screaming intensified. I felt like a sadist and began to decrease and even skip the therapy. I couldn't bear to hurt him and I would give in, holding my baby close to my chest until his sobs subsided. The more therapy I skipped, however, the more clogged his lungs became and the sicker he got. We were lucky that his colds didn't progress to pneumonia that first year, given my slacking off during periods of illness right when he needed his chest PT the most. After repeatedly hearing from all the doctors that more therapy was required during colds rather than less, I finally steeled myself to experiment with his next cold. When it arrived, instead of giving him less therapy, I completed morning and evening regimens with a third session in the middle of the day. Despite his protests, his cold quickly grew less intense, and his mood improved. I'd gotten the proof that I needed and vowed never to skip another day of chest therapy. When I shared my concern about hurting Russell at one of our appointments with Dr. Sullivan, he joked, "I've offered fifty bucks to the first parent who breaks a rib during chest PT!" If anyone could have won this morbid contest, it would have been me. My initial approach may have been tentative, but after I got the hang of it, I was soon whacking Russell with vehemence. I've come up with some weird rationalizations over the years, but the belief that my ardor would not only break up the mucus but toughen him up as well took the prize. As for me, our PT sessions did little to improve my singing, but I cultivated pretty impressive forearms!

I'd never been faced with a challenge this big before. The emotional roller coaster, which seemed to mostly head downhill with few uplifts, was taking its toll. I cried often. Even the loving support of family and friends didn't stop the ache in my heart. The only extended family members who lived nearby were my in-laws: Richard's mother, Geraldine, and step-father, Chuck. They came to visit us regularly, always bringing apple and cherry turnovers with them from a deli near their home in Friendship Heights in Northwest D.C. Geraldine was desperate to help. After hearing me complain about how hard it was to zero in on the prescribed 16 locations on Russell's tiny ribcage with our big hands during chest PT, she went looking for something that might help. She eventually found specially-crafted soft plastic cup "percussors" at a medical supply store. I was impressed by her proactive search and grateful for the clever find. The cups' small size and built-in handles made the whole process a lot easier. The percussors were also designed to create a suction effect, which enhanced the effectiveness of the therapy. (I don't know why no one at the CF clinic had ever thought to mention them.)

After about six months of trying to track exact minutes on a digital clock, I remembered the (3-minute) glass-and-sand egg timer from my mother's kitchen and purchased one. Over time, I also found a sectioned, hard foam pillow (called a "Body Slant") on which I could position Russell either flat or at a 90° angle—especially convenient for head-down positions. This large pillow allowed me to hold him in different positions with less strain on my back, and also meant that we could do chest PT in the living room in front of Sesame Street. Though I wasn't a big fan of television, this transformed morning chest PT from mindless torture to a daily regimen that could be endured with the support of entertainment. Around this time, I also started to make up stories about two little monkeys who lived deep in the jungles of Africa. Fueled by wonderful memories of a photographic safari I'd taken through a swath of East Africa in 1984, Mungo and Ludi (the monkeys) and their endless jungle exploits got us through many an evening chest PT session.

Once Russell's care was underway at the CF Clinic, we were assigned to a pulmonary fellow, a very polite young pediatrician who had gone on to specialize in pulmonary medicine. She seemed unusually fixated on getting through to me regarding Russell's prognosis—especially the life-threatening part. At first, her goal was merely perplexing but, after a while, hugely frustrating. Visit after visit, she would look at me very intently and insist on repeating the deadly course of the disease, beginning with a picture of mild infections and never-ending colds along with chronic digestive problems, such as diarrhea and stomach aches. She would then go on to describe the chronic lung infections and protracted coughing that he would develop, and the pneumonia and other even more serious drug-resistant bacterial infections that would require inpatient care one or more times a year. Each rendition would then conclude with a gruesome picture of permanent lung damage and eventual lung failure, i.e., death. "He will not get any healthier than he is now," she emphasized. I wondered at her need to repeat this litany over and over. At first, I tried to listen politely. But by the third or fourth conversation in the same vein, I found myself getting quite agitated.

Making matters worse, this particular doctor was not a native speaker of English and, though essentially fluent, she at times used a word that was ill-chosen and conveyed a slightly bizarre, if unintended, meaning. She had also apparently been raised in a culture that successfully schooled her to be extremely polite. Thus, not only was I obliged to suffer through repeated renditions of my child's morbid prognosis, I also had to endure detailed descriptions of his impending doom from someone with an ever-present smile on her face. As she started up again at one of his appointments, I finally put an end to her ceaseless predictions. "I heard the news loud and clear the first time I was told," I said rather forcefully, "and I have no need whatsoever to hear it again." No doubt, my tone of voice was unnecessarily stern, but at least that was the end of that.

I have devoted most of my adult professional life to combating prejudice and stereotypes in the context of anti-poverty work in urban minority communities. I was shocked, therefore, by the formation of two new and ugly biases on my part. I vowed to seek out American doctors (whatever that means), and I vowed to consult only with doctors who were at least as old as I was. I was eager to find a glitch in my son's diagnosis and to find doctors "better equipped" to give me positive news. In the end, I had to admit to myself that his prognosis would have sounded just as terrible coming from any messenger.

During the first year following Russell's diagnosis, I often called the hospital after hours for reassurance that his symptoms were no cause for alarm and to get advice on whether to start him on another round of antibiotics. A different fellow with the CF clinic was frequently on call in the evenings and on weekends. This young man—clearly an immigrant given his accent—was a good listener. After a number of brief, albeit emotion-laden (on my part) conversations with him, I noted how comforting his counsel had been and realized that it was his superior skill at communication that stood out. He paraphrased each of my questions back to me for clarification before answering, and he took the time to make sure that I understood his response and any instructions. "Is there anything else you would like to share with me before we talk about how to handle this?" he asked with compassion. Having met many uncommunicative doctors through the years, I came to respect this man's ability—whether innate or schooled, I will never know. Luckily, thanks to my interactions with him, my unpleasant biases about a doctor's ethnicity and age soon fell away.

Our experience with spina bifida and CF—both currently classified as genetic conditions—has prompted me to give some thought to the ethics surrounding genetic testing, specifically amniocentesis at 16 weeks or the *chorionic villus* test which is available even earlier in pregnancy. When I discovered I was pregnant with my first child at age 34, my obstetrician suggested that I consider having an amniocentesis—a test performed on the mother's amniotic fluid that, at that time, routinely screened for three conditions: Down syndrome, spina bifida, and a certain type of heart defect. I asked the doctor how the age-related risks of having a baby with Down syndrome compared with the risk that the amniocentesis test might itself cause a miscarriage (of a healthy fetus). "Given your age," she said, "the risks are exactly equivalent." It was difficult for me to place a fetus that I already felt moving in my womb at such grave risk. I chose to err on the side of caution regarding the baby's survival and did not have the test. When I became pregnant again (with Russell) at age 39, the midwives at the Maternity Center voiced concerns about the risk of birth defects. With the unqualified health of my firstborn under my belt, however, I blithely rejected the need for testing.

The irony of the availability of genetic testing in our case is that amniocentesis would have told us nothing about Russell's spina bifida (a birth defect) or his CF (an inherited condition). Because his spina bifida defect was mild and the signature mark on his back was closed, none of his spinal fluid would have leaked into my amniotic fluid to indicate spina bifida in the amniocentesis result. In addition, outside of Sweden where there had been a longstanding attempt to systematically eradicate CF mutations from the gene pool, at the time of my second pregnancy (1992), amniocentesis in the U.S. did not routinely screen for CF unless a family history indicated that the fetus could be at risk. Unaware of any history of CF in either of our families, my husband and I would not have even thought to request the additional analysis. So, strangely enough, in our case, prenatal testing would not have revealed either one of Russell's conditions.

It has occurred to me, in retrospect, however, that had I known that the fetus I was carrying would be afflicted with spina bifida and cystic fibrosis—both incurable life-threatening conditions that cause children to suffer—I would certainly have leaned toward having an abortion. It is perhaps overly simplistic to say that I am very grateful now that I did not know. Russell is one of my two best blessings that I count every day, and my delight in him is thoroughly unblemished by his health challenges. I suspect most parents feel this way after they come to love their child. But a fetal test would not have been able to predict how good Russell would feel about being alive or that his spina bifida would be minor, relatively speaking, and correctable. Nor would it have reassured me that he would be able to thrive despite his CF, with the support of alternative healing (which I describe later on). What is clear to me now is that just because advances in technology have made this type of information available to us, it doesn't mean that we necessarily have the ethical clarity or even the collective intelligence with which to handle it. I firmly support a woman's right to decide whether to pursue or end a pregnancy, but medical advances such genetic testing and the ethical questions and decisions they prompt are fraught with complexity.

In July 1993, a month before Russell's first birthday, I decided to have a tubal ligation (cauterization of a woman's fallopian tubes that results in permanent sterilization). The doctors at Children's Hospital had cautioned us that any ensuing children would not only be statistically very likely to have CF, they would also be at increased risk for a more severe manifestation of spina bifida. This was one instance in which I didn't need any additional information in order to know what to do.

While I was in "pre-op" before being wheeled into the operating room, the surgeon came to my bedside. Never having had surgery before, I didn't know if this was a common practice, but I was nervous about the procedure and heartened by his seemingly personal gesture. He told me that he wanted to make sure that I was clear in my desire to be sterilized given the fact that it would be irreversible. I responded with an emphatic

"Yes!" He cocked his head to one side, and I answered his unasked question with a brief countdown of Russell's woes. I begged him to cauterize each tube at least four times over. "I don't want to burden another child with such severe problems," I said, "and I don't ever want to be in the unbearable position where I am compelled to consider abortion." He understood.

At my post-surgical visit, the doctor admitted that he'd had a little trouble locating one of my tubes. When I started to protest, he immediately waved his hand to stop me. "Oh no," he interrupted, "You have nothing to worry about. I shared your story with the nurses before I began the operation; it even made one of them cry. They weren't about to let me close you up without finding that tube!" Even so, I made a half-joking threat that if I ever did become pregnant again, he'd be the first to know.

We had been spared the potential horrors of spina bifida—the shunts to the brain, cognitive impairment, paralysis, feeding and breathing tubes—but I held out little hope of mercy with cystic fibrosis. Life expectancy for a person with CF at the time of Russell's diagnosis (1993) was 29 years.[9,10] I couldn't bear the thought of my son's life ending prematurely. One day, I sat at our kitchen table with a friend of my husband's—a nice man with no children of his own, who had always shown particular kindness to our boys. He was asking me questions about Russell's CF and was obviously heartened by the news that Russell might well live to be 29.

"How old are you, Rob?" I asked.

"Thirty-two," he answered.

"Well," I said bluntly, "you'd be dead."

It was an unnecessarily cruel thing to say to someone who was trying so hard to be optimistic. Retorts like this often spilled out of me back then. To be honest, they still do—an overflow of bile caused by my just barely contained grief.

So many times, I have had to endure the "good news"—that Russell's CF was caught early allowing essential treatment to begin, that it was a "great time" to be diagnosed with CF given the promising advances in gene therapy and lung transplants, and so on. The uninitiated don't realize that these caveats aren't worth a damn to a mother in pain. Personally, I found much more sustenance when my good friend, Wendy, choked on her words as I shared the diagnosis with her over the phone.

"Oh my God," she sputtered through her tears, "*then he'll die?*"

Validation of the bottomless despair and fear I felt is what brought out my strength, not attempts to fabricate silver linings that were somehow supposed to mitigate the fact that my son was destined to die an untimely death. I've come to accept that most people run as fast and far away as they can get from dark emotions. The few friends who had the courage to feel the fear and despair with me was what I needed most, not to have them try to talk me out of those feelings. Occasional plunges into the fear and despair actually brought relief. And, eventually, the respite of relief helped to ground me and prepare me for the work to come.

Chapter 3

My Transformation

You wanna fly, you got to give up the shit that weighs you down.

Toni Morrison (1931-2019)

FROM THE OUTSET, MY ATTITUDE TOWARD THE SPINA BIFIDA team ranged from deference to complete awe. I had an unquestioned faith in the doctors' ability to fix my son's spinal cord defect, and I looked to them to call all the shots regarding his treatment. I dutifully glanced at the terrifying pamphlets about spina bifida that Dr. Shaer gave us, but as soon as we found out on day four that our baby's defect was mild (relatively speaking) and correctable, I halted my reading. Full-blown spina bifida was a nightmare that we had somehow missed by the skin of our teeth, and I had little incentive to learn more. The surgery to correct his defect was successful thanks to the prowess of the neurosurgical team at Children's Hospital. Once it was behind us, all I felt was tremendous relief.

When a diagnosis of cystic fibrosis was confirmed less than seven months later, the prediction that Russell would die pierced my heart like a hot knife through butter. For days following our first visit to the hospital's CF clinic, I wept uncontrollably and felt hopelessly paralyzed. I just couldn't fathom our bad luck. And the growing demands of two unrelated medical conditions were overwhelming—two clinics, in separate wings of the hospital, different teams of doctors, multiple sets of appointments and protocols. The enormous love I felt toward my son soon became fused with trepidation—what else was headed our way?

Somehow I managed to drag myself out of bed each morning, make breakfast for Gus, nurse Russell, take a shower, do the laundry, feed the dogs, have a glass of wine with my husband at dinnertime, *play* with my children. We had a life to live, and I sought relief in the ordinary tasks of each day. Richard and I were emotionally exhausted and wrung-out. After the CF diagnosis, neither of us was able to muster up enough energy to go back to work for weeks. The tension of interrupted income led to spotty arguing, though we rarely had the energy to do serious battle.

Eventually I climbed out of my stupor and arranged for childcare. Our neighbor and owner of the farm where we lived had a wonderful Nicaraguan housekeeper, whose sweet-tempered young adult daughter (whom we all called "Datoushe," since the Spanish version of Dietriche was hard for us to pronounce correctly) was willing to watch Russell while I worked from home. Luckily, there was sufficient demand for the fundraising and strategic planning skills I had accrued for me to launch a modestly lucrative consulting career. Work was a welcome diversion. It gave me a sense of purpose and accomplishment at a time when solutions to other more pressing problems seemed beyond my reach.

Richard received modest pay for managing the farm, but his

primary work took place in the woodworking shop he had set up in the other half of our converted barn. He was very talented, crafting exquisite shoji screens and inlay cabinets that he designed himself. Unfortunately, his meticulous efforts required a high price tag to offset his time, so most of his commissioned jobs entailed more mundane carpentry. Following each of Russell's diagnoses, Richard had a difficult time pulling himself together, putting in a bare minimum of hours to keep the farm from falling apart. He turned inward, troubled by his inability to protect his son compounded by an inability to support his family. His protracted downward spiral caused enormous tension between us and sparked repeated arguments about money.

In retrospect, I view Russell's ordeal with spina bifida and corrective surgery as mere boot camp for what was to come. The second assault on my baby's life, cystic fibrosis, was a lot harder to absorb. From the moment he was diagnosed, my mind was abuzz with stray questions. I had no idea how to sort through all of the new medical details. No matter how much I learned, I knew that I would never be able to catch up with the doctors, or counter their emphatic and repeated proclamations that my son would die young *no matter what*. I had never felt so powerless. I was desperate to do something but had no idea what to do. The pressure to act intensified each time the doctors reaffirmed that there was no hope. Despite the love that my children and extended family showered on me throughout this time, my heart was in constant pain. I had a beautiful little cherub of a baby, with pudgy cheeks, blue eyes, and Goldilocks curls; the thought of him dying, even well into the future, was unbearable.

One evening, looking into the bathroom mirror, I was appalled by the person staring back at me. I saw a woman in great distress, with wild eyes filled with both anger and dread. Her naked misery scared me and made me feel maternal—toward myself. I had been staring down into a dark abyss, not knowing how to back away from the edge. It wasn't just my son who was threatened; I was under attack by a horrid monster that I couldn't see but felt lurking behind every corner.

Out of the blue, I had a vision of a fire-breathing dragon with gigantic wings and a hideous spiked tail. In that moment, something powerful inside me shifted. Instead of being consumed by fear, I suddenly pictured a knight preparing to do battle with this huge mythological beast. Why am I trying to adjust to this terrifying nightmare? I asked myself. Why am I being so damned passive? There must be something I can do. I determined then and there to go on the offensive, to do anything and everything I possibly could to save my son. This moment changed not only my mothering style—it literally changed my personality. I couldn't afford to be caught up in petty insecurities or a lack of confidence. I had a child to rescue and a dragon to slay!

It was painfully clear to me that the conventionally trained doctors also recognized a dragon when they saw one. But somehow they were able to tolerate a prognosis that portended worsening illness, permanent damage, and an early death. Of course they would try to delay my son's decline as long as they could, but they weren't about to try and *save* him. They humbly acknowledged that this was well beyond their capacity. Obviously it was well outside my capacity too, but I had no interest in facing up to my insufficiencies, which were far more profound than theirs. I was on a mission, and it consumed me.

Admittedly, for a time, I was more like a knight errant, racing off blindly in one direction and then dashing off in another. I had no coherent plan in mind. I was fueled by desperation, and girded with the strong will of my Scottish ancestors and a ferocious maternal instinct to keep the dragon at bay. My first knightly act was fairly mundane: to rid our house of all dust, dirt, and animal hair. If CF was preparing to attack my baby's lungs, then I would do everything I could to protect his lungs from any avoidable threats. Since we lived on a farm, achieving a dust-free environment was an unrealistic goal, but I did what I could, using my new consulting income. I purchased washable electro-static filters for our forced-air heat and air conditioning system that were advertised to take 99% of dust and pollutants out of the air. I purchased a humidifier both to offset the drying caused by our woodstove and to weigh down the dust rather than allow it to float around in the air. Datoushe washed the linoleum floors in the kitchen, hallway, and bathroom regularly, and I kept an ever-present damp cloth in my hand to wipe window sills, tables, and any other flat surface that might collect dust. I put special "encasers" on all of our mattresses and pillows to reduce dust mites and kept a portable air filtration machine running 24 hours a day next to Russell's crib. I bought a top-of-the-line vacuum with replaceable filters to keep the wall-to-wall carpeting free of dust in the living room where Russell played with his toys. I installed a thick, coarse doormat outside the front door to trap as much dirt as possible before it came inside. My work was an uphill battle, what with two dogs, two cats, and a farmer-woodworker constantly tracking dirt and sawdust into our home. But I was finally doing something.

My goal was positive: to build up Russell's health, rather than simply fight disease. This focus on positive improvements was essential to our success. I wasn't trying to reduce my son's symptoms or simply postpone the inevitable decline; instead, I hoped to help him achieve optimal health. My stubborn commitment to this goal prevented me from compromising my standards for him. If my goal was truly his optimal health, then I couldn't cut corners or accept the status quo. I couldn't solely rely on the experts, and I couldn't wait for researchers to find a cure. Although these may well be reasonable approaches for a parent in my situation, to me they all felt like giving up. Each of us has to choose our battles and try to avoid battles that are a set-up for frustration and failure. I was, after all, told point blank that Russell's long-term survival could not be achieved. But losing this battle was out of the question.

The disease that threatened Russell was a routine professional encounter for the doctors, but for me, it was as if the front yard had suddenly been sown with landmines. I had no choice but to go forth gingerly on my hands and knees, inch by inch, moving in a careful but steadfast manner in order to clear away the threat.

In my own naïvely arrogant way, I persisted in trying to take the "fatal" out of my son's fatal prognosis. My emerging confidence gave me a fresh perspective on doctors, conventional Western medicine, and medical research. I felt freer to assess the gaps in medical care I observed, at the same time applauding everything that helped my son. The doctors could afford to be realistic, patient, skeptical, and acknowledge their limitations of time or money or knowledge. I couldn't. I simply couldn't let my son go—it's not only that I didn't want to, I couldn't. I didn't know how.

My mother hadn't raised me to stand up to people far more knowledgeable than I was. She had just barely graduated from high school herself, having refused to study or abide by the school's rules. Despite her scant formal education, however, during my childhood, I observed her sparring verbally with all sorts of professionals: doctors, lawyers, teachers, accountants. Her primary aim was to question everything and then freely posit her own theories about how things might be viewed differently. If she had any doubt as to whether the intellectual prowess of a modestly educated woman was equal to a man's, it never showed. Though I ended up with insecurities about my intellect that originated from her insatiable expectations, I never once doubted myself because of my gender. This is an important detail, given the still overwhelmingly male composition of the physician workforce in the U.S.

Russell's two diagnoses significantly complicated his medical care. Once he began having regular visits at both the spina bifida and CF clinics at Children's Hospital, it gradually dawned on me that no one was really in charge. No one was at the helm, responsible for oversight of all his care. No central person was taking stock of the multiple treatment regimens that were being implemented. Russell was being seen by seven clinicians based in two different specialty clinics—the pediatrician who coordinated the spina bifida clinic, a neurosurgeon, an orthopedic surgeon, a urologist, the nurse who coordinated the CF clinic, a pulmonologist, and the nutritionist on the CF team—as well as our general pediatrician. Yet none of them seemed to be looking at the big picture or regarding Russell in any kind of holistic way.

Both hospital clinics adopted a "team" approach that included regular discussions about Russell's status, though I suspect that once his corrective surgery was achieved, his case took up scant time in the spina bifida team discussions. The CF clinicians never mentioned his spina bifida to me, and the spina bifida clinicians never mentioned his CF—no one seemed to concern themselves with symptoms that other specialists were monitoring, or the collective array of treatments and tests that were being ordered. This was before electronic medical records were instituted—a welcome invention that, at least theoretically, gives today's doctors ready access to each patient's full information. Before electronic records were the norm, in order to stay current, Russell's clinicians would have had to exchange copies of the pen-and-paper charts they all kept. As far as I know, this never happened.

When I raised concerns about oversight with Dr. Brynelson,

our pediatrician, she acknowledged that the role of "coordinator" was more or less hers. She assured me that she reviewed the brief appointment notes that the spina bifida and CF teams forwarded to her, but she didn't proactively monitor what anyone was doing. She trusted that the specialists were attending to their defined and limited roles, ordering whatever screening tests or labs or prescription medications they felt were needed. She instead focused on the normal pediatric checklist of appropriate immunizations, child development, and growth.

Our current healthcare system is, of course, designed to function this way: primary care physicians (such as pediatricians) cover a broad array of topics to assess a patient's general health, while specialists concentrate on a narrow set of issues in greater depth. But the lack of oversight given to Russell's care as a whole struck me as bizarre. I became aware that no one was tracking how many x-rays or sonograms or blood draws were being ordered or with what frequency, and that no one but the pharmacist paid attention to the full array of prescribed medications. Furthermore, no one was thinking about the cumulative effect that all of these tests and medicine might be having on Russell as a whole person, a whole *baby*.

In the context of appointments, the absence of a holistic lens was even worse. Not only did each specialist focus solely on their specialty or their disease, some of them focused only on a specific organ or symptom(s) of interest. When Russell was examined by a urologist, for example, it was only bladder control and any abnormal retention of urine that claimed the doctor's attention.

At a routine spina bifida clinic appointment when Russell was around age two, the urologist marched into the exam room in his starched white coat and looked over his glasses at me. After grunting perfunctorily, he turned to the exam table where Russell was seated and began to remove his diapers without saying a word or even making eye contact with him. I was taken aback by the doctor's callous approach. The fact that Russell had to endure examination after examination by so many different and indifferent doctors drove me berserk. I wanted to protect my child from these strangers who didn't adore him or even know who he was beyond a cursory glance at a medical chart.

I put my arm around Russell's shoulders and stopped the urologist. "I'm sorry to interrupt," I said. "But before you continue, could you please greet my son directly and explain to him what it is that you're doing?"

"Oh, ah, sure, of course," the doctor muttered, clearly taken aback by my request.

This man had lost sight of the fact that this little penis was attached to a little human being who was constantly being poked and prodded, scrutinized like a bug under a microscope. The doctor was also insensitive as to how invasive his examinations might feel to a toddler whose sense of self was just beginning to emerge.

No doubt, confrontations like this one did not help my reputation at the hospital. Surely other parents must have had similar reactions, but I never witnessed another parent stand up to the doctors or question the validity of their generic protocols the way that I did. With all the wear and tear on Russell, it didn't take long for me to grow impatient with the whole world of modern medicine. Frankly, sometimes I even resented the doctors. A few of them displayed endless patience with my long lists of questions. But others seemed indifferent toward my efforts to learn and question and figure out solutions alongside them. Leave it to us, they seemed to say, and to the brilliant researchers who will one day discover a cure to save your son. With each successive appointment, however, "one day" seemed to fade further off into the distant future. I couldn't just wait—the dragon's hot breath was at my back.

Little by little, the tension of watching and waiting and complying got the better of me. I felt like a passenger in the back seat, headed downhill in some runaway car. No map, no confirmed route or destination, no master plan. At some point, my panic motivated me to clamber out of the back of the car and plunk myself down into the driver's seat (which was, after all, unoccupied). I didn't realize my lead role right from the beginning; I assumed that one of the doctors—maybe the CF specialist—would oversee Russell's case. After all, who was I to serve in such a critical role? I was no doctor! Who was I to judge which detail was critical to share with the other clinicians? Who was I to judge which examination, which test, which medication was necessary, and which one was not?

Eventually, I realized I was the only person monitoring who was doing what, when, and why. Perhaps more importantly, I was the only one witnessing the effect of all the doctors' independent decisions and actions on Russell. I had underestimated the value of my daily observations of his symptoms and health status. But now I realized that caring for my son day-in and day-out made me, and *only* me, qualified to be the driver of this vehicle. I wished someone had told me how to do this right from the beginning—or at least had told me that it needed to be done.

The truth is that if a child's health issues are at all complicated, as they were in Russell's case, and the parent doesn't take on the role of oversight, then coordination simply doesn't happen. So even though I didn't feel up to the task, the fact that no one else was doing it meant that I had to. I was idealistic as a young adult, convinced that most anything could be accomplished with sufficient perseverance and creativity. However skewed that optimistic mindset might be, it helped me to develop creative problem-solving skills as well as a bit of a Mighty Mouse complex. My response to my son's health challenges drew on this tendency. Besides, the alternatives to optimism—depression, alcohol, leaving it all up to the doctors, slowly watching him die—held little appeal.

Taking on this oversight role was a major challenge. For starters, I had absolutely no medical background. I knew precious little about the lungs and had no idea where that all-important CF organ, the pancreas, was even located, let alone what it did. Thus, one of my first endeavors was to learn all about CF. I had sheltered myself from the gruesome details of spina bifida, but I resolved to learn everything I possibly could about cystic fibrosis. I bought volumes of books on CF, anatomy and physiology textbooks, diagnostic guides, and a five-pound medical dictionary. The problem with the dictionary (aside from its weight and microscopic font) was that the definitions were all written in the same scientific Latin as the entries themselves. I often had to look up half the words used in a definition in order to understand the original entry. (Perhaps one day, someone will compile a user-friendly medical dictionary that affords parents and other laypeople crucial access to medical terminology.)

In my travels, I came across one book on CF (*Cystic Fibrosis: The Facts)* that successfully interwove medical and anatomical facts with personal anecdotes and touching testimonials.[1] My intellect was starving for information, and my heart was starving for comfort; I found this book to be an unusually humane rendition of the disease.

Armed with a shelf of new books, I began to learn about my son's disease and the basics of how the body functions. I studied the exocrine system, the digestive system, the respiratory system, and even the nervous system, given Russell's history of spina bifida. I was relentless in my search for knowledge and, for a time, not particularly good company for anyone who wasn't keen on being enlightened about the critical role of the pancreas, cellular-level transport of chloride, or *in utero* formation of the neural tube. Friends and relatives began to send me articles on all sorts of related topics, and I went to the National Library of Medicine in Bethesda, Maryland, in addition to searching the burgeoning Internet, looking for clues to a cure.

Several months after Russell's diagnosis with CF, I considered signing up for a basic course in anatomy and physiology at the local community college. Finding a babysitter for an early morning class was impossible, however, and my husband and I couldn't seem to resolve our conflicting schedules. I soon realized that Richard didn't share my ambition to fully understand CF or to explore research and alternative treatments. Eventually, he all but abdicated Russell's health care to me. I questioned my ability to make monumental decisions on my own and resented his absence. I was also aware that my obsession with saving my son added tension to an already beleaguered marriage, but I was unwilling to stop. In the end, Richard's non-involvement made for a simpler arrangement. I suppose it also signified his confidence in me.

The learning proved invaluable. I soon found I could follow along with the doctors as they talked in medical lingo about Russell's treatment and prognosis. I started to gain confidence and asked more questions, especially when new tests were ordered. Much later, I learned from Russell's medical records that, as soon as he had been admitted to Children's Hospital as a 12-hour-old newborn, he received x-rays of his spine; sonograms of his spine, head, kidneys, and bladder; and a special x-ray video of his urinary tract called a Voiding Cysto-Urethrogram (or VCUG). The battery of tests also included a chest x-ray that had been taken at the local hospital the night before his transfer to Children's Hospital.

Of course, I am grateful that modern medicine jumped in as soon as my son's birth defect surfaced, but all these tests, many involving exposure to radiation, were conducted within 24 hours of his birth (not to mention without our permission). I wonder if there might have been room for greater restraint with all the testing. Even if truly necessary, Russell was not in an emergency situation. Perhaps the tests could have been spread out over a week or even a month to allow his fragile newborn body time to recuperate from successive zapping, rather than barraging him all at once.

The pattern of test after test did not stop. The spina bifida doctors wanted to repeat sonograms of his kidneys every few months to reconfirm resolution of a minor reflux detected in his urinary tract immediately following birth, and they wanted to take x-rays to rule out a hip anomaly associated with spina bifida. The CF doctor ordered repeated chest x-rays to monitor the progressive lung damage anticipated with CF, and he ordered frequent blood tests to monitor Russell's electrolytes, vitamin levels, and the presence of infections or allergy-induced proteins in his blood.

Aside from the discomfort or anxiety that these tests caused Russell as a baby, I was concerned about the possible risks of so much testing. Though the amount of radiation used in x-rays has been drastically reduced over the years, radiation causes cancer. To my knowledge, the two clinics weren't conferring with each other about the x-rays they ordered, and I was not equipped to judge whether the cumulative radiation posed a danger for a young child.

Thus, I began to question the necessity of every single test. Of all the behaviors I exhibited as a take-charge mother, questioning the doctors' recommendations must have been irksome. But, it worked. My demands for the best way forward pushed them to think things through again, consider different and less risky options, and bring the unique characteristics of my little boy into focus instead of allowing them to lean so heavily on a generic set of CF or spina bifida protocols.

My goal was not to impede the use of technology in monitoring my son's health status. My hope was to take Russell out of the doctors' generic lens, urging them to view him as an individual who required unique consideration in terms of tests and treatment. It was easy to conclude that the schedule of appointments and routine tests related to his spina bifida were all part of a generic protocol (i.e., generally accepted procedures to be applied to any child with spina bifida). However, his particular defect was extremely minor in comparison with those of the clinic's other patients. Some of the tests were used to rule out more serious problems that were unlikely to accompany his minor defect. Rather than design an approach tailored to Russell's unique needs, however, the checklist of things to watch for stayed the same, with an underlying message of "Consider yourselves lucky—it could be a lot worse."

Each time I asked whether there was a need to conduct a screening or test, given the specific nature of his defect, I was treated with disdain and dismissed as a foolhardy mother who wasn't truly committed to her child's well-being. The doctor would check her watch, impatient to end our conversation. Even when I explained that Russell was also receiving x-rays and CT scans (computerized tomography) related to his cystic fibrosis, and that I was worried about cumulative radiation exposure, my concerns were ignored. I often left appointments feeling angry and consumed with self-doubt. Russell's medical conditions were new to me and only barely understandable, yet here I was arguing against the seasoned wisdom of specialists. What was I thinking?

I was well out of my league much of the time, especially in discussions about genetic mutations or the cellular-level cause and effect of CF, and the CF doctor was clearly taken aback by my aggressive search for answers. I suppose I could have simply trusted the experts—him, the researchers, the enzyme and medicine manufacturers—to do what was needed in terms of treatment. But I was no longer in the habit of automatically trusting anyone, especially when the doctors admitted that they could not save my son. I also wanted to be collaborative, to be viewed as a mother with a brain, not someone who meddled in affairs better left to the white coats.

One day, when discussing the various brands of pancreatic enzymes that were available, I asked Dr. Sullivan why the quantities of protease, amylase, and lipase differed in Russell's enzymes; what was the balance that was needed, and how do the enzymes interact with each other?

The doctor was stunned that I knew enough to even ask these types of questions. "You're the first parent in 20 years of practice to ever ask me about enzyme dosage!" he exclaimed. After returning home, I looked up everything I could in medical dictionaries or anatomy and physiology textbooks. Was I that unusual? I was smart. I could understand big words. The fact that I was trying to learn as much as possible in my quest to help Russell may have temporarily intrigued Dr. Sullivan, but he clearly valued my compliance above all else.

One conversation with Dr. Sullivan followed another. When he emphasized the promise of gene therapy "down the road," I pressed him to explain the role of the protein that is defective in the cells of CF lungs. I had been reading articles about genetic research, and I was hungry to understand what I had read.

After about 30 minutes of enduring my questions, Dr. Sullivan paused and suggested gingerly, "Lindsay, perhaps your role as a parent doesn't require quite so much detail." What did he mean by detail?

I heatedly countered, "It's not like I'm getting intellectual satisfaction out of this. I would never have voluntarily chosen a deadly disease to research if I hadn't been forced into this situation by Russell's diagnosis!"

Oops, I suddenly realized, that's exactly what he has chosen to do. I was so impatient to understand this disease that it made me quick to anger. It's a miracle no doctor has ever lost their temper with me. Perhaps their remove from the emotional quicksand in which I found myself enabled them to be endlessly patient. My thirst to understand the inner workings of the CF-affected body and the implications for treatment was never quenched. The information I waded through was highly technical, and there were times when I floundered or felt intimidated by unfamiliar terms and jargon. What always helped was the thought that if Russell could put up with the physical challenges of having CF, at least I could try to understand it. Time would tell whether my zealous efforts contributed anything meaningful to the mix.

The doctors' insistence on viewing Russell through a generic lens, coupled with a handful of incidents, caused me to finally lose all remaining blind faith I had in the medical establishment. One of these incidents occurred around age one. Russell finished eating his supper, after which I gave him a dose of his new antibiotic. Within moments, he began a high-pitched scream that didn't stop. After walking him around the living room for close to an hour, it suddenly occurred to me that maybe he was being pinched by his clothing or diaper. As I undressed him, I noticed a furious red and bumpy rash all over his chest—as clear a case of hives as I'd ever seen. A call to the pediatrician and a quickly administered dose of Benadryl got us through the night.

What caused this allergic reaction? Yogurt? Vanilla pudding? Maybe there were additives? In my effort to tease out the culprit, I called our pharmacist the next morning and asked if my son's new antibiotic (Cephalexin, or its brand name Keflex), which he had taken for the first time that night, might have caused his allergic reaction. She said it was quite possible and suggested that we stop using it and switch to a different drug.

I then called Dr. Sullivan at the hospital to ask if he would prescribe a different antibiotic. He was reluctant to rule out an entire "family" of antibiotics, given Russell's likely future need to alternate between antibiotics, since bacteria can build up resistance. Russell might suffer from infections of greater magnitude and severity. The doctor suggested that we test the hypothesis that Cephalexin had been the real culprit and try another dose. When I expressed concern about chancing a serious allergic reaction at home, he suggested that I contact our pediatrician and give Russell another dose in her office. "If problems arise," he reassured me, "Russell can always be transferred to the hospital."

I hung up and called our pediatrician. She said she would be reluctant to conduct such a test in her office, preferring that he instead be at the hospital clinic in case he had an adverse reaction that required an emergency response. I also called the pharmacist back for her opinion. She too was uncomfortable at the suggestion of a test that risked another reaction. By mid-day, we still hadn't resolved the issue. When I called Dr. Sullivan back, he was unimpressed with either the pediatrician's or the pharmacist's concerns. I was unimpressed with his casual demeanor, and I remained firm. "Okay, well, I'm happy to switch him to Pediazole for now," said Dr. Sullivan, "and experiment with a dose of Cephalexin the next time you come in to the hospital."

When Russell's next appointment rolled around, I refused to test the Cephalexin and risk an allergic reaction. For a number of years, Russell alternated between two antibiotics, Pediazole and Augmentin, taking them on an as-needed basis, and we never clearly pinpointed the cause of his allergic reaction.

A second incident occurred when Russell was several months shy of two. A routine blood test revealed a number of immature white cell "bands," possibly indicating a precursor condition to leukemia.[2] In my follow-up phone call with Dr. Sullivan, he talked of spinal taps and other tests. I panicked. Another dragon. I fantasized that I could whisk Russell off to the British Columbian wilderness where I would simply let him die, peacefully, without machines or tests or drug therapies or all the other horrors of modern medicine. If the universe wanted this child to die so badly that it dished out not one, not two, but *three* life-threatening conditions, then I would at least make sure he could die in peace. I refused the spinal tap, which would have been painful for Russell, and insisted on a repeat blood test instead. This second test revealed completely normal white cells, and the crisis passed. Dr. Sullivan shrugged it off as a mistake at the lab, and I learned the hard way to view diagnoses and test results in a measured light.

Later on in Russell's second year, a third incident occurred when a routine blood test revealed an excessive level of IgE (a type of immunoglobulin), suggesting that he was having an allergic reaction.[3] He had no symptoms of an allergy and no known allergens. Dr. Sullivan suggested radioallergosorbent serum (or RAST) tests that would be conducted with blood samples. Russell's RAST tests came back negative for most allergens and, all in all, were not terribly revealing. His IgE level continued to be unacceptably high at the next visit several months later, however, causing innumerable heated debates between Dr.

Sullivan and me about his suggested use of steroids to bring Russell's IgE level back down. I finally asked if Russell shouldn't be seen by an allergist before we introduced something as serious as steroids. Dr. Sullivan acquiesced and recommended a pediatric allergist associated with the hospital.

The allergist conducted a series of "scratch" tests on Russell's back, which revealed mild allergies to dairy, cockroaches, and Brazil nuts. The allergist also offered to conduct a different kind of skin test that would entail implanting potential allergens under the skin and watching for responses, including the possibility of anaphylactic shock. I refused these more accurate but risky tests. In contrast to Dr. Sullivan, the allergist told me he was not concerned by Russell's high IgE level, given the complete lack of observable allergic symptoms. Eventually, my son's IgE level normalized and we never figured out why it had been so high.

Despite Dr. Sullivan's imperfections, I appreciated that he always greeted Russell warmly and handled him gently while examining him. But my annoyance at these incidents started to eat away at my estimation of Dr. Sullivan's credibility and judgment. I began to view all the doctors as highly skilled, but fallible, technicians. I was no longer willing to simply comply or automatically do as I was instructed. Perhaps in direct proportion to how much my veneration of the doctors waned, my confidence in my own judgment grew. As soon as I started flexing this muscle, the doctors' pedestals were gone. I had evolved into a proactive caretaker who was assertive, questioning, and in charge.

From my perspective, no test was harmless, no medication was without side effects, and no examination was required unless there was a clear rationale. I questioned everything. Doctors' instructions often came in incomplete snippets, without full explanations or rationales. They expected me to trust quick judgments based on a 10 to 15-minute visit with them every three months. The tendency of all the pediatric specialists was to assume "ownership" of medical decisions relating to "their" specialty, organ, or symptom. The insertion of my judgment and critical thinking into their decision-making re-asserted the fact that my son (their patient) was *mine* not theirs. I did my best to be polite and respectful, or at least civil, but my primary concern was the well-being of my son.

Frankly, the clinical recommendations I received didn't always appear to be based on critical, let alone forward thinking. The hospital nutritionist, for example, advised me, "Russell should eat all those things that you and I should stay away from, in order to put on weight." She urged me to give him as much pizza, French fries, hamburgers, and shakes from fast food outlets as he would eat. When I voiced concerns with Dr. Sullivan that Russell might develop clogged arteries and heart disease later in life, he countered with the anecdote that "in all my years, I've never had a CF patient with high cholesterol." Maybe that's because *you've never had a patient reach 50*, I muttered sarcastically to myself.

Further, I knew from experience that whenever Russell spent time at the beach, his sinuses and lungs became notably clear of swelling and mucus, and his voice lost its nasal quality. But when I asked Dr. Sullivan at our next appointment, "Does living by the seashore make a difference for kids with CF?" I was told no. I looked forward to a time when my son was older and more comfortable with gadgets, so that I could experiment with having him inhale a mild saline solution with the use of the Steam Inhaler I had purchased. It seemed to me that it might make a difference. Sure enough, after the positive findings of an Australian study were released in 2004, daily home-based treatments using nebulizers to inhale an aerosolized "hypertonic" or high salt content solution became part of the CF protocol. But my adventures with Russell were taking place in the 1990's, before research had confirmed what was easily observable to me as his parent.

Further, I considered the discovery that the CFTR protein in lung cells (which was defective in CF lungs) was involved in the front-line defense against bacterial infection in addition to transporting chloride in and out of the cell. It made me wonder about the impact of CF on the immune system—something that I had never heard the doctors discuss. I wondered if the directive to "shut down" that the constant use of antibiotics relayed to the immune system might make things worse in lungs that were already insufficiently protected because of the defective CFTR protein. At the same time, there was conjecture that inflammation in the lungs and the sinuses (and perhaps elsewhere in the body) was an indicator of immune system overdrive.

I also began to wonder why the CF gene kept being passed down for thousands of years. Given the fact that only a generation ago, children with CF routinely died in infancy, why and how could the gene even survive? Was there a hidden advantage to a genetic mutation that resulted in the loss of life?[4] There had to be answers to all my questions—answers that might shed light on the solution.

The doctors' negative outlook on my son's long-term health was so entrenched that I worried that their treatment approach was short-sighted as a result. They saw Russell as temporarily treading water, holding his head just above the waterline while hungry sharks circled underneath, whereas I was hell-bent on his having the energy to swim long distance with a school of playful dolphins.

It was Richard's acupuncturist who initiated my exploration of alternative healing. When Richard told her about Russell's diagnosis with CF at one of his appointments, she offered to treat Russell for free. I was eager for us to try it. What did we have to lose by trying something new? This question was quickly followed by an even more persuasive thought: We had far too much to lose by *not* trying it!

I wasn't initially convinced that acupuncture had the capacity to alter my son's long-term prognosis, but what I did see after only a few treatments was an unmistakable decrease in symptoms following each session. His runny nose cleared up, his appetite improved, his energy rebounded, and he rekindled a keen interest in the world around him. My baby's true spirit began to emerge, and he started to laugh more frequently than cry. It turned all of our lives around! Each day began to feel like a gift instead of a death sentence, and I was inspired to go even further in the direction of alternative healing.

Acupuncture was like a tiny little carrot dangling on a string way off in the distance. I moved toward it, starving to reclaim hope. In private moments, I even timidly started to question his prognosis: Maybe the doctors are wrong? Maybe it *is* possible to slow this dreadful march toward an early death? Maybe there are treatments out there that the doctors don't know about? Could something totally outside the medical mainstream compete with a fatal prognosis dictated by his DNA? I knew the value of alternative healing because of my own positive experiences as a young adult, but I didn't know which approach might help Russell. I decided to find out.

Eventually, I added five alternative healing modalities into Russell's regimen: after he started acupuncture treatments, I found a pediatrician who prescribed homeopathic remedies. The homeopath recommended we also see a nutritionist she knew well. Then, with help from my sister, I found an osteopath. A year later, I finally found an herbalist. Each modality helped to resolve different CF symptoms: thinning the mucus in Russell's lungs or reducing inflammation in his sinuses, improving his appetite and increasing his absorption of nutrients which led to weight gain, and strengthening his overall constitution.

Once the alternative healing treatments began, and my son's symptoms lessened, I began to nurture a fanciful picture of his future. Our alternative healing practitioners placed emphasis on the positive changes Russell experienced, which caused the weight of his fatal prognosis to slowly shift. He would live to be

30, no, 50, no, 90! I knew my thinking was outrageous, heretical, even crazy. But once I started to feel optimistic, I began to crave it even more.

Several months after Russell's CF diagnosis, I got a phone call from Dr. Shaer, the pediatrician with the spina bifida clinic at the hospital. She asked me how we were coping with his disease.

"We're doing okay," I said wearily. "Well, I mean, at least my son doesn't have cancer. I really don't know how parents cope with something like that."

A silence followed. Finally, Dr. Shaer blurted out her confusion. "Lindsay, how can you possibly think that cancer would be any harder?" she asked. "CF is one of the worst diseases there is. At least some cancers can be cured!"

Dr. Shaer's reaction made me aware that I was in a weird state of denial. I have since redefined this "denial" as deliberate defiance, an energizing force, rather than a state of unconscious or passive denial. I only knew that I was grateful. I was no longer overwhelmed with despair, the hopeless despair that I imagined mothers of children with cancer must feel. Somehow I knew cancer would be worse.

I suspect that many parents in my situation try to fortify themselves, as I did, with the thought that out there somewhere there is a situation much worse than their own. Perhaps it makes the challenge at hand slightly more bearable. I was oddly aware of my state of denial and welcomed it, knowing that I was protecting myself against painful scenarios I could not face. This artificial "step up" energized me and made me feel strong and bold in my delusion that I could actually save my son's life.

My transformation into a self-assured take-charge mother changed how I viewed everything, including my marriage. Communication with Richard had always been thorny. But the added stress of our child's health challenges, coupled with my husband's reluctance to join me in my fervent efforts to save our son, took a final toll on our relationship. Richard and I separated in 1995, when Gus was seven and Russell was just shy of three.

The boys and I left the farm and moved 20 miles north to Frederick, Maryland, a quaint Civil War-era city where we would live for the next four years. I found a young, ambitious mortgage agent who miraculously helped me secure a loan, despite my erratic income and current self-employment, and I was able to buy my first house. There was plenty of work for me in Baltimore's emerging nonprofit sector, and my consulting business took off. Most work assignments could be completed at a distance via email and phone, with occasional meetings necessitating a 45-minute drive to Baltimore or D.C. Working from home meant that I could arrange my work life around the boys' elementary and nursery school schedules, an ideal set-up for a working single mother who couldn't afford a nanny or childcare after school.

Richard went through a difficult period after our separation. He lost his marriage, full-time parenting of his boys, and, eventually, his job and home on the farm as well. After a few months of sleeping on friends' floors, he found a new home of his own in Takoma Park, a small city in Maryland just across the

Washington, D.C. line. Once re-settled, he drove to and from Frederick every other weekend to collect his sons—a commitment that continued until the high school years, when peers beckoned the boys away from time with parents or family. Though he was originally somewhat reluctant to have children, once his sons were born, Richard was hooked. Ironically, after our divorce, he spent more focused time with his sons. And though their contact was limited by living apart, the boys knew he was only a phone call away. Shortly after our move, I also found a seasoned child therapist to help me support the boys' emotional upheaval during this big transition.

I had spent many years living alone as a young adult, but the loss of our marriage was hard for me too. I began to suffer from a panoply of minor health issues, unrelenting insomnia being the worst. Somewhere amid the added stress of single parenting and shouldering most of the financial burden alone, I found the strength to establish a new life. And, thankfully, once I got the hang of it, I actually found the change exhilarating.

Separating from my husband and an oppressive marriage (which, in all fairness, was equally oppressive for him) was liberating in a number of ways. In the beginning, I found it tricky to assume the dual role of both nurturing mother and disciplining father. I felt androgynous, pulled in opposing directions, and found myself being both loving and firm with my boys in new ways. Without the constant pressure of my husband's criticism and disagreement with my parenting methods, I was finally able to parent my way. I became freer with my children, more open to spontaneous jaunts and adventures, laughing with them to the point of tears.

The dictum of doing things my way overflowed into other areas of my life. I continued to pursue my consulting career, which flourished. I could decorate our house according to my own whims and taste, fixing it up as I wanted, without having to negotiate with a spouse. I painted the kitchen woodwork teal, turned the huge attic on the third floor into a home office, and had French doors installed throughout the house to bring in more light. The Mason & Hamlin baby grand piano I inherited from my grandmother took up the entire dining room. I planted a native redbud tree and a non-native Scotch broom bush out front, put in a tiny fish pond out back, and built a low fieldstone wall around a modest flower garden. The outdoor work did my soul (and body) good.

City life was an adjustment for the boys. Gus had left his best friend Aidan behind on the farm. They had been inseparable for seven years, literally since Gus's birth, and Gus was frustrated that he could no longer simply yell "Bye!" and run out the front door to go play. Furthermore, we didn't know anyone in this new city. After our move, the boys and I would walk throughout the neighborhood in the evenings, "scouting" for other children. In no time, we happily discovered another family with two boys around the same ages living down the street. Miraculously, there was even a friend for me—their mother, Teresa.

As we settled into our new home, little by little, the farm became a nostalgic memory. The boys eagerly anticipated

Richard's arrival on his alternate weekends and were always overjoyed to see him. Gus missed his father terribly after our separation and began to have bouts of intense anger; Russell missed Richard too, but he was very young and adapted more easily. When they returned on Sunday nights, our reunions were heavenly for me—I missed my boys terribly while they were gone. But re-adjusting back into our household sometimes entailed angry words between Gus and me.

"I don't need to go to bed yet!" he'd insist, despite his obvious fatigue.

"You have school tomorrow! Now get to bed!" I'd call to him up the stairs.

"Dad doesn't make me!" he'd retort grumpily.

I knew it was hard for him to say goodbye to his father, but I didn't realize just how torn Gus felt until he made a quiet plea one evening.

"Mommy, I don't know where my home is," he said following yet another battle over bedtime.

"Oh sweetie, you have two homes now—one with me and Russell, and the other with your dad and Russell. I know it's confusing and I'm so sorry," I said, wanting to help him make sense of our fractured family and his divided loyalties. The divorce had been mandatory for my personal well-being, but it was painful to witness just how hard separation from their father was for my boys.

Building a new life with my sons and launching a consulting career nurtured my self-confidence. I began to trust my gut, something the women of my generation were taught not to do. I trusted my instincts as a mother and my own innate healing capacity. Even before Russell's actual diagnosis with CF, I caught myself doing odd things, gestures and physical movements to heal him. For example, as a baby, when Russell caught a cold and was overwhelmed with thick mucus in his lungs, I instinctively thumped against his chest and back to help him clear the mucus. Other CF parents have told me they did the same thing pre-diagnosis.

Far stranger, during those early days, I found myself pulling at Russell's chest without touching him. I would move toward his chest with an open hand, clench something in my fist that I could not see or feel but had a sense was there, and pull it out of his chest. I found these actions bizarre, but felt compelled to continue. Though I didn't know what I was doing, I was convinced on a purely instinctual level that I was pulling mucus out of his lungs. My odd "treatments" seemed to benefit him, clearing his airways in the process. Years later, I learned that what I had been doing was a rough facsimile of hands-on healing methods used in Reiki or other intuitive healing.

At times, I would sit with Russell in my lap, him facing me with his little legs wrapped around my hips, reminding me of a mother monkey and her baby. I would close my eyes and sit quietly, breathing deeply and slowly, in and out, offering him "energy" through my chest into his. These times soothed him like nothing else. I came to feel this energy transfer quite clearly and even became alarmed one time as I felt him suck away too much of my own energy. It was a reminder that I needed to take care of myself if I were to continue to be strong enough to care for him.

Such energy exchanges are real. Energy fields surround all animate objects, and energy is continuously being transferred from one organism to another. I believe that our energy "feeding" was a primal ability that I accessed. It was healing for both him and for me. Unfortunately, mothers are taught to belittle or dismiss their innate ability to heal their own children and, instead, to elevate the doctor's ability to identify symptoms and prescribe treatments. Parents' descriptions of a child's ills are often given scant weight, cut short by impatient practitioners with an eye on the clock and minds focused on their standard checklist. Rather than being peripheral, however, a mother's (or father's) active role in healing can be pivotal to a child's recuperation and well-being. No one knows a child the way a doting mother does, and no one can flood her child's little body with warmth and goodness the way a mother can. True love, deep love, goes a long way toward healing.

One weekend when the boys were off with their father, I rented the movie *Lorenzo's Oil*, Hollywood's rendition of a true story about parents who were determined to find a cure to their son's rare, untreatable condition (adrenoleukodystrophy or ALD). I watched the story unfold through a flood of tears: the medical establishment's ease in condemning a small child to death; the doctors' insensitivity to the parents' suffering and the huge challenges assumed by Lorenzo's parents; the pivotal role of a curiosity-driven scientist; the aunt's courage to step in as a guinea pig for their experimental treatments; and the major implications of their discovery (invention, really) for other children who shared Lorenzo's terrible affliction. Their story made me realize that any doubts I had about defeating Russell's deadly disease were only in my mind—there was really nothing but a lack of confidence to keep me from forging ahead. This realization was key to my transformation and helped me to appreciate both the doctors' vast knowledge and my own creative intelligence. I no longer aimed to know as much clinical detail as they did, but I continued to pick their brains in order to individualize Russell's treatment. Lorenzo's story encouraged me to take my own scientific theories seriously and to keep looking for answers that I hoped were out there somewhere.

Chapter 4

Acupuncture

Faith is taking the first step even when you don't see the whole staircase.

Dr. Martin Luther King, Jr. (1929-1968)

FOR YEARS, POLLEN IN BOTH THE SPRING AND FALL activated my husband Richard's allergies, giving him flu-like symptoms that landed him in bed, sometimes for a week at a time. Washington, D.C. is a beautiful city filled with hundreds of species of exotic trees, shrubs, and grasses—gifts to American presidents from countless foreign dignitaries over the years. But unfortunately, for anyone who suffers from allergies, an unintended consequence of all this beauty is a never-ending parade of pollens.

One day in the fall of 1992, while visiting with our friend, Daniel, at his Japanese import gift store in Dupont Circle, Richard picked up a flyer advertising acupuncture as he headed out of the store. The flyer claimed that acupuncture treatments could provide relief from a variety of ailments, including allergies. For years, Richard had tried allergy shots and multiple medications for symptom relief, but nothing had worked. So when he showed me the flyer and its claim about allergy relief, I urged him to give acupuncture a try.

Unbeknownst to us at the time, Richard's bringing home this flyer was not only his introduction to acupuncture—it was the first step in Russell's odyssey with alternative healing as well.

I had experienced acupuncture myself while living in Boston as a young adult. Pharmaceuticals had failed to curb painful menstrual cramps that surfaced following the insertion of an IUD (intrauterine contraceptive device) called the Dalkon Shield.[4] Even several years after its removal, my monthly cramps hadn't eased up at all. The pain compelled me to stay in bed for an entire day each cycle, wreaking havoc on my work life. The gynecologist and I exhausted a long list of pharmaceuticals trying to get rid of my cramps, to no avail.

No one I knew had experienced acupuncture (this was the 1970's), but I heard about a local acupuncturist who had been trained in Traditional Chinese Medicine in England and decided to see if acupuncture might help lessen the cramps. At my first appointment, the acupuncturist placed needles in "source" points located in the triangular webbing between the thumb and forefinger of each hand. She then left me lying on my back on the treatment table in a darkened room for about twenty minutes, with the needles still in my hands. After this first treatment, I went home and, as if drugged, slept practically non-stop for three days. Another of my early treatments caused an intense outburst of weeping (for no apparent reason) which the acupuncturist said was quite common. As the months passed, I noticed a significant decrease in painful cramps and became a convert to the possibilities offered by acupuncture. I continued treatments for about six months until I could no longer afford them. (The cramps finally went away completely a decade later when I had my first child.)

Richard soon started treatments with Mary White—the acupuncturist whose flyer he had brought home. Mary had just graduated from acupuncture school and was seeking new clients to fill the private practice she had recently established in Columbia, Maryland. For the first couple of months of treatments, Richard made the 45-minute drive back and forth to Mary's office every two weeks. Eventually his appointments spread out to once every three and then four weeks. The following spring, after only five months of acupuncture, Richard sailed through allergy season with nary a sniffle, despite an unusually high pollen count. The difference was astounding. In addition to his allergic symptoms being gone, he also exuded a new calm, taking stressors in stride where before he might have reacted with quick frustration. Without understanding how it could be so, I credited acupuncture with the unexpected change in Richard's attitude as well as his lack of allergy symptoms.

At each appointment, Mary asked Richard to give her a full picture of his physical, emotional, and psychological state in order to select which acupuncture points to treat. She would ask about his digestion, his sleeping, his moods, his energy level, his work life, his home life—all of which indicated to her which meridians and points needed stimulation. In April, when his monthly appointment with Mary followed on the heels of Russell's diagnosis with CF, Richard shared our most recent trauma with her as part of his ritual pre-treatment interview. As she listened to the story of Russell's now second serious diagnosis, Mary made a silent vow to help our son and extended an offer to treat our baby for free. She acknowledged to Richard that she had had no prior experience treating children and wanted to take some time to investigate children's acupuncture before initiating her treatment of Russell. She also said that she would prefer to treat him in our home where he would be more at ease than in an unknown and impersonal office setting. Given our shaky finances, the "free-of-charge" held as much appeal as anything else. Without even consulting me, Richard jumped at her offer and scheduled a time for her to come out to the farm.

Mary came to our home for the first time in early May, a month after Russell's diagnosis with CF. After introducing ourselves, Mary and I sat on the couch (with me holding Russell in my lap) while she grilled me gently with a multitude of questions about Russell's daily life and well-being. Her questions were almost mundane: What does he like to eat? What does he like to do? Are his moods changeable? What upsets him? Does he sleep well? How does he react to new people or new situations? After a while, I became impatient with what felt like a frivolous non-medical line of questioning and interrupted her. "Don't you need information about the spina bifida and cystic fibrosis?" I asked. Russell was still a very sick little baby, and his symptoms colored his entire existence. I couldn't believe we were spending all this time on his eating and sleeping habits or moods, when we had more serious topics to cover!

She told me that these medical details were not really necessary and went on to explain that Traditional Chinese Medicine doesn't approach health challenges (she never once used the word "disease") in the same way that Western medicine does. Reading into my perplexed expression, she could see that I wanted badly to convey at least some of the medical details. She quickly adjusted her seating to face me more squarely and said with a smile, "But if you would like to describe his medical diagnoses, I'll be glad to listen." That was all the permission I needed to launch into the gobs of technical detail that I had learned over the previous eight months for which I had had no prior outlet. Poor Mary. I was still attempting to make sense of something too big and scary to grasp.

I had no idea what to expect, but Mary took me completely by surprise. She was a quiet, slim, spiritual soul with a gentle voice and affect, who had made an unlikely migration from international trade law to Traditional Chinese Medicine. Her strong healing skills, honed in close to 600 hours of supervised clinical practice, were amplified by a sharp legalistic mind mixed with a soft spiritual nature. I soon became transfixed by her explanations of acupuncture and the beautifully allegoric names of points, such as *Cloud Gate* (a point along the lung meridian on the chest) and *Hard Bargain* (a point along the stomach meridian located on the second toe). When I hungered for more concrete detail, she gave me physiological explanations of how Russell's symptoms could be caused by an organ being "out of balance" or the normal flow of "*chi*" (or energy) being blocked. Her lessons freely crisscrossed between the realms of science and spirit, and I was soon aware that we were embarking on a journey of healing unlike any I'd ever known.

Russell was only eight months old when he started receiving acupuncture. Our desperation about his dire prognosis undoubtedly predisposed us to trying an approach that was so far outside the boundaries of mainstream medicine. The complete disappearance of Richard's allergy symptoms after Mary started treating him was also very persuasive. Even so, for a long while, I juggled contradictory perspectives—on the one hand, I was a skeptic who was sure that only the doctors had the appropriate knowledge and therefore the authority to decide what would help my son battle this serious disease; on the other hand, in spite of the doctors' pessimism (or maybe because of it), I was a desperate dreamer intent on delving into anything that might better Russell's odds.

Acupuncture is an ancient form of healing that originated in China thousands of years ago. There is no written record of its origins or early use, but one story that has been handed down is that Chinese healers close to the battlefield noticed that warriors who sustained non-fatal injuries caused by an arrow or spear often experienced an improvement in a health condition completely unrelated to the injury (essentially a positive if unexpected side effect of sustaining their wound).[1] This inspired healers to embark on an exploration of pressure points that eventually revealed a total of 12 primary meridians in the body and hundreds of points located along each of those meridians, as well as the impact that stimulation of each point had on organs and major bodily functions. It required, no doubt, a methodical approach and lengthy period of experimentation in order to fully understand and codify this approach to human healing.

Acupuncture is based on the principle that a fundamental life energy called *chi* flows along energy channels (or meridians) located throughout the body, entering and exiting at an organized series of precise locations or "points." Each meridian corresponds to a different organ or bodily function and represents both the physical and psycho-spiritual aspects of those functions. Acupuncture also acknowledges five major elements of existence: water, wood, fire, earth, and metal. Each of these elements is associated with a pair of organs that correlate with physiological functions in the body. Chinese medicine posits that any blockage to the flow of *chi* impacts organs and, over time, can compromise their function. Blockages can also cause one or more of the elements to become unbalanced, also compromising health. As points along meridians are stimulated with special needles or fingertip pressure, the flow of *chi* is unblocked and rekindled. As a result, the elements are essentially recalibrated and put back into a properly balanced state, and the organs or physiological functions that were impeded are corrected. Balance is a crucial concept in Chinese medicine and is always the end goal of healing.

These beliefs about energy and the five elements diverge dramatically from the beliefs that frame our Western medical science, although they are not at all mutually exclusive and can even be seen as parallel or complementary.[2] Around the time that Mary started treating Russell in 1993, acupuncture was just beginning to gain credibility in the U.S. and recent changes in State regulations had made it possible for licensed acupuncturists to practice in Maryland without the supervision of a physician. Mary earned a Master of Acupuncture degree (M.Ac.) from the Tai Sophia Institute—a highly respected acupuncture school founded in the 1970's in Columbia, Maryland.[3] She was also licensed by the Maryland Board of Acupuncture (L.Ac.), and held a Diplomate of Acupuncture (Dipl.Ac.) from the National Commission for the Certification of Acupuncturists (NCCA). Her credentials simply backed up the intuitive sense I had that Mary was an extraordinary healer. They are important guides for the novice, however, when attempting to distinguish a thoroughly trained and experienced professional from the mail-order variety.

Russell was absolutely enchanted with Mary, fascinated by her long dangly earrings and the wooden meditation beads that wound around her wrist. He wasn't walking yet, but drawn in by her gentle spirit, he would crawl onto her lap to get a closer look. She always insisted on sitting on the floor of the rustic milk barn where we lived, in order to be accessible to a crawling baby. This also placed her within reach of our pack of curious cats and dogs who would maul her in a good-natured sort of way before plunking down beside "their" baby to keep watch.

For Russell's first acupuncture treatment, Mary inserted several needles just above and below the dramatic 3-inch horizontal scar on his lower back (a vestige of the surgery to correct his tethered cord).

"It's possible that these pathways were interrupted by the development of scar tissue following surgery," she explained. "This treatment will create a new bridge for the energy to flow."

From the start, Mary was very relaxed and tender with Russell. No one had to hold him down. She would gently lay him on the floor and roll him over onto his stomach to treat his back, or tenderly cradle his foot in her hand while she quickly inserted and then removed an acupuncture needle—talking quietly to him the whole time. Russell's older brother, Gus, just five years old at the time, watched these treatments with wide-eyed fascination.

As Russell's treatments progressed, Mary inserted needles into ankle, knee, wrist, and face points. If he felt any pain, it was momentary and slight. Unlike babies or small children receiving shots at the doctor, however, he never once cried or recoiled from Mary. One time, she treated a point located on the top of his foot and he immediately convulsed into giggles. There was no other possible explanation for his spontaneous joy than that he had experienced a lovely sensation of energy ripple through his body. We dubbed the point—where he was treated any number of times thereafter and always with the same effect—his "giggle point."

Mary cautioned me that it often takes a year, or a complete cycle of the four seasons, for a person to begin to reap the full benefits of acupuncture treatments. I had witnessed the impressive impact that acupuncture had had on Richard's allergies in well under a year and didn't need a lot of convincing that Russell might also benefit. I was, of course, keen about the potential effect on Russell's lungs and sinuses. But what I really hoped was that the acupuncture would help him holistically and not simply relieve his symptoms. Even though I was still unsure of what all of this meant, I wanted acupuncture to strengthen his basic constitution and unblock the flow of energy throughout his body, helping to make him as healthy and strong as possible. My hope was to free him of any extraneous burdens that he might have now or in the future, so that his body could focus its primary attention on the challenges of CF.

Mary most often treated Russell's water element, but also his wood, earth, and metal elements. (She concluded that he manifested plenty of fire already, so this element rarely required stimulation.) By treating and rebalancing his **water** element, Mary was working to strengthen his spine (a critical goal, given his history of spina bifida and subsequent surgery on his spinal cord), keep his electrolytes in balance, and generally balance all of his bodily fluids. There is also a taste associated with each of the elements according to Chinese medicine. The water element is associated with salt—a major issue in the context of CF. (Interestingly enough, even as a baby, being by the sea—a setting that combined water and salt—rejuvenated him like no other place.) Both the CF doctor and Mary encouraged Russell to eat salty foods. The doctor's aim was to replenish the sodium chloride that was lost through excessive sweating, while Mary's aim was to strengthen Russell's water element, bones, and overall vigor, and ultimately help him to get the most out of his inherited vitality and constitution.

The **wood** element is considered one of the most important pediatric elements, because it promotes growth during the enormously critical period of childhood and also serves to bolster the immune system. The CF doctor had told us that good growth was a significant factor in a child's long-term prognosis. (Russell's initial diagnosis with "failure to thrive"—in his case, a lack of weight gain and growth despite an appropriate daily intake of calories—contributed as much to his eventual diagnosis with CF as his other symptoms.) By treating Russell's wood element, Mary worked to promote growth and to protect him from the daily onslaught of bacteria and viruses that threatened to develop into serious infections of the lungs.

The **earth** element, also considered a vitally important pediatric element, is associated with digestion and assimilation. It is especially important to treat when children have a condition such as CF that can lead to "wasting." By treating and rebalancing Russell's earth element, Mary was working to increase his appetite and strengthen his capacity to metabolize food and assimilate essential nutrients. Russell's "giggle point" on his foot, which Mary treated often, stimulated this earth element.

Finally, the **metal** element is involved with the taking in and letting go of energy at all levels. It is associated with the important elimination functions of the colon and the lungs, both clearly pertinent in Russell's case. By treating his metal element, Mary was working to strengthen the capacity of his colon to absorb nutrients and to eliminate waste. These treatments also helped to strengthen the capacity of his lungs to inhale and exhale, so that he was able to take in a greater quantity of oxygen and empty his lungs more fully. This element also helped him to clear his lungs of the lethal mucus typical of CF. Another function of the metal element is to create a protective layer of energy on the skin, called *wei ch'i*, which helps to generally protect against the invasion of germs.

Nine months after first initiating Russell's acupuncture, I began to notice a distinct pattern. He was just over a year and a half and had endured a second long winter fraught with chronic ear infections and almost continuous antibiotics. His acupuncture treatments, usually geared toward rebalancing his water or wood elements, began to have a noticeable and positive effect. Almost immediately after his treatments, his appetite and energy level increased. By the next day, the mucus in his nose lessened, his coughing decreased, and smiles, giggles, and his true happy nature would all reemerge. This rebound, little by little, would then slowly dissipate such that, as the three-week intervals between acupuncture treatments came to a close, his nose would be runny again, he would be coughing again, and his energy level, mood, and appetite would all be low.

Thus, by the time Mary came back to our home to treat Russell, he was generally run-down and cranky again. This never discouraged her, even though she didn't witness the improvements that Richard and I observed. She would listen carefully to my reports of Russell's rebound and ask me for as much detail about his steady subsequent decline as I could remember. (This is a perfect example of how a parent's observations are valued by alternative healing practitioners.) The acupuncture treatment he received at the appointment would then turn the decline around completely in a matter of minutes, transforming Russell back into a happy, energized, and hungry baby.

At first, I tended to dismiss the improvements that I repeatedly observed as wishful thinking. How could a tiny little needle inserted into one tiny little spot make a baby feel so much better? How could treating a point on his foot clear up the mucus in his nose, or strengthen his appetite or improve his mood? It wasn't logical. Yet I witnessed this dramatic transformation over and over again with each successive treatment. Eventually, when the positive turnaround started to last longer and longer between appointments, the lack of logic no longer mattered.

Once four full seasons of acupuncture had passed, Russell's uplift spanned the full three weeks between treatments. At that point, the aim of his treatments was no longer to improve his condition, but became instead to sustain the good results. I still didn't understand how acupuncture worked, but I couldn't deny that it was working. Everyone noticed the improvement in Russell's energy and mood and appearance—even the doctors. There was no way to explain away his rejuvenation as the power of suggestion, particularly since he was a baby and pre-verbal. And even if my positive attitude toward Mary and acupuncture caused a temporary lift in his mood, this couldn't possibly sustain his well-being over time. Though acupuncture was not being credited by the skeptical members of our family or the doctors, everyone felt compelled to applaud the steady improvement in his health.

For that first year, Mary came out to our home in Darnestown, making the 45-minute drive from her own home in Columbia. These house calls—considered outdated and an exaggeration of a doctor's normal commitment by many—assisted Russell in feeling that Mary was someone to be trusted. Her visits were just another part of his everyday life, and all of us were there to observe his treatments and comfortably interact with Mary ourselves. When she first began treating him, Mary came every other week for two months. Following that initial period, she tapered down to once every three to four weeks. By the time a year passed, Russell had grown comfortable with his treatments and she asked me to start bringing him to her office in Columbia instead of continuing her home visits. I was actually glad. Eliminating her commute helped to assuage the mounting guilt I felt at not paying her anything for Russell's treatments.

After a year of acupuncture, Russell's rebound in health and increased energy filled him with joy, simply because he felt so good most of the time. This is an ambitious goal in the context of CF—a disease that debilitates the broad-reaching exocrine system and typically causes its victims to feel consistently lousy. Strengthening each of the elements and their functions early on in life helps to keep a child in a vigorous state, especially in the context of a medical challenge where the child's health may be compromised. The resultant good growth, assimilation of nutrients, proper elimination, protection from germs, and overall vigor make for a healthy and happy child. The earlier this holistic rebalance and reinvigoration occurs in a child's life, the less time there is for the child's body to fully imprint (or adjust to) any negative health burdens. Such an early revitalization, of course, improves the child's long-term prognosis.

The major difference between the conventional medical approach and acupuncture was that Russell's acupuncture treatments were primarily focused on the positive—building on his inherited constitutional strengths and enhancing his vigor or foundational energy—where conventional medicine sought to suppress negative symptoms and stave off the predicted decline for as long as possible. Mary sought to renew and then sustain his organs' functionality as well as build up his innate capacity to ward off disease. Acupuncture supported him on a much deeper level than merely controlling his symptoms or slowing the progression of CF. It was premised on the belief that his body had an innate ability to change and correct the imbalances, essentially revert back to its originally intended state of good health, despite a genetic code and prognosis that conventional medicine believed to be immutable.

In the early years, Russell's renewed vigor on the playground, his clear lungs, his ability to effectively fight off germs, and his steady climb back up the growth chart due to his improved assimilation of nutrients all contrasted sharply with the predicted decline. The doctors not only acknowledged a general lack of deterioration, they admitted that he was actually becoming healthier as evidenced by improved lab results, weight gain, and a decrease in head colds and infections. I was amazed that acupuncture was having such a profound influence on both his health and his quality of life. I started to consider that there might be a lasting impact that would go beyond the current rebound that we were witnessing. Hope began to seep in around the edges and give me relief from endless worrying.

After separating from my husband in 1995 and becoming a single parent, I realized how critical my own well-being was to my ability to nurture my children, and I decided to take proactive steps toward protecting my health. I asked Mary to start treating me in addition to treating Russell. Today, acupuncture is no longer a novelty, and licensed practitioners abound. Yet acupuncture is still surprisingly uncommon among my friends and acquaintances, and I don't know anyone who has sought out acupuncture treatments for their baby. Thus, even though my primary aim in this book is to describe Russell's experience of alternative healing, I share a bit of my own experience to give readers who have never tried acupuncture an idea of what it's like.

Acupuncture produces sensations unlike anything else I've ever experienced. Frankly, I'm often at a loss for words as to how to describe treatments, because the physical sensations and concepts of healing are so completely outside our American medical experience (and the English language).

Sometimes when a point is stimulated, the effect is somewhat painful, like a mild electric shock. Other points are incredibly subtle and can even be soothing, sending a gentle buzz or ripple of energy through my hand or up my leg. Sometimes I feel the precise point where the needle is inserted, and then also have an immediate sensation somewhere else in my body. Occasionally, I can feel a point (without looking at it) before the needle is even inserted. When I first started acupuncture with Mary, I often "saw" my treatments as a momentary flash of bright light, rather than feeling it in any sort of physical way. Though these experiences didn't make any sense according to my Western logic, I came to accept them as real.

One time, while lying on my back, Mary treated me just below each eye and then lower down on my face to the side of each nostril. I closed my eyes and distinctly felt a tear slowly roll down one cheek, connecting the upper point to the lower one.

"What are those points called?" I asked without opening my eyes.

"*Received Tears*," Mary answered.

"Wow," I said, without yet divulging the sensation of a tear rolling down my cheek. "Are the upper and lower points connected somehow?"

"Yes, they are—they're entry and exit points on adjacent meridians."

I reached up and felt my cheek and was stunned to find it bone dry. I suddenly realized that, since I was lying flat on my back, if there had been a real tear, gravity would have caused the tear to roll off the side of my face at my temple, not roll horizontally toward my chin. I shivered slightly and told her what I had experienced. She was as excited as I was, though my experience was well within the norm for acupuncture and came as no great surprise to her.

Another time, she treated kidney points on either side of my breastbone. I confirmed the treatment on my left side, and she then walked around to the other side of the table in order to treat my right side. She inserted the needle but I felt absolutely nothing. Sometimes Mary could tell from the feel of the needle whether or not her aim was off. But much of the time, she asked me to confirm. "Did you feel that?" she asked, already convinced that she might be slightly off. "I don't think you got it," I said, "I didn't feel anything." Her second insertion was also off. "Did you feel *that*?" she asked. "No," I said. As she continued to feel around with her finger and prepared to insert the needle for a third time, I suddenly very distinctly felt where the point was located. "Wait!" I said, "I feel the point. It's just over here," indicating the spot with my finger. Sure enough, when she inserted the needle where I had indicated, she hit the point like a bull's-eye. "I felt it!" I declared. I was thoroughly taken aback by my accuracy. Though I had little knowledge of the whereabouts of points or meridians, my body had clearly communicated to me exactly where the point was located. This notion was a lot more problematic for me to take in than for Mary. Over the years, she had heard many an amazing story about acupuncture, including one about monks who treated each other at a distance, without even touching.

During my treatments, needles were sometimes reluctant to come out, as if there were a tiny creature just below the surface of the skin gripping that needle tip for all it's worth, causing a little pitch tent of skin at the insertion point. The stimulation of a point can literally create a vortex, or gathering of intense *chi,* which can cause a kind of suction effect when the acupuncturist goes to remove the needle. It wasn't at all painful and made me laugh, renewing my emphatic belief that, when imbalanced, these points crave attention.

At the beginning of each of my treatments, just as she had done with Richard, Mary asked me to tell her all about my physical, emotional, and psychological state. Once she grew to know me well after several years of treatments, she would simply ask me, "What do you need from your treatment today?" Sometimes I would give her a quick response, such as, "I haven't been sleeping well. I'd love to be able to fall asleep more quickly and stay asleep through the night." Over time, I grew comfortable with less concrete and more metaphorical descriptions. One acupuncture appointment coincided with a recently diagnosed breast abscess and major stress from a work assignment. Instead of going into all of this detail when she asked what I needed, however, I simply told her, "I need endurance, faith, and calm." For the uninitiated, this must seem rather peculiar. All I can say is that after that particular treatment, my energy level, self-confidence, and overall sense of calm were all restored.

Mary always listened closely to my description of how each treatment felt with both enthusiasm and awe. Even after years of training and practice, she was still reverent toward acupuncture's effects. Though she understood thoroughly the scientific whys and wherefores of the body's meridians and the need to unblock and restore the flow of energy, Mary was also convinced that the true reason that acupuncture works is that it taps into the greater energy of the Universe. She saw herself merely as forging a link with this endless energy source, rather than actively making something happen in a conventional medical sense. This unique respect for the key role that the Universe plays in healing has done my soul good. As an avowed atheist for most of my adult life (perhaps more of an agnostic as I age), as well as a conventionally-schooled public health researcher who values empirical evidence, I've had to work at being open to these types of foreign concepts. In the end, though I still do not fully understand how acupuncture works, I cannot argue with its observable and lasting results.

One time, an appointment with Mary coincided with my having just lost my 84-year-old mother-in-law, Geraldine, in a horrible car accident. Geraldine was from a different generation, and we often disagreed about a woman's proper role in life. But she doted on her grandsons and, because of that, held a special place in my heart. For several years, I had been trying to entice her to come live with me and the boys in our home in Frederick, so that I could take care of her as she aged. But she was a stubbornly independent woman—an attribute I admired—and insisted on remaining alone in her home in northwest Washington, D.C. The day of the accident, she and a friend of hers who was in her 90's had gone out for a pleasure drive in the countryside. The police later surmised that an errant driver had sped toward them around a blind curve, crossing into their lane and forcing Geraldine's car off the road and into a phone pole. Both women died on impact. The violence of her death shocked us all.

At this particular appointment, Mary began her routine questioning about my well-being while the boys sat quietly in the next room, subdued with the weight of their own sadness at losing their grandmother. Upon hearing about the grief I was experiencing, Mary became very still, almost meditative. Once I was lying comfortably on the table, she suggested that we begin my treatment with the aptly named "Palace of Weariness"—points located in the center of each palm. The point felt like a bee sting, with the stinging continuing for a good 10 to 15 seconds after the needles were removed. She then said that she was going to treat points called "Supreme Radiance" located on my feet to support me in my state of exhaustion. "It's kind of like a 'Club Med' point," she joked. As she turned away to get a fresh needle, I suddenly realized that I already knew at least generally where these points were located—somewhere on the top of my feet. I didn't say anything. Sure enough, that was where she inserted the needles. She continued on, describing the next point she planned to treat, called "Heavenly Pivot." Without her revealing anything about its location, I knew this point would be somewhere on my stomach. It was indeed located on either side of my belly button.

"I can tell where you're going to treat me!" I said with amazement. "I knew you were going to treat the top of my foot and then somewhere on my stomach before you treated me. How can I possibly know that?" I asked.

She smiled, and without answering my question, said that she'd like to treat a fourth and final point. "Do you know where it is?" she asked with a twinkle in her eye before divulging a word about the point she had in mind.

I closed my eyes. "Yup. It's right here," I answered in surprise, pointing to the slight dips in the middle of my lowest ribs.

"Yes," she said, "It's called 'Gate of Hope'."

"How on earth could I know where you're going to treat me?"

"Well," she said, "some people are very in tune with their bodies and they can actually tell which points need to be stimulated."

"Do you have other patients who know?" I asked.

"Sure," she responded. I was dumbfounded. At that

moment, I wished that all the cynics of the world could experience acupuncture for themselves and delight in this mysterious healing practice firsthand. The next morning, I woke up with a sense of renewed calm and felt energized for the first time in weeks.

Medical diagnoses and acupuncture aside, life went on. In early 1999, the boys and I moved again. I had landed a long-term consulting assignment with a hospital in Baltimore, and the hour-long daily commute between Frederick and Baltimore on top of very long and demanding workdays was taking a toll. With the move to Baltimore, we now had a slightly shorter drive to Columbia, and Russell and I continued our acupuncture treatments with Mary. Soon after our move, Mary suggested that she start treating Gus as well, not because he had any health problems, but because acupuncture could help keep him healthy. Frankly, it hadn't occurred to me that Gus would even benefit from acupuncture because he was so healthy, but I readily agreed with Mary's suggestion and welcomed the thought of Gus actively joining his brother and me in this amazing realm. I also made Mary promise to accept payment for Gus' treatments. (I had been paying her for my treatments, but she still refused to accept payment for Russell's.)

I have an indelible picture in my mind of Gus's first acupuncture treatment at age 11. He sat in a straight-backed chair, facing backwards per Mary's instructions, with his shirt off and his long arms draped over the back of the chair.

As soon as he sat down, he resumed reading his book and ignored us, as if nothing unusual were happening. Mary used a pen to mark the points that she planned to treat down the length of his back on either side of his spine for an initial "clearing" treatment. She then inserted at least a dozen needles one by one and left them in for 15 to 20 minutes. Gus sat very still, engrossed in *Forgotten Realms* or *Star Wars*—some worn out paperback that he was rereading for the umpteenth time. It made us all chuckle to watch him take in this new experience in such an offhand manner.

The goal of Gus's clearing treatment was to rebalance all five elements so that he would be more receptive to the acupuncture treatments that would follow. As Mary inserted the needles, starting low on Gus's back and proceeding upwards to just below his neck, Russell (then age 7) was mesmerized. He had been receiving his own treatments for years, but he obviously found it rather entertaining to observe someone else undergo acupuncture—especially his big brother. I suspect he was also hoping to catch Gus flinching at the insertion of a needle, but there was little chance of that happening. Gus had already hit puberty and was an emerging athlete—he wasn't about to acknowledge any discomfort. In any event, treatment of these back points doesn't tend to be painful. Because of his strong health, after a few months of regular treatments, Mary let Gus decide for himself whether or not he needed a future treatment. From then on, he requested only sporadic follow-up treatments, usually to support better sleeping habits.

I briefly attended a CF parent support group in the first year following Russell's diagnosis, and I shared with the other parents that Russell was being treated by an acupuncturist. Their previous exposure to alternative healing had apparently been minimal. One father was flabbergasted that we allowed an acupuncturist to stick needles into our baby "like some sort of Voodoo doll!" Without any firsthand experience, he understandably imagined that acupuncture would be a terribly painful procedure. "Needles" is really a misnomer, as the steel used to make acupuncture needles is extraordinarily thin and pliable (you can actually bend them). The diameter is much smaller than that of a hollow needle used to inject fluids. In fact, the needles that acupuncturists use are so tiny that their insertion is hardly felt at all and, unlike a normal pin prick, rarely draws any blood. If there is any pain or discomfort, it is caused by the stimulation of the actual point rather than the needle insertion itself. I know this to be true from my own experience. Occasionally, Mary had to treat a point more than once. If she was off on her calculations as to where the point was located, I literally could not feel the needle's insertion at all. This is how we both knew she had missed the actual point. What's more, she always used children's needles with Russell, which have an even smaller diameter than adult needles, to minimize any discomfort.

For the first few years, Russell rarely balked at the

needles. Later, as a toddler, he would insist on choosing which ankle or which wrist Mary would treat. Normally, an individual is treated on the same meridians on both sides of the body during a treatment, i.e., treating a point just above the right ankle is followed by the insertion of a needle in the same location just above the left ankle. Children are more easily stimulated, however, and until Russell reached adolescence, Mary found it sufficient to treat points on just one side. As a baby and toddler, he was frequently treated on only a single point in a treatment session.

Once Russell reached age five, he was too old to automatically submit to his treatments anymore and yet too young to fathom the purpose and positive benefits of acupuncture. Mary was beginning to treat several points during his treatment sessions, and the points she treated were becoming more varied and (for Russell) unpredictable. Some of them were not painful, exactly, but they were definitely a bit uncomfortable. She and I were often obliged to spend a few moments encouraging him before treatments, explaining that, while the treatment might hurt a little bit, his health would benefit as a result—a concept that wasn't terribly persuasive for a five-year-old. I often stooped to bribery with a special meal if he was particularly reluctant to have a certain point treated. (A promise to stop at Boston Market on the way home to get him two chicken breasts and mashed potatoes with gravy usually did the trick.)

Russell also had nasal polyps, which are commonly

associated with CF. Nasal polyps are soft, non-cancerous, "sac-like swellings" that grow on the lining of the sinuses. The acupuncture points close to his nose, which Mary treated to reduce inflammation of his nasal passages and shrink polyps, were particularly unpleasant for him. As he grew older, he outgrew this reluctance and would hop right up onto the table and receive treatments without any complaint. No doubt it helped that Gus was usually there to observe, if not to receive his own treatment, and that I was also there to be treated. It had simply become part of our family's routine health care.

During the early years, it seemed as if we were always in the car, driving to some doctor or alternative practitioner who was located at least an hour away. But every third Saturday, I was motivated like a pilgrim to drive to Columbia, mindless of the lengthy round trip, so that Mary could continue to heal my little boy. The boys were both avid readers at a young age, and being in the car was just another opportunity for them to sink into a favorite book. I also caved in to their requests for hand-held sports games, drawing the line at games with a theme of violence.

Appointments with Mary always began and ended with warm hugs that displayed the mutual affection cultivated between us. She fine-tuned Russell's energy balance, taking as much time as necessary to listen carefully to his (and my) renderings of any changes in his sleeping or eating patterns, or complaints of nasal congestion or polyps, in order to determine the appropriate treatment. In addition to the positive impact that acupuncture had on Russell's health, Mary offered me a totally different perspective on both his condition (labeled by Western medicine as cystic fibrosis) and his supposedly fatal prognosis. In contrast to the doctors' chorus announcing Russell's impending demise, she was wildly enthusiastic about how healthy he was, how strong he was, how wise his body was, and how capable of healing it was. She never doubted that he would be able to surmount this major health challenge. Her enthusiasm was contagious and fueled a hungry fire in me that might otherwise have been extinguished by the CF doctor's stubborn belief in a negative outcome. The moral support that I reaped from my conversations with Mary—wherein we blithely defied any and all life-threatening dictates—allowed me time to breathe, collect myself, and focus on the positive. It was not just the power of positive thinking that we were engaged in, however, it was the absolute conviction that my son's little body did indeed have the ability to heal itself. I held tight to a glorious new vision of Russell's good health, stamina, and longevity.

In 2005, Mary made a personal decision to end her acupuncture practice. I was devastated. She had been treating Russell for 12 years. At our last scheduled appointment, I gave her an unusual fossil that my sister had brought back from a trip to Sozopol, a little Bulgarian town on the coast of the Black Sea. I told Mary that, just as the seashell had imprinted on this stone despite the shell itself having disappeared long ago, her acupuncture treatments had indelibly imprinted on Russell, permanently changing him for the better. I told her how grateful I was for her healing ability and her generosity over many years. I said all of this, of course, with tears streaming down my cheeks. I truly believed what I said about the permanent imprint—her treatment of Russell had contributed to a striking difference in his health. But I was also petrified that he would go downhill without her.

A few weeks later, Mary called to tell me that she had changed her mind, in part because of the impression that the fossil metaphor had made on her. We kept seeing her for a few months after that, but eventually she circled back to her decision to end her practice. For more than a decade, Mary had refused to accept payment for Russell's treatments, stating simply that "it is an honor to treat him." I will always be indebted to her for the foundational work she contributed to his well-being.

After Mary stopped her practice, we went for a couple of years without any acupuncture. I didn't like what I observed in Russell during this hiatus—increased susceptibility to tree pollen in the early spring that manifested as a constantly runny nose and coughing at night, and constant trouble with stomach aches and decreased appetite. He was indeed going downhill—my worst fear—but I couldn't imagine finding anyone else that I would trust with my child and respect as much as I had respected Mary. A friend finally told me about a licensed acupuncturist in the Baltimore area named Melanie Birch who had treated her, and even more important to me, her children. I contacted Melanie, and Russell and I started receiving treatments again in early 2007 and continue to this day.

Melanie is herself an amazing healer, and it was easy to become re-committed to acupuncture. She shares Mary's optimism and belief in acupuncture's ability to influence health at a profound level. As with many alternative healers, Melanie offers treatments in her home. Thus, not only do we see her on our visits, we often catch a glimpse of her lovely daughter and are greeted enthusiastically by their fluffy-haired little dog, Tiger. Her home is a spiritual haven, with beautiful colors and paintings all about. She greets both Russell and me with warm hugs. One of us then waits in her living room with Tiger happily installed on our lap, while the other goes upstairs for a private 30 to 40 minute treatment.

I love re-examining everything on the wall with each visit as I lie still on Melanie's padded treatment table—the etchings of Chinese characters, the large poster delineating the meridians of the body and the five elements, her bookcase filled with books on an array of unusual healing topics. Melanie exudes warmth and compassion, and she's an incredible listener. I typically enter the room, plunk down on a chair, and immediately unload a long list of woes or, if it's been a good day, excitedly rattle off all of my promising projects. She has a very playful demeanor too, and even though what she is doing is serious and carefully thought through, she and I often end up laughing.

At one appointment, Melanie seemed to insert needles everywhere—points on my feet, my ankles, my stomach, my arms, and even on the very top of my scalp. I started kidding her about the bountiful number of needles.

"You're gettin' a little wild here, girlfriend... are you just gonna keep going until you run out of needles?" I asked.

She giggled, "I'm like a mad scientist today!"

After she inserts the needles, Melanie checks and re-checks the six pulses that she can feel on each of my wrists, just as Mary used to do, to determine if there is an additional point that needs stimulation in order to fully "balance" my pulses. Once Melanie is satisfied that she has stimulated the correct array of points, she dims the light and asks if I want music while she leaves me alone with the needles still in for 20 minutes or so. I always want music. Her selections are wonderfully eclectic, running from Michael Franti, to Buddhist chanting, to Native American flutes and drums. I often doze off during this time alone, with needles sticking out all over my body. Treatments are so calming that sometimes I feel as if I'm floating when it's time to come back downstairs. I usually chat with Melanie for a short while to get my feet firmly planted on the ground before I drive back home.

When we started acupuncture with Melanie, Russell was

a shy 14-year-old, especially around adults he didn't know well. Conversation between the two of them was scant, and he didn't provide much of an answer to her questions about his current state of health or well-being. I respected his emerging adolescence, and since he didn't have any anxiety about being treated, instead of being with him during his treatments as I had when Mary was treating him, I began a new practice of staying out of the room. I didn't think to share my observations about him with Melanie as I had routinely done with Mary when he was a young child. Melanie was instead obliged to rely on Russell's pulses and her interpretation of his coloring and demeanor to shed light on which points she needed to treat. Once she shared with me how little he was telling her in terms of how he had been doing since his last treatment, I felt free to make a comment or two about a symptom or trend that I had noticed before they went off without me into the treatment room. Melanie was always grateful for the added information.

The primary aim of Melanie's treatment during Russell's teenage years was to keep his body clear of the excess heat and dampness associated with chronic antibiotic use. She also treated points that would improve the functioning of his immune system, which might otherwise be stagnating from the antibiotics essentially directing his immune system to shut down. In addition, her frequent treatment of stomach and liver points enhanced his ability to metabolize nutrients.

Unlike Mary's treatments throughout Russell's childhood,

which focused on every element *except* fire, Melanie focused on strengthening his overall constitution, which meant that she often did treat his **fire** or heart element. The fire element impacts four organ systems in two groupings according to Chinese medicine: the heart and the small intestine in one grouping, and the "heart protector" (or pericardium) and the "triple heater" which regulates fluids and body temperature in the other grouping. Russell often suffered from overheating (he preferred to sleep with just a sheet and an electric fan even in the dead of winter) and excessive sweating. Treatments of his fire element helped to correct the underlying imbalance that contributed to both of these tendencies.

Melanie eventually observed that Russell's treatments were "holding better." She also told me that Russell had gotten past his shyness and their communication had improved. Through the years, Russell always showed an immediate and visible resurgence of energy after his treatments. I hoped that his positive attitude toward acupuncture as a child would deepen as he grew older and had the intellectual ability to link the treatments with a reduction of his symptoms and overall improved well-being.

Chapter 5

Homeopathy

Hope is a very unruly emotion…

Gloria Steinem (1934 -)

AS SOON AS RUSSELL WAS DIAGNOSED WITH CYSTIC FIBROSIS, the CF specialist started him on pancreatic enzymes to support his digestion. The doctor also switched him to a "big gun" antibiotic to quell his constant ear and sinus infections. By the time we started acupuncture with Mary White a month later, the severe diarrhea (steatorrhea) was largely gone, and the severity of his cough had lessened. But he still manifested many of the symptoms typical in the early stages of CF—stomach aches, loose and frequent stools, poor growth, excessive perspiration, stuffy nose, constant cough, low energy, and significant ups and downs in appetite. Though I was optimistic that the acupuncture treatments would help, I worried that acupuncture alone wouldn't be enough to battle a disease as monstrous as CF. So I kept exploring to see what other types of alternative healing were out there that might help my son.

I had been exposed to homeopathy as a young adult while studying music in Paris in the 1970's. When I started to feel a bit blue after a few months of living abroad, my French roommate offered to take me to see her physician. After a brief interview, the physician (an M.D.) diagnosed my mild depression and prescribed the homeopathic remedy *Pulsatilla*. The remedy consisted of tiny white globes that I was instructed to place under my tongue, where they would slowly dissolve. They tasted like sugar. I was to avoid eating for an hour both before and after taking the remedy. Though nothing else about my life in Paris changed, after taking the *Pulsatilla*, the depression lifted in a matter of days.

Once back in the U.S. the following spring, I temporarily set aside my piano studies and looked for a job. I was soon hired as a cashier in an organic food store where I became intrigued by our customers' keen interest in nutrition and herbs. I bought every book the store sold on these topics. (Luckily, in 1977, there weren't the hundreds of books on these topics that there are today, or I would have gone broke in short order.) Six months later, I was accepted into graduate school at the New England Conservatory and left my job to re-immerse myself in the piano. But having had daily conversations with customers and fellow workers about alternative healing for even that short amount of time whetted my appetite.

A decade and a half later in 1993, when I found myself exploring alternative healing again, this time on behalf of my son, homeopathy was still a novelty in the U.S. I had no idea how to find a homeopath. (There was no "H for Homeopath" in the Yellow Pages.). So I started by asking friends and acquaintances if they had heard of any homeopaths practicing in the D.C. area. Most of the people I asked didn't even know what a homeopath was, but among the few that did, the name Ioana Razi came up repeatedly as a wonderful homeopath who specialized in children.

I soon discovered that Dr. Razi was a conventionally trained, Board-certified pediatrician who used homeopathy in her routine care of children. Her medical practice was so popular that it was sometimes closed to new patients for years at a time. My friend, Ginger, offered up Dr. Razi's name to me like forbidden fruit. "She's terrific," Ginger said, "but I fear you may never get in. Her practice is usually filled." When I called Dr. Razi's office to request an appointment, the receptionist confirmed Ginger's prediction and discouraged me from calling back. "It's unlikely that Dr. Razi will be accepting any new patients for the foreseeable future," she said.

I really wanted to try homeopathy as part of Russell's healing plan, and I was determined to take him to a seasoned practitioner. After hanging up the phone, I sat down and wrote Dr. Razi a long letter describing Russell's dramatic medical history with a closing plea, asking for her help. A week after mailing the letter, I received a call from Dr. Razi's receptionist who expressed her own surprise that she was calling me back to offer us an appointment. The caveat was that Dr. Razi's care would be limited to providing homeopathic care; she would not be able to serve as Russell's general pediatrician. That was fine with me since we already had a pediatrician (Dr. Brynelson), and I was perfectly happy to stick with her for Russell's primary care.

In mid-May, I drove an hour south to Washington, D.C. with 9-month-old Russell asleep in the backseat for our first appointment with Dr. Razi. I was very excited. I parked our car in a tiny parking space in the alley behind her house in D.C.'s upscale Georgetown neighborhood. Russell complained sleepily as we wound our way through a small backyard lush with flowering bushes until the jumble of red wagons, hula-hoops, and child-size vehicles caught his eye.

The waiting room was just as inviting, with a huge comfy couch, overflowing bookshelves, and toys scattered in all directions. What a difference from the impersonal and sterile hospital environment. Dr. Razi soon emerged from her office with a little girl and mother, hugging them both warmly as they said their goodbyes. The doctor's brightly colored skirt and profusion of wild black hair suggested an exotic heritage (which turned out to be a mix of Greek and Romanian), but I was mostly struck by her warm smile and strong maternal presence.

As soon as Dr. Razi saw us, Russell garnered all of her attention. She whisked him out of my arms, turning to introduce herself to me almost as an afterthought as she led the way back to her exam room. She nodded to a chair for me to sit in and gently lowered Russell down onto the fresh blanket that was already spread out on the floor to begin his physical examination.

Russell stared up at Dr. Razi with a look of baby wonder, clearly entranced by this beautiful stranger who was treating him with such tenderness. She talked to him quietly and smiled reassuringly as she began her examination of his whole body. She gently placed her hand on the still-open "soft spot" on the top of his skull. She listened to his lungs and palpated his abdomen all over, and she looked closely at his fingernails and toenails—cooing to him the whole time. After she finished, she replaced his wet diaper with a clean one, gently kissed his forehead, and placed a toy or two within his reach to keep him occupied. I was mystified by her loving approach toward my baby—something none of the doctors at the hospital had ever displayed. As with Mary, I found myself observing a health practitioner who took a very personal, almost intimate approach to health care and healing.

Dr. Razi then sat down at her desk and, turning her full attention to me for the first time, proceeded down a long list of questions. Every once in a while, she glanced back at Russell who was happily engrossed on the floor with an assortment of toys, as if to weigh my responses against her own observations. As Mary had done during Russell's first acupuncture treatment, Dr. Razi asked me all about him—his likes and dislikes, his sleeping habits, his energy level, his moods. Her questions went far beyond what a physician would normally ask.

"How is he with his older brother?" she asked at one point.

"He adores him," I responded, "although he recently bit down quite hard on Gus's nose..."

"Oh my," she said, "and what did Gus do?"

"He didn't do anything—he was remarkably restrained."

"That's impressive for a 5-year old!" she said.

"How is Russell around animals?" she asked, continuing down

her list. "What does he like to do the most?" "Are there any activities that he shies away from?" "What kind of food is he most drawn to?" Her questions about physical symptoms came last, and I got the impression that they were only a part of what was important to her regarding Russell's health status. She had a general knowledge of spina bifida but clearly knew quite a lot about cystic fibrosis. She was very intrigued by my reports of the constant changes in his hair and skin color, and asked for a lot of detail about his ear infections and cough, colic and crying fits, diarrhea, mood swings, growth trends, and the constant ups and downs of his appetite and energy level. She listened carefully to each reflection that I shared and kept asking follow-up questions until she was satisfied that she had been given a thorough answer. I found myself sharing observations about my son that I hadn't even realized I had made.

Just as our appointment was drawing to a close, I mentioned to Dr. Razi that Russell was experiencing trouble swallowing his enzymes. He had only recently begun to eat solid food, and the strangely-shaped enzymes that the CF doctor had prescribed to help with digestion often caught in his throat, causing him to gag. She immediately asked me if I knew what true choking looked like.

"Oh sure," I responded proudly, "we took 'Baby Life' classes."

"How long ago?" she asked with a raised eyebrow.

"Four years ago, with our first child," I said.

She ignored my lame vote of self-confidence and went on to describe in detail the difference between the mere unpleasantness of gagging versus the life-threatening act of choking. In the event that he should actually choke (turn gray, stop breathing, and go limp), I was to perform the infant version of the Heimlich maneuver. She took Russell out of my arms again and sat back down to demonstrate. Turning him over onto his stomach on her lap, with his head tilted downward at a 90° angle over her thighs and knees, she pretended to whack him forcefully in and down on his back (i.e., "up" toward his lowered head).

She looked up at me and said firmly, "Lindsay, you'll need to hit him hard if he's really choking."

I was dutifully traumatized and we went back to discussing solutions to his harmless gagging. Most of her advice was filled with reassurance that I was doing a good job as his mother—something I was starving to hear. Her sympathy brought me close to tears. She assured me that she would be back in touch soon, after she had had enough time to lay out an individualized plan of homeopathic remedies.

At home the next morning, Russell sat in his highchair in the kitchen watching my every move as I tore off a small piece of bagel for him in his ongoing exploration of real food. He took a nibble, happily mouthed it for a while, and then swallowed. The swallow was arduous and somehow incomplete. As I watched in horror, he turned from his normally very pale skin to gray. He didn't cough or make any sound at all, and within moments, he stopped breathing. Seemingly right on cue, he was manifesting all of the ghastly symptoms of true choking that Dr. Razi had described the previous day. When he began to go limp and faint away, I came to life. Ripping the tray off his high chair, I positioned him on my lap face-down at an angle just as Dr. Razi had directed, and whacked him. Nothing happened. I made a flash judgment that a cracked rib was preferable to having him die and, begging his pardon, I gritted my teeth and *really* whacked him. Out popped the morsel of bagel and Russell gasped for breath. As soon as his lungs refilled with air, he began to wail and I clutched him to my chest for a long time as we both sobbed and trembled. Dr. Razi's instructions had literally saved his life. The irony of it all—that here Russell had two life-threatening conditions but could just as easily die from choking on a stupid bagel—was not lost on me.

Dr. Razi was eager to help Russell. She had completed her medical residency years before at Georgetown University Hospital which, at the time, housed the only CF clinic in Washington, D.C. When we met her, she had no other current patients with CF, but because of prior experience with the disease during her residency rotations in the hospital clinic, she was well-versed in its symptoms and progressive deterioration. Dr. Razi had a stellar reputation, and I looked forward to her help. But I also wanted to be an educated consumer so that she and I could work together as a team. I resolved to learn how homeopathy worked and searched the stacks in the library and local bookstores to find books about the homeopathic approach and its origins.

I purchased a copy of Paul Herscu's book, *The Homeopathic Treatment of Children*, and was struck by Dr. Herscu's assertion that a holistic assessment of a child's well-being was necessary in order to accurately prescribe homeopathic remedies.[1] This full assessment would be expected to cover not just physical or medical topics, such as healthy growth and development or challenges, but the child's psychological, intellectual, and emotional make-up as well. In his book, Dr. Herscu described eight "pediatric constitutional types or patterns of illness." Each type was differentiated by a unique slate of physical, emotional, and mental characteristics. In turn, each type corresponded to specific homeopathic remedies that should be considered for a child with that particular constitutional type or pattern of illness.

Though this was all new territory to me, the *Calcarea Carbonica* constitutional type that Dr. Herscu described gave an uncannily comprehensive description of Russell's diverse physical issues, including "spinal disorders (and spina bifida), problems with metabolism and failure to thrive, vomiting after nursing, voluminous diarrhea, profuse perspiration, problems with excess catarrh (mucus), coughing fits, cradle cap, frequent ear infections, round face with fat rolls, and delayed walking," as well as some of his personality quirks, such as "strong character (mind of his own) and curiosity." There were a few aspects that did not match—"slow and plodding intellect, fearful, obstinate nature, and eye problems"—but overall, it was amazing just how many of the characteristics and symptoms did match. *Calcarea Carbonica* seemed likely to be his "type." A couple of weeks after our first appointment, Dr. Razi called to inform me that she had indeed decided to prescribe *Calcarea Carbonica* as Russell's very first homeopathic remedy.

Before he was to start this remedy, however, Dr. Razi asked my permission to speak with Mary White. She wanted to ask Mary to interrupt Russell's acupuncture treatments briefly during the first course of the *Calcarea Carbonica* remedy, so that the homeopathic remedy could work on its own without any interference. I looked forward to their discussing Russell's case together. In retrospect, not counting the time that the spina bifida pediatrician walked in on our CF clinic orientation, the conversation between Dr. Razi and Mary White was the only instance I can remember in which any of our practitioners (conventional or alternative) consulted with one another.

Following our initial in-person meeting with Dr. Razi, she and I continued to communicate via scheduled consultations over the phone. During each call, she would listen patiently to my observations about Russell's current state and ask follow-up questions in order to determine which homeopathic remedy would be helpful. She would then either send the remedy to me through the mail or I would drive to Bethesda to purchase the remedy at a very unusual pharmacy that sold a spectrum of nutritional, herbal, and homeopathic products, in addition to a normal line-up of prescription medicine. (Nowadays, most health food stores sell homeopathic remedies, although they usually stock a limited array.)

Over time, Dr. Razi prescribed a number of remedies, including *Teucrium Marum* and *Thuja Occidentalis* for nasal polyps; and *Natrum Carbonicum, Natrum Muriaticum, Kali Bichromicum, Pulsatilla, Hepar Sulphuris Calcareum, Calcarea*

Sulphurica, and *Cinchona Officinalis* to ward off symptoms of a cold, support the expectoration of mucus, and reduce excessive sweating. She carefully selected each remedy and its dosage to address a specific symptom or weakness (or collection of symptoms) that was most paramount for Russell at the time. I was thrilled to see her craft an individualized regimen for him; nothing was standard or generic. In addition, he was given only one remedy at a time, the norm for homeopathy, so that Dr. Razi would be able to gauge each remedy's effectiveness (supported by my observations at home).

No one really understands how or why homeopathy works. No doubt this is what troubles the skeptics most, many of whom casually dismiss homeopathy as utter nonsense. The scientific basis of Traditional Chinese Medicine and acupuncture does not conflict with conventional Western medical beliefs but, instead, suggests a drastically different understanding of disease and healing. The theories underlying homeopathic medicine, however, clash rather daringly with a pharmaceutical approach.

In a brief online discussion of homeopathy, the National Center for Complementary and Alternative Medicine (NCCAM) at NIH states: "Several key concepts of homeopathy are inconsistent with fundamental concepts of chemistry and physics."[2] NCCAM goes on to acknowledge that "there are significant challenges in carrying out rigorous clinical research on homeopathic remedies." In other words, because the basis of homeopathy differs from the basis of Western medical science, and because the accepted research methodology has not been an appropriate vehicle with which to study it, homeopathy continues to be dismissed by the medical establishment. Is it reasonable to dismiss something that we don't understand simply because we don't understand it? Or because we don't yet know how to study it? Despite NCCAM's views, the homeopathic remedies sold in the U.S. have been deemed harmless enough to warrant approval by the Food and Drug Administration.

In my reading, I learned that "Homeopathy" was invented by a German physician named Samuel Hahnemann in the early 19th century. After many years of medical practice, Dr. Hahnemann grew disenchanted with the medical profession and its usage of what he felt were unacceptably primitive treatments, such as blood-letting. He closed down his practice and combined his linguistic abilities with his medical knowledge to launch a new profession as translator of medical texts into German. At one point, one of the texts he was translating for a professor in London described the use of quinine, an organic substance extracted from the bark of the *cinchona* bush, to treat malaria. (Quinine's medicinal properties were originally discovered by the Quechua people living in the Andes Mountains of South America.) Dr. Hahnemann suspected that the professor's explanation of why quinine was effective in treating malaria was inaccurate, and he took it upon himself to explore the matter further.

Dr. Hahnemann's unlikely investigation began with a series of experiments on himself. He observed that when he took quinine without malaria being present, it actually induced malarial-like symptoms. This strange observation compelled him to experiment further with quinine and other plants (and eventually with minerals as well), using himself and willing medical colleagues as guinea pigs. His ongoing observations led to his belief that curative properties worked because they contained the capacity to cause the very symptoms that they were used to treat—a "like cures like" theory that became the foundation of homeopathic medicine. Ignoring the fact that this belief had no basis in the conventional medical theory of the day, he was compelled to continue his experiments for a period of years.

Doctors throughout Europe who heard about Dr. Hahnemann and his experiments streamed into Germany to disprove his outrageous theories. Some of them feared that, if he were allowed to continue, his theories could threaten the very basis of "modern" medicine. However, according to George Vithoulkas, a modern day practitioner and teacher of homeopathy, once the critics saw Dr. Hahnemann's work firsthand, even the most skeptical among them were eventually won over, often joining his efforts to further develop an entirely new approach to healing.[3]

Dr. Hahnemann and his team of medical colleagues combed through the annals of medical history looking for accounts of poisonous and non-poisonous plants (as well as toxic and non-toxic minerals and metals) and their effects on the body. Using as many different substances as he could find, he continued to test his "like cures like" theory, documenting the impact that the curative treatments derived from these substances had on healthy individuals. The documented results of these experiments were then compiled into a multi-volume homeopathic *Materia Medica Pura* that describes some 5,000 homeopathic remedies. Homeopaths today are expected to spend many hours studying these remedies before working directly with patients.[4]

The primary working principle of homeopathy is that the human body itself will mount a healing offensive if given the correct and, importantly, subtle message. In fact, homeopathic remedies derived from plants and minerals are given in dosages of such dilution that molecules of the original source (the plant or the mineral) are no longer traceable. Further, one of the more curious facts of homeopathy is that the greater the dilution of a remedy (in other words, the lower the dosage by conventional medicine's definition), the greater its impact.[5] This, of course, goes completely against the grain of Western pharmaceutical thought where "more is better" in terms of a higher dosage having a stronger impact. This mystifying basis for homeopathic healing has only served to intensify the charges of quackery that are sometimes leveled against it.

There are several problems with anyone blithely dismissing homeopathy as quackery. First, despite NIH's skepticism, homeopathic remedies have been rigorously studied in Europe (including by a Nobel Prize winning scientist) and found to be particularly effective with chronic diseases such as fibromyalgia, behavioral conditions such as ADHD, and detoxification following arsenic poisoning.[6] Second, since Dr. Hahnemann's discoveries and development of the homeopathic approach in Germany, Europeans have come to widely accept homeopathy as a low-cost, effective, and virtually risk-free medical treatment. In cases of mild illness, many conventionally trained physicians across Europe prescribe homeopathic remedies in lieu of pharmaceutical drugs, such as the *Pulsatilla* remedy given to me by a French physician.

Due to homeopathy's widespread use, European pharmacists are routinely trained to give their customers counsel on homeopathic remedies as well as on what Americans would consider to be more conventional pharmaceutical options. Out of curiosity, on a recent trip to Spain, I walked into the first half dozen pharmacies that I passed on the street to see what was routinely sold. Every one of the pharmacies sold an array of over-the-counter homeopathic remedies (plus nutritional supplements and herbal tonics) alongside aspirin and cough syrup. When I tried to convey my surprise in broken Spanish that homeopathic remedies were sold in regular pharmacies, each of the pharmacists asked insistently what symptoms I was hoping to treat, thinking I was instead asking for their advice.

Many Americans are using the same low-cost, effective, and non-toxic homeopathic remedies that are sold in Europe. Boiron, the world's largest homeopathic manufacturer (headquartered in France and founded by pharmacist brothers, Jean and Henri Boiron), has opened manufacturing and distribution outlets on both the East and West Coasts of the U.S. (as well as other locations throughout the world). Boiron remedies are now available over-the-counter in health food and nutritional supplement stores and selected pharmacies all across the U.S. Hopefully, the increase in American consumption will pique physicians' curiosity and increase the demand for government-sponsored research.

In our second year of consultations with Dr. Razi, she ordered a special *Escherichia coli* remedy from England that was specifically designed to treat the pancreatic insufficiency of CF. We had to wait several months for it to arrive. Dr. Razi assured me that this remedy, which was derived from a much-feared bacteria that could cause kidney failure in young children, would be perfectly safe to give to Russell. I knew that vaccines contained the actual viral agent they were designed to protect against, and that some vaccines such as polio even contained live molecules. I had allowed Russell to be vaccinated with the usual slate of pediatric vaccines, because they were considered to be at least generally safe, but the idea of giving him anything as deadly as *E. coli* frightened me.[7] Dr. Razi patiently reassured me multiple times, and though I was still nervous, I finally decided to simply trust her. She instructed me to give him a specific number of chewable "tablets" each day for a period of several weeks. Once that initial period of time passed, we would consult again to discuss its effect and any need for further treatment.

Russell's stools were still far from normal at this stage—the steatorrhea had ended, but his stools were still abnormally frequent and loose, and his diapers often contained greasy yellow globules of undigested fat. The day following his first dosage of the *E. coli* remedy, his stools suddenly turned green and foamy and voluminous—frighteningly reminiscent of his pre-diagnosis steatorrhea. I called Dr. Razi in a panic. Much to my amazement, she was very encouraged.

"This is an *excellent* response!" she said with excitement.

I was puzzled by what she explained was a "homeopathic aggravation," when a remedy initially causes symptoms to worsen. This was utterly counter-intuitive, but I continued to give Russell the *E. coli* remedy for the allotted time anyway. As Dr. Razi predicted, his stools calmed down within days and eventually normalized to a much greater degree than ever before.

It may seem odd that I tended to question the conventional doctors so thoroughly and yet trusted practitioners whose alternative approaches were still considered by many to be quite strange and unproven (again, it was the early 1990's). In retrospect, I can see that it was the highly individualized and compassionate attention that the alternative practitioners gave to Russell as a unique child with unique strengths and needs, coupled with the observable improvements in his well-being once they began to treat him, that convinced me to trust them. Furthermore, I was impressed by the extremely thorough and positive nature of both Mary White's and Dr. Razi's approaches.

After the boys and I first moved from the farm following the separation from my husband, I kept them enrolled at their old Montessori school in order to maintain consistency in at least one area of their lives. This made for a 45-minute commute to and from school each day. Russell, who was then three years old, began to suffer from car sickness on the way to school in the morning, and he often vomited while in the car. I grew concerned about his losing the nutritional benefit of a whole meal each day as well as the benefit of the nutritional supplements that he took with his breakfast (described in Chapter 7). In one of my phone consultations with Dr. Razi, I mentioned his car sickness. She instructed me to give him *Cocculus Indicus*, a homeopathic remedy for just this problem. Within three days, his car sickness was gone and she suggested that we discontinue the remedy. After a number of months, the problem returned and the remedy again worked its miracle in short order. He hasn't suffered from car sickness since.

Despite the noticeable and positive impact that homeopathic remedies had on Russell, I had trouble understanding how something so diluted could possibly have an influence on the body. It confused me that remedies made from toxic materials, such as the deadly *E. coli* bacteria or poisonous berries from the cockle vine in the *Cocculus Indicus* remedy, were beneficial to one's health. I gradually developed my own theory that a homeopathic remedy introduces a "message" into the body that is derived from a hint or faint "shadow" of a plant or mineral substance that remains in the remedy despite the extreme dilution. The fact that scientists have been unable to detect a residual molecule of the original plant or mineral in homeopathic remedies doesn't bother me—it's entirely possible that science has yet to develop the capacity to measure or even recognize something that small.[8]

Though extremely subtle, the message in a homeopathic remedy is definitely recognized by the body, and the body responds accordingly. I have wondered if the subtlety and faintness of the message is precisely why homeopathy works. Remedies are not diluted simply because the original substance has toxic properties. During his experimentation, Dr. Hahnemann discovered that the more times over that a remedy was diluted (and successed or shaken), the more powerful its effect. In fact, the homeopathic remedies that we buy today have been diluted hundreds, thousands, and even hundreds of thousands of times before they are considered ready to be taken. I have wondered if it is precisely because the message is so faint that the body is inspired to mount a focused response in order to correctly interpret and fully respond to the message. The remedy thus mobilizes the body in a way that conventional pharmaceutical products do not.

When a patient is given antibiotics to quell an infection, for example, the medicine itself kills the targeted bacteria (as well as other good or bad bacteria that happen to be present). The body doesn't do the killing; in fact, the immune system is essentially ignored while the medicine does the killing. In contrast, homeopathy's value is that it mobilizes the body to initiate its own healing. The diluted homeopathic remedy is not going to do the work, therefore the body must.

There needn't be a contest between homeopathic and conventional medicine. Homeopathy has been proven to be effective in resolving certain conditions (such as car sickness, arthritis, or digestive disturbances) where conventional medicine is effective for resolving others (such as re-setting broken bones, organ transplants, or the surgical correction of birth defects). There are still other conditions, such as cancer or CF, where patients may benefit enormously from the use of both homeopathic and conventional approaches.

Because Dr. Razi was not Russell's general pediatrician, we didn't visit her in person or even communicate with her by phone with any kind of regularity. I tended to contact her only when a new problem surfaced (such as car sickness) or when a stubborn problem wouldn't go away (such as nasal polyps) to see if she knew of a homeopathic remedy that would help. I didn't try to figure out which remedy to use on my own because the volume of remedies, the nuanced differences between them, and the complex parsing out of Russell's specific needs was far more than a novice could possibly handle.

As Russell emerged from toddlerhood into boyhood, his nasal polyps became more prominent. They were the most stubborn of all his CF symptoms, most of which had decreased significantly by then (some, such as stomach aches and diarrhea, had disappeared completely). Nasal polyps are common in people with CF, although doctors do not know what causes them or how to prevent or shrink them. At times, he could barely breathe through his nose and would breathe almost exclusively through his mouth. Though not exactly a dangerous practice, mouth-breathing interferes with both the cleaning action of the cilia in the nostrils and the healthy stimulation of the sinuses that take place during normal nose-breathing. As far as I knew, polyps were more of a nuisance than a serious threat to Russell's health, but I was disappointed that neither acupuncture nor the homeopathic remedies had gotten rid of them.

We hadn't been to see Dr. Razi for two years when I decided to make an in-person appointment. I hoped that if she were to examine Russell and see the polyps for herself, she might be inspired to design a more aggressive homeopathic approach. My goal was to avoid using the steroidal nasal sprays repeatedly offered by the CF specialist. Dr. Brynelson, our pediatrician, had cautioned me that long-term use of steroidal spray might truncate Russell's final height (though not by much). When Russell's nose was thoroughly stuffed up, I sometimes relented and used the nasal spray anyway. But I never noted much of an impact on the polyps.

At our appointment, Dr. Razi examined Russell's nasal passages and classified the polyps as moderate. I wasn't surprised as he had been breathing more easily through his nose during the two weeks leading up to our appointment. We had also been using the homeopathic remedy she had prescribed over the phone (*Teucrium Marum*) as well as an Ayurvedic herbal remedy (*Calamus Nasja*) that our herbalist had suggested we try (described in Chapter 8). But the polyps were frustratingly chronic and often a lot worse than they were on this particular day. I also knew that they were likely to recur.

"When he can't breathe well through his nose, why do you assume it's due to the polyps?" Dr. Razi asked.

"I assume that the polyps are what's blocking his nasal passage," I answered, wondering if this were a trick question.

"It could be polyps, he certainly has polyps, but it could also be due simply to inflammation of his sinus passages," she said. "When he's on antibiotics, does the breathing through his nose improve?"

"Yes," I answered.

"That would suggest that inflammation (which the antibiotics help to reduce) is also contributing to the blockage, and not only the polyps," she said.

I sat there confused and frustrated. How was I to know what was blocking his breathing? I couldn't see into his sinuses and wouldn't have known what to look for anyway. I wanted so desperately to have her knowledge, I wanted to know *everything* she and all the other doctors knew so that I could battle this damned disease full on. I hated the slow dribble of information and endless learning curve that never seemed to get me anywhere.

Dr. Razi took the conversation back to the polyps. "What do you think causes the polyps to flare up when they do?" she asked me.

"I think they might be caused by allergies," I said.

"Why do you think this?" I loved that she valued my observations, even though her probing questions often brought me to the frustrating conclusion: "I don't know."

I explained that his nose seemed to be especially blocked in the spring, when the locust, tulip poplar, and horse chestnut trees started to flower in Maryland. For weeks each year, a thick layer of green pollen coated the windshield of my car each morning—a perfect visual of the pollen that his sinuses were battling. I added that his nose also tended to be blocked in the early fall, coinciding with the flowering of ragweed.

"Hmmm," she said thoughtfully.

I could practically see the wheels turning in her mind as she sorted through what I had told her. She turned to Russell (then three years old) and asked him what he liked to eat. He headed down a strange road, talking about how much he loved candy. He was rarely allowed to have any candy, and I had just refused to buy him some on the way to the appointment with Dr. Razi. Evidently, it was still on his mind. I was embarrassed that I'd look like a bad mother, but I kept quiet, trusting Dr. Razi to adequately explore the subject with him. She did, and eventually he shared the real list of his current favorite foods: mango, tuna fish, and potato chips. This list made total sense to Dr. Razi, given the large quantities of enzymes, protein, and salt that these three foods respectively contained. Dr. Razi and Mary White both encouraged me to trust Russell's food cravings and allow him to eat as much of a particular food as he wanted (so long as he didn't crave something void of benefit like candy) even if it meant eating essentially the same meal over and over. He often craved something for days or even weeks on end and then suddenly didn't want it anymore.

We went on to discuss his other food preferences, digestion, stools, energy level, moods, and sleeping habits. It always felt good during an appointment with one of our alternative health practitioners when they asked lots of questions about Russell and his health. (Though Dr. Razi is a conventionally trained M.D., I still think of her as "alternative," largely because of her holistic approach.) Unlike the brief exams of the conventional doctors (with the exception of our pediatrician), the unusually broad questioning of our alternative practitioners helped them to get a full picture of Russell's personality and health status. It also led to a more caring discussion about him as a whole person who had unique likes and dislikes, habits, behaviors, and needs. The alternative practitioners didn't look at just one part of him (or one *organ*) the way the conventional doctors did. And because the alternative practitioners felt a need to know his status thoroughly before they could decide how to proceed, they were prepared to take their time. There were no rushed 10-minute appointments with either Mary White *or* Dr. Razi; visits with them typically lasted well over an hour. And they certainly didn't have a generic approach that they used with every patient, which was how it felt at both the spina bifida and CF clinics.

For his nasal polyps, Dr. Razi decided that we should try *Calcarea Carbonica* again, but this time using a low maintenance dose for two months. This led to a temporary calming down of his polyps, but they kept recurring and did not completely disappear. Russell eventually required surgery to remove the nasal polyps during his early teens. After "shopping around" for a surgeon, I settled on Dr. Maria Peña, the otolaryngology or ENT (ear, nose, and throat) surgeon at Children's Hospital. For the first time, I learned from her that polyps were much more than a nuisance. She explained that, as polyps grow, the cartilage in the nose can actually be worn away—this had occurred in Russell's case without our knowing it until it was revealed on pre-surgical computerized tomography screenings (CT scans). She said that polyps come and go mysteriously (at least the doctors don't know why), and that it was hard to predict whether or not they would regrow after surgery.

Dr. Peña also said that, in her experience, steroids in a nasal spray had little to no impact on the growth of polyps. This helped to alleviate my guilt at having turned down the CF specialist's repeated suggestion to use the steroidal nasal spray when Russell was little. Over a four-year period, during middle and high school, Russell had a total of three surgeries to remove the polyps. They never totally disappeared but thankfully, so far, they haven't grown back enough to warrant additional surgery.

Though Dr. Razi was more like a special consultant to us than a general pediatrician, I often asked for her advice on non-homeopathic topics such as antibiotic use. Our regular pediatrician and the CF specialist eventually trusted my judgment about when to prescribe Russell antibiotics, and the standing pharmacy prescriptions always had plenty of refills available. Sometimes I didn't even notify the doctors when I placed him on antibiotics unless I had a particular question or concern. When I did consult them, they both consistently erred on the side of using antibiotics rather than risk waiting to see if an infection would resolve on its own or have it worsen instead. They also knew that I was a careful observer of my son's ups and downs, and that I didn't worry unnecessarily.

In contrast, Dr. Razi encouraged me to keep decreasing our use of antibiotics, which I admitted to using three or four times a year. By the time he reached age five, she urged me to avoid the "lest syndrome"—that he should be on prophylactic antibiotics when sick lest the cold or other virus should develop into more serious CF complications. She implied that this strategy of preventive antibiotics, which may well be essential for children who experienced more severe CF symptoms, was a false premise for Russell, given his extraordinarily good health and lack of symptoms. (The weight she placed on his lack of symptoms called to mind the discussion I had had with the pediatric allergist who did not want to treat Russell's positive IgE test result in the absence of any allergic symptoms.) Stating what the acupuncturist had said before her, Dr. Razi said that, far from the minor colds and viruses that Russell encountered being a constant threat to his health, she believed that they in fact served to challenge and thus strengthen his immune system. His full recuperation and lack of complications with a recent and nasty bout of a viral para-influenza was a good indication that he had what it took to meet these types of challenges, even without the conventional chest physiotherapy which I had stopped at around age four.

I admitted to Dr. Razi that when Russell became sick, and particularly when he developed a cough, it was nearly impossible for me to simply relax and trust that he would be fine without antibiotics. I said that what I really needed at those times was someone to hold my hand and help me make that judgment call. Once again, Dr. Razi complimented me on the good care I was giving my child, and even called me "courageous." It was all I could do not to succumb to tears. I desperately needed reassurance that I was doing all that I could to protect my son from this terrifying disease, this looming dragon that threatened to carry him away.

When I was confronted with differing opinions about what to do, I could never be certain that I was making the right judgment call. The CF specialist was certainly sensitive to how scary it was to be the parent of a child with a fatal prognosis, and he displayed enormous patience with me and my endless questions. But I always suspected that he and the other doctors would have preferred me to simply take their advice rather than question everything. When I didn't agree with them, it was never seen as an opportunity for them to consider their advice in a different light.

In complete contrast, the alternative practitioners encouraged me to question and debate the unknowns—they respected my tendency to weigh decisions about Russell very carefully and not to simply do as I was told. They viewed critical thinking as a strength and fundamental component of responsible parenting. Dr. Razi, in particular, was always happy to take as much time as was needed in each appointment to answer all of my questions. She considered my education as Russell's parent to be part of her job. And just as with our appointments with Mary, Dr. Razi ended our appointments with warm hugs, her hand gently patting my back. At least for a moment, her respectful handling of my questions and her compassionate touch soothed away my worries.

In addition to homeopathic remedies, Dr. Razi gave me lots of practical suggestions during Russell's early years (though none were ever quite as spectacular as teaching me the Heimlich maneuver). She suggested including plenty of papaya and mango in Russell's diet because their high natural enzyme content would support his digestion. She also suggested that I use only sea salt in Russell's food and consider giving him natural kelp supplements, so that he would ingest naturally-occurring sea minerals as well as the salt. Once he was old enough to use it, she urged me to purchase a hand-held "flutter valve" to encourage expectoration of any excess mucus in his lungs. He barely had a cough anymore, but she was focused on prevention. Her bar for his health status was high—something I valued about all of our alternative practitioners.

Unlike any of the other doctors or practitioners we encountered, alternative and conventional alike, Dr. Razi also considered the health of the other members of our family. She noted the potential for symptoms in carriers of the CF gene, such as increased phlegm. She explained that research had revealed that individuals who carry only one mutation (and thus do not manifest the full gamut of CF symptoms) are also at risk of manifesting CF symptoms, though to a much less severe degree. This discussion brought to mind Richard's allergies, and I wondered if his being a carrier exacerbated the symptoms triggered by pollen in the spring and the fall. It was so like Dr.

Razi to contemplate things to such a holistic degree that she not only considered the full spectrum of Russell's health, but also Russell's *family's* health!

Eventually we transitioned from Dr. Razi's homeopathic care to that of Dr. Peter Hinderberger, a homeopathic physician (M.D., Ph.D., and D.I.Hom.) and colleague of Dr. Razi's, who had attended medical school and received homeopathic training in Switzerland. He had emigrated to the U.S. and settled in Baltimore years before; I first met him when our sons were classmates at the Waldorf School. Because Dr. Hinderberger's vast experience was equivalent to that of Dr. Razi's and also his practice was located five minutes from our home, I started taking Russell to see him instead. We continued to see Dr. Hinderberger sporadically over the years, as needed.

After witnessing the positive benefits that Russell experienced with homeopathic remedies over a period of years, I became convinced of its value for my own health care. As an example, in 2014, I noticed a strange whitish translucent patch on my lower eyelid. I went to an eye surgeon who recommended that I get a biopsy to rule out basal cell carcinoma. If the biopsy report revealed cancer, the surgeon planned to follow up with Mohs micrographic surgery, a procedure that entailed taking successive "slices" of tissue and looking at them under a microscope until a slice was clear of cancer. I, of course, asked him a lot of questions, with a focus on whether or not my eyelid would function normally after the procedure. "If we need to, we can take skin from behind your ear or some other location to piece your eyelid back together," he said to reassure me. Even though he was a reputable cosmetic eye surgeon, the thought of reconstructing a perfectly good eyelid was quite distasteful. And just because he could do something didn't mean I wanted to give him free license.

So I asked more questions. Eventually, the surgeon interrupted me. "You're over-thinking this," he said impatiently, evidently weary of all my questions. What I wanted to say back was, "Yes, and perhaps, Doctor, you're under-thinking this," but I didn't want to be as rude to him as he had just been to me. I had obviously gone over the allotted time for a quick exam and tidy wrap-up, and he apparently had better things to do than satisfy my concerns. In his mind, he knew exactly what to do. All he needed me to do was agree with him. I left his office without agreeing to the biopsy. I already knew a bit about basal cell carcinoma, that it was typically slow-growing and unlikely to metastasize (or spread to another part of my body). I wasn't scared by the diagnosis and needed a little time to decide what to do.

Eventually, I went back to the eye surgeon and asked him to do a biopsy. After thinking it through (not to be confused with overthinking), I decided that it made more sense to find out for certain whether or not the patch was cancerous, even though I was convinced that basal cell carcinoma was nothing to get worked up about. In the end, the biopsy did reveal basal cell but instead of immediately opting for the Moh's micrographic procedure that might necessitate an unsavory reconstruction scenario, I went to see Dr. Hinderberger.

Even though the patch of basal cell appeared to be quite small, it was located close to my tear duct. Dr. Hinderberger noted the possibility that my eyelid and tear duct might require extensive reconstructive surgery after the cancer was removed (a risk that the surgeon himself had noted). Dr. Hinderberger suggested that there was an alternative to surgery. He instructed me to inject a remedy made from mistletoe (*Viscum Abietis*) into my abdomen three times a week for a period of six months to see if the cancer would resolve on its own (i.e., without surgery). Mistletoe is a parasitic shrub that grows on trees, such as birch and fir, and is considered poisonous. As a homeopathic remedy, mistletoe has been used in Europe for the better part of a century because of its anti-cancer properties. Dr. Hinderberger also prescribed homeopathic eye drops made from ant venom (*Bambusa Formica*) to help my eyelid rebuild itself following the removal of a tissue sample during the biopsy. After six months of mistletoe injections, he would want me to see a dermatologist to determine if the basal cells were truly gone. I was thrilled to have an opportunity to test an alternative to surgery.

As I left Dr. Hinderberger's office, I had a satisfying (and sublimely adolescent) vision of the stodgy eye surgeon's face should he learn that, after thinking it over sufficiently, I had decided to go with highly diluted homeopathic remedies made from poisonous substances (mistletoe and ant venom) rather than place my faith in a surgical outcome. Perhaps his categorizing me as "overthinking" would be quickly replaced with "out of her mind."

Chapter 6

Osteopathy

Seek health in your patients; any fool can find disease.

Dr. Andrew Taylor Still (1828-1917)

SEVERAL YEARS BEFORE MY FIRST SON WAS BORN, MY SISTER Faith moved from New England to Kirksville, Missouri—home to the nation's oldest school of osteopathic medicine. Soon after settling in, Faith met Janie Koss, whose husband, Rick, was an osteopath, and they all became good friends. In fact, my sister found that she was literally surrounded by osteopaths in her new hometown—her gynecologist was an osteopath, her children's pediatrician was an osteopath, and most of the primary care doctors in private practice or specialists on staff at the local hospital were as well. When Russell was diagnosed with CF, Faith had already been in Kirksville for a number of years. She confided her worries about his scary prognosis to her friends, Janie and Rick. Rick convinced her that osteopathy would be a valuable addition to Russell's overall treatment for CF, and he recommended that I take Russell to see Harold Goodman in nearby Silver Spring, Maryland—an osteopath he knew personally and spoke of very highly.

I myself had been treated by an osteopath in the early 1970's when I was an undergraduate student at music school in Boston. Practicing the piano hour after hour had wreaked havoc with my neck, shoulders, and arms, and when I complained about these sporadic pains to my mother, she took me to see her osteopath in Concord, Massachusetts. The osteopath realigned my spine and neck by placing me in odd positions and gently forcing my bones to shift. The treatments were painless but quite strange—I could actually feel and hear my spinal column "click" back into place. The treatments helped to reduce the pain, though I didn't end up any wiser about how osteopathy worked or what an osteopathic treatment accomplished beyond pain relief. This earlier experience helped me to be open to Rick's suggestion years later, that we consider osteopathic help for Russell.

I called Dr. Goodman's office to make an appointment and discovered that he didn't accept insurance; we would have to pay for his services upfront and then ask to be reimbursed by our insurance carrier. Money was scarce in those days, and I didn't feel that I could commit to paying for expensive osteopathic treatments without assurance that at least a portion of the cost would be covered by insurance. Osteopaths or D.O.s (Doctor of Osteopathy) were equally as trained as M.D.s, but in the early 1990's at least, they were a rarity on the East Coast. But since Dr. Goodman was a doctor, I was optimistic that his treatments would be covered. My repeated requests over the phone to the insurance company, an HMO, were fruitless, so eventually I put a request in writing, asking them to cover Dr. Goodman's osteopathic treatments. The insurance company finally agreed to pay for an initial consultation. After the consultation, when I went back to request approval for ongoing treatments with Dr. Goodman, however, the insurance company illogically refused to pay for any actual treatments. The cost of Russell's treatments with Dr. Goodman was going to be exorbitant, but I was determined to try osteopathy, especially given its focus on spinal column health and Russell's history of spina bifida. Cost be damned!

Russell began his treatments with Dr. Goodman in September, a month after his first birthday. Dr. Goodman is a short, round man with a delightful expression of merriment about the eyes. Even when we talked about serious matters, he looked as if he were barely containing the urge to chuckle. We were still at the beginning of our journey into alternative healing, and I had no idea what to make of him or his treatment approach. Luckily, there was no placing my baby in odd positions and "cracking" his spine as the osteopath had done to me many years before. Instead, for most of the first appointment, Russell lay face up on the treatment table while Dr. Goodman sat on a low stool gently cradling Russell's head in his hands. Dr. Goodman sat very still in the same position with his eyes closed for close to 30 minutes. I didn't have the slightest idea what he was doing, except that he was concentrating intensely. Still a baby at the time, Russell was not at all pleased to be constricted, and he intermittently began to cry despite my efforts to distract him.

When we returned for Russell's second treatment, I came

armed with an assortment of books and toys from home to keep him happy while the doctor treated him. I was worried that Dr. Goodman would be distracted or even annoyed by my redoubled efforts to keep Russell entertained, but the doctor assured me that it didn't bother him at all. In fact, he often giggled (with his eyes still closed) when Russell laughed, but otherwise he seemed completely undisturbed. We continued bi-weekly and then monthly osteopathic treatments for about six months, at which point I could no longer afford them. I am quite sure that Russell benefited considerably from Dr. Goodman's work, especially given how early in my son's life the treatments occurred.

Osteopathy was conceived in the late 1800's by an American medical doctor named Andrew Taylor Still who, in his service as a field surgeon during the Civil War, gained new insight about how the body heals.[1] (I find it interesting that both acupuncture and osteopathy share an origin on the battlefield.) Dr. Still's primary finding was that, with the use of "hands-on therapy," soldiers could withstand infection better and their wounds tended to heal more quickly. He went on to extrapolate that, under the proper circumstances (referring to a combination of the interior environment of the body and external stimuli), the body had the inherent capacity to heal itself. Dr. Still's original intention was not to start a separate field of medicine but rather to integrate his findings into current medical thought, but he found his medical colleagues to be thoroughly unreceptive to his new ideas. After the war ended, Dr. Still remained determined to further develop this hands-on therapy despite his colleagues' resistance, and he founded the American School of Osteopathy in Kirksville, Missouri in 1892. Today, the renamed "A.T. Still University" trains more than 3,000 osteopathic doctors each year.

Osteopaths are recognized by the American Medical Association in all 50 states as fully trained Board-certified physicians. They are licensed to perform surgery, prescribe medicine, provide specialty care, and deliver babies, among other medical procedures. Students of osteopathy not only complete the same standard four years of medical training as students enrolled in conventional "allopathic" medical schools; they are also required to complete many additional hours of training in osteopathic manipulation. Most osteopaths (D.O.) end up practicing primary care or specialty medicine—just as physicians (M.D.) do. But some osteopaths choose, as Dr. Goodman and the other osteopaths that we have encountered did, to specialize in osteopathic manipulation rather than practice general medicine.

I think osteopath Ted Miller captures the essence of osteopathic manipulation particularly well:

> The manual techniques used by D.O's [Doctors of Osteopathy] involve using one's hands on the patient's body in ways that range from the most direct and forceful to the most indirect, subtle, and low-force. Some of the commonly used techniques include what is called "high-velocity thrust manipulation" (similar to the "adjustments" used by chiropractors); muscle energy techniques, which are used to stretch tight muscles; and

non-force techniques such as "strain/counterstrain," "myofascial release therapy" or "unwinding," and cranial technique.

> The approach that I use in my practice [for some patients] is the application of non-force "unwinding" myofascial release and cranial osteopathic techniques to help catalyze the body's inherent capacity to unwind and dissolve these restrictions. All we do is gently lay our hands on some part of the body and **wait**. We wait for an internal unwinding, a softening, to begin. As the process continues, we have a sense of when to gently pull with traction, and when to press with compression, all for the sake of enhancing the **body's** inherent healing capacity.[2]

I love Dr. Miller's description of how the body unwinds in response to a gentle (and trained) laying on of the hands. When I receive osteopathic treatments myself from Dr. Goodman, I find it easy to relax and absorb the energy coming through his hands. I also literally feel the tissue around my joints relax and shift.

As the years passed and more books were published on the topic of alternative healing, I became quite familiar with several modalities. I also learned quite a bit in my conversations with Russell's alternative practitioners. I began to hear recurring themes about "healing energy" and the "re-balancing of energy," both in my discussions with our practitioners and in the books that I was reading. A key aspect of this energy theme seemed to be somewhat ethereal or spiritual, which I found unsettling. As my own treatments with Mary White and Harold Goodman continued, however, I couldn't ignore the evidence that there was indeed some kind of life force flowing inside of my body as well as an apparently unlimited source completely outside my body from which I was able to draw more energy.

When the boys and I moved from the farm to the city, we often took walks around the neighborhood after supper. One evening, we discovered nearby Hood College campus and its wondrous array of hundred-year-old trees. I immediately fell in love with an enormous beech tree; its huge splayed trunk and gray wrinkled skin reminding me of elephants. Though I'd always loved nature, I'd never been a literal hugger of trees, but it became a habit of mine to make solo visits to this particular tree. Over time, I became aware of a subtle vibration that I felt underneath its huge canopy of red leaves. As I stood there, any tension that I brought with me seemed to dissipate and wash away, and I always left the tree able to breathe more deeply. Even though it seemed far-fetched, I wondered if the universal life force and energy I was learning about was also shared by this massive tree. I didn't really need an answer; standing under its branches covered in shivering leaves made me feel better and I visited the tree often.

One of the first books about alternative healing that I read was *Spontaneous Healing* by Andrew Weil.[3] Dr. Weil, a Harvard Medical School graduate, is now a renowned expert in integrative medicine—the combined or integrated use of both alternative and conventional medicine. This early book was written before he became world-famous and his concept of integrative medicine became popularized. The topics that he wrote about were still considered quite controversial and even strange. Dr. Weil described his global meanderings through jungles and deserts in search of "the perfect shaman" (or healer). He noted his surprise, after many years of futile searching, at finding just such a healer in "his own backyard" in Arizona, in the form of an osteopath named Robert Fulford. Dr. Fulford was revered by his peers and many other alternative health practitioners as a rare and exceptionally gifted hands-on healer. He had treated thousands of people (including children) over his many decades of osteopathic practice, often treating them only once, yet somehow catalyzing remarkable improvements in their health. Dr. Weil described Dr. Fulford's approach in the book as "nonviolent medicine that did not suppress disease but rather encouraged the body's own healing potential to express itself." There were stories of people who had suffered debilitating illness for years whose problems simply went away after being treated by Dr. Fulford—stories that were as hard to believe as they were mouth-watering.

Coincidentally, my sister's friend Rick in Kirksville had become Dr. Fulford's protégé, traveling and lecturing with him across the country (sometimes lecturing for him, given his advanced age). In 1996, at a friend's Christmas party, my sister took Rick aside and asked him if Dr. Fulford actually treated patients anymore. Rick acknowledged that he did, but since he was now in his 90's, Dr. Fulford only treated children, because their treatments required less physical effort. Rick told my sister story after story of how Dr. Fulford's gentle hands-on osteopathic healing had changed so many people's lives. When Faith asked Rick if I should take Russell to see him, Rick immediately wrote down Dr. Fulford's home phone number in Ohio (where he had settled post-retirement) with instructions for me to call.

While I had read Dr. Weil's book, and had an idea of just how revered Dr. Fulford was, my sister had had the benefit of listening firsthand to Rick's observations of Dr. Fulford's mythic abilities—she convinced me that this was a chance of a lifetime. I figured "Why not?" based on her trust in Rick, and I placed a call to Dr. Fulford the following day. He answered the phone himself and listened quietly to my request for an appointment.

"I will be happy to see your son. But I won't be seeing any patients again until after the 5th of January, when the earth's energy is on the rise again," he said. "You can give me a call back then."

We hung up. I was both mystified and terribly let down. I called Rick for reassurance. He explained that, because the earth's energy level is so low around the time of the winter solstice, Dr. Fulford wanted to wait until the energy level came back up before seeing patients. I didn't really understand what this meant but decided it was a good sign for a doctor to be in touch with nature's cycles.

I called Dr. Fulford again a few weeks later as instructed and, in late January, took Russell out to Ohio to see him. Russell was four years old. In preparation, I bought a copy of Dr. Fulford's recently published book, *Dr. Fulford's Touch of Life*, and devoured it quickly, amazed at how similar our world views were—not just about medicine and healing, but about politics and education too. I felt primed for our visit.

After our flight from Maryland to Ohio, the boys and I checked into our hotel near the Cincinnati airport and set out the next morning in a rental car toward Dr. Fulford's home a couple of hours south. Dr. Fulford lived in a modest one-story ranch house on the cul-de-sac of a sprawling retirement community. He opened the door himself and immediately looked down at my children with a wonderful twinkle in his eye. He had obviously been a large man in his youth but was now stooped over with age. He had a shock of white hair and massive hands bent with arthritis—I hoped they could still work their magic.

Once we settled into his examining room, Dr. Fulford looked over at Russell as if deep in thought. By this time, Russell had been on a solid regimen of acupuncture, homeopathy, and nutrition for three years, as well as having had several months of osteopathic treatments with Dr. Goodman early on. He had responded dramatically and now suffered from very few of the CF symptoms he had endured as a baby, as well as there being no evidence of the general decline anticipated with a CF diagnosis. Someone with an untrained eye would never have suspected that Russell was in anything but perfect health. Dr. Fulford had treated thousands of children during his more than 60 years of active osteopathic practice. I also knew from our phone conversation that he had treated a number of children with CF. He knew exactly what to look for and was well-versed in the spectrum of severity that can accompany CF. His first question caught me completely off guard.

"Why do they think he has CF?" he asked, observing Russell intently.

"Well, ummm, he had all the classic CF symptoms as a baby, and he's had the diagnostic and DNA tests to confirm it," I replied awkwardly, thinking he must have known all this.

"I see," he said. He paused.

"Well, he doesn't have the affect of a child with CF," Dr. Fulford observed, "so why do they think he *still* has it?"

I was too stunned to respond. Just what exactly was he implying? That one could recuperate from a genetic disease? This notion was like an irresistible but potentially traitorous muse—compelling but also extremely discomfiting to me—and I found myself literally holding my breath. I remembered back to my earlier discussion with Rick over the phone, and his mention of Dr. Fulford's ability to observe someone across a crowded room and accurately pinpoint their condition or illness. Prickles went up my spine, and I wondered if this might be how Alice felt during her inane conversations with the Cheshire Cat.

"Well, ahhh… I don't know," I said, fumbling with my words, "that's just how they approach CF—you know, that once you have it, you always will."

"Hmmm," Dr. Fulford replied.

"But I don't think he does anymore," I suddenly gushed, feeling positively reckless for articulating such a preposterous thought out loud.

"Hmmm," he replied again, nodding thoughtfully.

He helped Russell climb up on the treatment table, joking with him in a quiet, reassuring manner. Russell seemed intrigued by this slow-moving but light-hearted old man. Gus and I sat in chairs nearby. Dr. Fulford reached for the steno pad and pencil on his desk, and asked me about Russell's medical history. I gave him a drastically abbreviated recounting of the spina bifida, the corrective surgery, and the subsequent diagnosis with CF.

"Anything else?" he asked in a low calm voice. He seemed thoroughly unruffled by Russell's double whammy.

"Isn't that enough?" I couldn't resist responding, weighed down by having to once again acknowledge Russell's terrifying medical history.

Dr. Fulford began his physical examination by feeling Russell's pelvic bones.

"His left hip is out," he said. "It's not sitting in the joint properly."

His comment called to mind a walk in the park that the boys and I had taken a few days ago, with Russell once again complaining that "my legs hurt" and begging me to let him ride in the stroller. During the walk, I chastised myself for even bringing the stroller and, more, for babying him all his life as if he were crippled. As if it were Russell's fault, I had scolded him that, if his legs checked out with both Dr. Fulford (the trip to Ohio was imminent) and the orthopedic surgeon (we would see her during Russell's check-up at the spina bifida clinic upon our return), I was going to give the stroller away. I gulped guiltily at

Dr. Fulford's observation. *No wonder Russell has been complaining about his legs hurting,* I thought to myself, *his damned hip was out of place!*

Dr. Fulford repositioned Russell's hip ever so gently and began to work on his lower back.

"His sacrum is out," Dr. Fulford said. "What was his birth like?"

Having just read his book, I knew he was asking about the first yell—essential, according to Dr. Fulford, to realign the body and return the ribcage back to its proper position after a baby crams its way through the narrow birth canal. I told him that Russell was born yelling.

"Hmmm, that's good," he replied thoughtfully. "Well, my guess is that when they did his back surgery, they inadvertently put his sacrum (or tailbone) out. The sacrum is connected to the diaphragmatic muscles, which are connected to the lungs." He then positioned his enormous hands on Russell's chest.

"His ribcage is completely locked and he probably hasn't been able to get a full breath since the surgery on his spinal cord. That's probably what kicked off the CF. Most doctors don't understand this life force. It's very delicate."

I was stunned. No one, not one doctor, had ever contemplated a connection between Russell's spina bifida and cystic fibrosis. The doctors in both the CF and spina bifida clinics minded their own business, so to speak, and didn't seem to concern themselves with the cause (or symptoms) associated with the other clinic's specialty—even though the child in front of them had both diagnoses. At one point, I myself had conjectured that perhaps they were both caused by my own nutritional deficiencies, but then realized that, if that were the case, there were likely to be thousands or even millions of other kids with both conditions. (There weren't any that I knew of.)

What on earth was Dr. Fulford implying? I was already somewhat convinced that genetics were not destiny, but rather an indication of vulnerability or, at most, a predisposition. Geneticists had said as much in media interviews when discussing the recent discoveries of breast cancer and obesity genes. But *CF*? No one had ever suggested that Russell's body had any choice about whether or not to manifest the symptoms of CF.

There had been recent speculation that as many as 70% of all men who present as sterile may have CF, and that the obstruction of their *vas deferens* (one of the many ducts included in the exocrine system affected by CF) is its only manifestation. In other words, these men produce viable sperm, but the sperm are unable to make their way past the CF-induced mucus plug in the *vas deferens*, such that their semen doesn't contain any actual sperm. The thought had occurred to me that a DNA sampling of the whole American population might reveal just how many individuals have the CF mutation, not just as carriers but with the full-fledged CF double mutation without any apparent symptoms. If the sample being studied is limited to the DNA of individuals who have already been diagnosed with CF, then our knowledge doesn't include anything about the DNA of individuals who have not manifested symptoms and therefore have *not* been tested for CF. Perhaps, in contrast to the accepted wisdom, genes aren't always the predictor of bad health but, instead, are a road map that gives us greater insight into *potential* problems, or even a confirmation of something (a mutation) that has previously taken place and not necessarily a prediction of what is irreversibly to come. In truth, the field of genetics is so new, and our understanding of DNA is still so incomplete, that I can only imagine what corrections of "truth" will evolve over time.

Was Dr. Fulford really saying that the surgery displaced Russell's sacrum, and that this displacement then caused a blockage in the "life force" (so beautifully defined in his book), a blockage which, in turn, launched the CF vulnerability? Unfortunately for me, Dr. Fulford was a man of few words. I guessed that this had less to do with old age than his innate disposition. I desperately needed clarification and elaboration, but for some reason was compelled to merely watch and listen.

Dr. Fulford completed Russell's treatment using an electrically-powered percussion "hammer," a soft rubber vibrating instrument that, I learned later, he himself had designed by modifying a furniture polishing tool. He used it on Russell's spine, head, and ribcage without any objection from Russell. Before he started Russell's actual treatment, Dr. Fulford could barely make Russell's ribcage move left to right; but following the treatment it moved around as easily as a bowl of jello—the difference was remarkable. I asked him if the chest therapy that I athletically performed on Russell morning and night could have contributed to the locking up of his ribcage.

Dr. Fulford shrugged, "I suppose it's possible. It depends how hard you do it."

I cringed at the implication. (A couple of years later, in a conversation with Larry Culp, then editor and publisher of the newsletter, *Network: Quarterly News From and For the Adult Cystic Fibrosis Community*, I learned that this locking up of the ribcage is a major issue for people with CF, preventing the proper inflation of the lungs and inhibiting deep breathing. Interestingly enough, Larry shared with me that he himself had gained relief from osteopathic treatments, which loosened his ribcage and allowed his breathing to deepen.)

"There are alternative exercises that you could do," Dr. Fulford offered.

He briefly demonstrated a couple of them, and suggested that I seek further instruction and arrange for Russell to have regular osteopathic treatments every six to twelve weeks with an osteopath closer to home. He gave me several names to contact.

As our appointment with Dr. Fulford came to a close, I asked him how much I owed him.

"I charge twenty-five dollars," he said.

I mentally compared his ridiculously modest fee with the close to $1,500 that I had spent on three plane tickets to Ohio, hotel room, and rental car. Feeling like a crass tourist, I asked Dr. Fulford to sign my copy of his book. When I apologized for asking, he said matter-of-factly, "Oh, they all ask." I also took a photograph of him with his arm around Russell, wanting Russell to have this reminder of Dr. Fulford when he was older.

At the front door ready to leave, I found myself in a state of complete mental disarray, questioning the validity of what had just occurred. Was it something unbelievably big and meaningful, or something ridiculously non-existent?

"Why did you come all this way to see me?" Dr. Fulford suddenly asked, seeming to read my mind.

I was no longer sure. Our visit with him had lasted no more than an hour and my brain was overflowing with incomplete explanations. I was no longer certain of his mythic reputation.

"You were recommended so highly by a number of friends," I answered.

"Oh," he answered, "I just wondered. I had a child here last week from Tokyo."

Was he really questioning his own ability and worth, I wondered, or was he simply fishing for a compliment? *Or was he a mind-reader and reassuring me that his reputation was well-deserved?* Now I was hopelessly confused.

The drive back to Cincinnati took several hours due to a torrential downpour. I was oddly grateful to be distracted by the need to concentrate on my driving. Once we arrived back at the hotel, the boys and I changed into bathing suits and went to soak in the whirlpool in the hotel's enormous atrium, which also sported large cages of colorful, squawking parrots. After a while, we went back to our room, dried off, and went to the hotel's restaurant where Gus and Russell ate a huge supper while I picked at my food. Later, with the boys immersed in Nintendo (this hotel was fast becoming their idea of heaven...), I called my sister.

"I don't know what to tell you, Faithy," I said. "It was so confusing and all done in this very low-key, matter-of-fact manner. I don't even begin to know if something happened, or if nothing happened."

"You have done a huge thing for Russell, Lindsay," she reassured me firmly.

I started to share what Dr. Fulford had theorized about the connection between spina bifida and CF but stopped abruptly when I realized that I wanted to take time to think this through on my own before exposing it to anyone else's thinking. I hung up, promising to call her back to describe the rest of our experience after we arrived home the next day.

Later that evening as we were brushing our teeth, I asked Russell offhandedly, "So, Russell, what did you think of Dr. Fulford?"

"He was a *good* man," he replied with emphasis, "a *good* man."

Ah, Russell, such an old soul you are...

When we finally arrived back home in Maryland, one of the first things I did was pull out Andrew Weil's book to re-read the chapter on Dr. Fulford. Hmmm, I thought, there are an awful lot of extremely well-informed people out there who are convinced that Dr. Fulford knows what he's doing. Later that evening, I called Rick Koss, intending to ask him to share my still unanswered questions about Russell's prognosis with Dr. Fulford and to then please get back to me with the doctor's fuller explanations. As it turned out, Rick was able to interpret Dr. Fulford's brief comments and fill in the blanks himself.

Rick agreed with my assumptions exactly. Dr. Fulford's theory was that an extraneous (and obviously unintended) consequence of Russell's surgery had been the displacement of his sacrum, which had then blocked the life force and served as a catalyst for what had previously been merely a "blueprint" for CF to go into action. I could barely believe my ears. It brought back the gruesome picture of Russell right after his back surgery at five weeks old, and the powerful gut sense I had had that, despite the fact that his spinal cord defect had been successfully repaired, the surgery had somehow done something hugely wrong to him. I also suddenly remembered that Russell's CF symptoms had first surfaced right after the surgery. (Later on, Richard and a handful of close friends and family members all confirmed the validity of this memory—that my complaints about his CF symptoms only started after his surgery.)

I felt as if the pieces of a gigantic 3,000-piece jigsaw puzzle were finally falling into place, after years of thought and query and confusion. Unfortunately, it also raised the specter of self-blame. If I had taken folic acid supplements before conceiving Russell, he might not have had spina bifida in the first place. And if Russell hadn't required corrective surgery, maybe the CF would never have manifested. I felt a heavy sadness in my heart; preventive health suddenly took on a whole new dimension.

Toward the end of my phone conversation with Rick, I said with enormous trepidation, "Okay, Rick, play God for a moment and answer me this... If the CF manifested because of a blockage to Russell's life force that occurred during his surgery, and if that blockage to his life force has now been removed as a result of Dr. Fulford's treatment this past week, then what are we talking about? *Did Dr. Fulford cure Russell's CF?*"

I waited breathlessly for his response, my throat practically closing with the tension.

He said without even hesitating, "Oh, it's entirely possible. I've seen 'Doc' do incredible things before. Time and again, he's had amazing results. But what he does is so contrary to standard medical theories that the results are not even publishable. This life force is everything. What Dr. Fulford meant by a 'delicate' life force is that it's extremely *subtle*, but it's not at all fragile. We'll have to wait and see what results this treatment may reap for Russell."

Wait and see... Wait and see... Oh my God, I thought wildly, I will die waiting and never get to see! But that, of course, was exactly my wish: that my little boy would outlive me.

"We recreate our bodies every two years," Rick continued, "with a complete set of new bones every three months. That's been scientifically proven, but unfortunately it hasn't been incorporated into modern medical theories of healing. It's very possible that, over a period of time, Russell's body will unlearn the condition of CF."

"How can it be that this life force, the very essence of healing, is not even considered in conventional medicine?" I wondered out loud to Rick. "It's like a locomotive taking off from the station without the rest of the train or any of its passengers."

Before we hung up, I indulged myself and said, "You know, Rick, it's strange. I've had such an awful week since going out to see Dr. Fulford. I think it must have brought up all of the grief that I've been suppressing for the past four years."

"Oh yes," he said calmly, "Doc often treats parents right along with the kids."

The next day I called our pediatrician, Dr. Brynelson, to request referrals for Russell's appointments scheduled later that week at both the CF and spina bifida clinics. I had no intention of breathing a word to her about Dr. Fulford, but as soon as she came on the phone, it all came pouring out. She completely shocked me by being both intrigued and supportive. She promised to fax me an article in a recent issue of *Pediatrics in Review* in which the author suggested that pediatricians ought to be at least conversant with alternative healing, and recalled her osteopathic resident friends of yesteryear.[4]

I had always liked Dr. Brynelson. She had a real knack with my boys, getting them to talk about recent sports headlines or books they were reading even while she poked them in the stomach or gave them a shot in the arm. She had also always been very supportive of me and patient with my questions. I could tell that she regarded us as a team that took care of Russell together, and I appreciated how well she knew him and his brother. But she hadn't yet expressed much interest in the alternative treatments that Russell had been receiving. After she reacted so positively to our experience with Dr. Fulford, I began to consider her in a different light. She wasn't one of "us" exactly, but I no longer simply viewed her as one of "them." It gave me hope.

Beginning around the time that Russell turned two, I had been repeatedly urged by the orthopedic surgeon with the hospital's spina bifida clinic to have Russell's hips x-rayed to rule out a dislocation of the hip that can accompany spina bifida.[5] (When present, this hip anomaly can require early intervention in the form of corrective surgery.) I was in the habit of discouraging any unnecessary tests, especially x-rays, and had repeatedly refused the request for hip x-rays. The orthopedist obviously found my repeated questioning of her recommendation vexing, but her concern was a generic one and she was unable to convince me that x-rays were necessary absent any symptoms or a concern specific to Russell. I was not willing to agree to an x-ray to simply enable her to cross "hip anomaly" off her generic checklist.

After our trip to Ohio, it dawned on me that perhaps there had been something wrong with Russell's hips. Dr. Fulford had in fact observed that one of his hips was "out of position," but he had gently (and apparently successfully) put it back into place. Russell had not complained once about his legs hurting in the months since his treatment with Dr. Fulford. Was it possible that this "malpositioning" was the very thing that the orthopedic surgeon was asking to screen for? Was it also possible that, had we never been to see Dr. Fulford and had I allowed the x-ray, his hip would have been treated surgically instead of gently and non-invasively by an osteopath? I will never know.

A couple of weeks after returning from seeing Dr. Fulford, I made an appointment for Russell with Dr. Lisa Chun, an osteopath closer to home whom Dr. Fulford had recommended. Dr. Chun was a soft spoken Chinese American with a quiet intensity and ready smile. It turned out that she had been making the drive to Ohio for four years to study under Dr. Fulford. In addition to being a doctor of osteopathy, she was licensed to practice acupuncture and was also studying homeopathy. The breadth of her training and interest in alternative healing made her very appealing. I began taking Russell to her for osteopathic treatments every two to four months.

Dr. Chun made a point of starting each appointment with a conversation with Russell that would put him at ease, asking him questions about the toy or book that he had brought with him. He was very shy as a child, but she was a little shy herself, and he warmed up to her gentle approach. She would then examine him and adjust any bone that had strayed out of alignment—often one rib or a knee. She and I talked while she treated him, which helped to further clarify my thoughts about Dr. Fulford. I felt that we were in good hands.

At one of our first appointments, Dr. Chun also showed me how to perform the gentle lung clearance exercises that Dr. Fulford had suggested. The minute we got home that day, I tested them out. The first exercise was designed to realign the ribs and the muscles surrounding the ribs. Russell lay flat on his back on the bed with me straddling him on my knees but without placing any weight on him. I placed my hands, palms down, on each of side of his breast bone, essentially covering the surface of one lung with each hand. I then very gently and rhythmically pressed up and down about ten times. Afterwards, I asked him to cough and clear his lungs of any mucus.

The second exercise encouraged a more vigorous clearing of the lungs. Again, Russell lay on his back on the bed and I straddled him on my knees without placing any weight on him. I placed my hands on the two lung areas of his ribcage as in the first exercise. I then asked him to take in an enormous breath and, as soon as he started to exhale, I pressed down on his chest further and further until the exhalation was completed, and then very quickly pulled my hands away. This caused both an unusually thorough exhalation and an abrupt subsequent inhalation which helped to clear away mucus at a deeper level. It was also followed by deliberate coughing.

The third exercise stimulated the circulation of primal energy or *chi* throughout the body. Again, Russell lay on his back comfortably on the bed. This time, I sat on the end of the bed just beyond his feet, while he flexed his feet upward (as if his feet were flat on the floor had he been standing up). I then rhythmically pushed on the ball or pad of his feet with the palm of my hands, causing his whole body to very gently bob up in the direction of his head and back down toward me. I did this for about 15 seconds and then stretched his feet gently downward.

Finally, with Russell still lying on his back and me sitting to one side, the fourth exercise entailed my folding his knees up to his chest, and then gently rocking his folded legs from right to left. This exercise assisted the *chi* to circulate more easily and also helped to keep the back of his ribcage loose and flexible. Russell was thrilled that we would substitute the rigorous 40-minute sessions of me thumping him on his chest, sides, and back with these new mystifyingly gentle exercises.

With Dr. Chun's reassurance, as well as the ongoing supervision of the CF specialist whom I trusted to detect any increase in mucus accumulation in Russell's lungs, I stopped doing the conventional chest physiotherapy that we had been taught at the hospital altogether—something I had been doing without fail, morning and night, for four years. Instead of thumping Russell so hard that it hurt him, these new gentle exercises that I learned from Dr. Fulford and Dr. Chun became our new nightly regimen.

One evening, a couple of days after stopping the old regimen and initiating these new exercises, Russell jumped up on my double bed and began to wriggle around, dancing and playing an imaginary electric guitar, singing a wild and crazy song at the top of his lungs. Gus and I both began to laugh hard, which of course only encouraged further antics. I had to admit that Russell was displaying a new abundance of energy and vigor. The next evening at bedtime, Russell renewed the "guitar" playing. In fact, this little performance of his took on nightly regularity until Gus and I both became worn out. I finally jokingly threatened to take Russell back to Ohio to ask Dr. Fulford to undo whatever it was that he had done during Russell's treatment so that we could have our quiet, mild-mannered, little boy back. Naturally, I was only kidding but the difference in Russell's physical well-being and even personality were incredible. Our entire family became elated that Russell was feeling so good. He was blossoming into an outgoing, funny, energetic, playful child right before our eyes. Months after returning from seeing Dr. Fulford, when Richard asked Russell whether his legs still hurt him, Russell responded, "Nope. Dr. Fulford fixed them!" We had taken many long walks in the park without the stroller since our trip to Ohio with nary a complaint from Russell about his legs.[6]

Given Dr. Fulford's advanced age (he was 92 years old when we saw him), I had been afraid that he might literally die before he would have an opportunity to treat Russell. After reading his book and then meeting him in person, I fancied that his humble but steadfast crusade to unearth the truths about healing and the life force would enable him to live forever. Unfortunately, Dr. Fulford proved to be mortal. He passed away in June of 1997, just five months after we saw him in his home in Ohio. I was so very grateful that Russell had a chance to be touched by him.

After I learned of his death, I sat at my computer and wrote a poem, mourning this incredibly wise healer's passing through a torrent of tears:

I am used to pushing mountains of one sort or another—
The combined gift of karma and tough beginnings
Having created a distorted nature of monstrous strength.
This mountain (CF) also compels me by its enormity,
 if not by its utter necessity,

So I readily, quickly, assume the stance of warrior.

You have removed this mountain with your enormous gentle hands,
This massive challenge to my son's life,
And I crumble into utter exhaustion and delayed grief.

It has vanished in a great cloud of mist
The dragon now casting only a faint shadow.
It is now my task to believe
And to slowly, steadfastly erase the imprint in my own mind.
"My son is cured. My son is cured," I repeat to myself.
"He is well. He is well. He is well."

You have saved us, me right along with my son,
And I will be eternally grateful.
May the gods bless you, wherever you may be,
And extol your gifts as we do.

While at the beach in the summer of 1997, Russell (age 5) began to manifest an awkward gait, a limp of sorts, and it seemed that one leg might be shorter than the other. I was such an avid (read: slightly neurotic) observer of my son that, whenever I noticed something the least bit "off," I had to question whether or not I was observing anything real. The awkwardness of his gait continued throughout the whole vacation, and when we returned home and attended our regular appointment with Dr. Chun in late August, she corroborated my worry by noting that the left leg was indeed shorter than the right by as much as an eighth of an inch (which doesn't sound like much, but it was enough to concern her). She treated him, but I reluctantly decided to have his hips x-rayed at our upcoming spina bifida check-up at the hospital anyway. I certainly didn't want to risk ignoring an anomaly that might affect him down the road. The x-ray showed no hip anomaly, and the limp completely disappeared in a few weeks' time. By our next appointment with Dr. Chun in October, his legs were back to equal length and my concern ended. This was perhaps an example of the potential for parents and doctors alike to scrutinize a special needs child too carefully.

Over time, Russell began to be able to feel bone misalignments himself, and he would direct Dr. Chun to the specific part of his body that needed adjusting. While there was rarely anything grossly out of alignment, I considered Dr. Chun's regular treatments—particularly adjustments of his ribcage—to be vital. Breathing deeply is essential, not only to enable adequate oxygen intake, but also to allow for full exhalations and continuous clearing of the lungs. As a baby and toddler, Russell's face would sometimes turn blue around his mouth, indicating an inadequate supply of oxygen. When the ribs are stuck in an inappropriate position, the ribcage is prevented from fully expanding, causing shallower breathing—a problem that is already commonplace when CF lungs are clogged with mucus.

Before we left his care (when Russell was around age 5), I asked the CF specialist at Children's Hospital why he urged us to continue chest physiotherapy even though Russell had no serious lung issues. He suggested that keeping it in Russell's daily regimen was a good idea, because otherwise he would become accustomed to not having it done. One day, the doctor assured me, Russell would definitely need it. The doctor had no crystal ball, but he was absolutely convinced that Russell's demise was inevitable and not that far down the road. A few years later, at Russell's annual physical with the pediatrician at age 8, Dr. Brynelson found his lungs to be completely clear of mucus. The harsh chest PT, which I had not done for almost four years at that point, was clearly no longer needed to keep his lungs free of mucus. From that point forward, Russell's respiratory tests continued to indicate excellent oxygen levels in his blood and strong lung activity. This is surely a result of the osteopathic treatments as well as the rest of his alternative healing regimen.

Eventually, our osteopath Dr. Chun moved to the Hawaiian Islands (if only we had been able to follow her there). We tried out the new osteopath who took over her practice on several occasions, but I didn't take to him. As a result, Russell's regular osteopathic treatments, which had been continuous for six years, came to an end.

Age 5 months

Richard and the boys

Russell, 7 months, and Gus, age 5

Always cuddling

Russell, age 1, and Gus, age 5

With my mother, age 2

With Granny Geraldine

A rare shot of all four of us

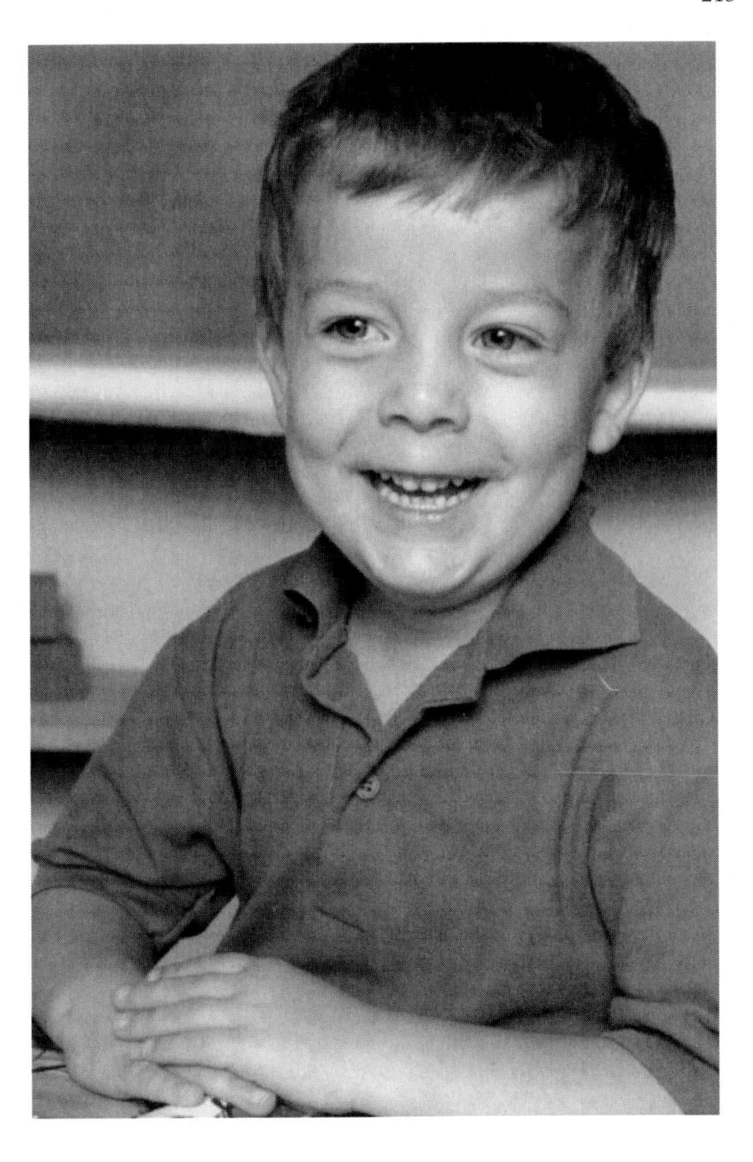

Nursery School, age 3

Russell, age 4, with Dr. Fulford in Ohio

Russell and Gus at karate

Surprise trip to St. John

The beach! Age 7

Maine

(Russell, age 6, and Gus, age 10)

Baltimore

(Russell, age 8, and Gus, age 12)

At a wedding, age 10

Maine again

(Russell, age 13, and Gus, age 17)

With my sister Faith (at left)

My brother Geoff

Gus is off to college!

Striking a pose

Always the ham!

Russell at college, age 21

Camden Russell, age 3, and Uncle Russell, age 25

Chapter 7

Nutrition

Hope is the thing with feathers that perches in the soul – and sings the tunes without the words – and never stops at all.

Emily Dickinson (1830-1886)

SOON AFTER WE BEGAN OUR HOMEOPATHIC CONSULTATIONS with Dr. Razi, she suggested that I work with a nutritionist to help design a nutritional plan for Russell. Dr. Razi knew that CF caused serious nutritional deficiencies, and that an appropriate diet and nutritional supplementation would be critically important for him. She recommended a nutritionist named Kelly Dorfman, who maintained a thriving nutritional counseling practice in her home in an upscale Maryland suburb off the Washington, D.C. beltway.

By the time we had our first visit with Kelly in mid-October, Russell was 14 months old. It had been six months since his diagnosis with CF. He had been having acupuncture treatments for about five months, he had been taking various homeopathic remedies for four months, and he had just started osteopathic treatments the month before. His CF symptoms were less pronounced than when he was first diagnosed, but they were still in evidence and he had not yet begun to exhibit any major rebound in health or growth.

Kelly greeted us at her door with a warm smile. Dr. Razi had cautioned me, "Don't let Kelly's youthfulness fool you. She knows everything there is to know about nutrition." I was glad to be forewarned. Kelly was a petite and pretty woman whose appearance and cheerful "Hi!" definitely made her appear quite young—until she began to speak authoritatively about nutrition. As she ushered me into her tidy home office, I noticed the collection of framed diplomas and professional licenses on the wall and became further excited at the prospect of her help.[1]

Kelly began our interview by asking me to share details about Russell's medical history that I felt were relevant. I started with a description of the myriad symptoms that surfaced after his spinal cord surgery, including steatorrhea, his need to nurse practically non-stop around the clock, croupy cough, colic, ear and sinus infections, pasty white skin pallor, and how the color of his hair constantly changed. I noted that these classic symptoms of CF went on for months before they were finally taken seriously by our new pediatrician.

I told Kelly that as soon as a CF diagnosis had been confirmed, Russell began treatment at the CF clinic at Children's Hospital. As soon as the CF specialist placed Russell on a regimen of pancreatic enzymes with each meal, his steatorrhea quickly transformed back into the normally loose yellow stools of breastfed babies. I said that now that we were beginning to dabble with solid foods, they caused an occasional build-up of orange grease in his stools (that coated his diaper) and even a sporadic reoccurrence of the steatorrhea, indicating to me that the supplemental enzymes were not enough to eliminate his digestive challenges.

Russell sat on the rug while Kelly and I talked, playing contentedly with several new toys I brought from the mountain of gifts that his adoring paternal grandparents had given him on his first birthday. I had tucked away a handful of unopened toys for just this type of occasion.

Kelly took notes as I described his many symptoms, occasionally glancing down at Russell. It both relieved and frightened me to have her confirm my suspicion that both the odd pallor of his skin and changing hair color indicated nutritional deficiencies. I was hungry to share my worries and fears with each new healer, and just as hungry to share my half-baked theories and self-educated guesses. The alternative healers represented fresh hope to me, and I was often so flooded with relief upon meeting a practitioner for the first time that tears streamed down my cheeks from the moment of introductions. My unchecked emotions embarrassed me, but I usually just kept talking as a way to push through the emotion and regain my composure. With the addition of each new healer, Russell's health team grew more robust, and I felt less alone. I was grateful that the alternative practitioners were not at all intimidated by the enormity of the threat posed by CF, not because they didn't know enough about the disease, but because they each had had experience treating individuals with scary prognoses that conventional doctors had been unable to help.

Kelly started down an endless list of questions that zeroed in on Russell's diet and digestion: "How much does he eat on an average day?" "Do you give him dairy products or foods containing wheat?" "What foods does he like?" "What foods does he dislike?" "Are there any foods that he seems to crave?" "Does he have a tendency toward thirst?" "Does he ever turn down food?" "Does he ever vomit after eating?" "Does he get rashes or hives?" "Is he ever constipated?" "How often does he have diarrhea?" "What foods are followed by a stomach ache?" She asked me for as much detail as I could recall about his eating habits, moods, energy level, sleeping habits, bowel movements, and complaints of indigestion. She also asked me what I thought was behind the ups and downs in his appetite. And she asked me to describe the trends in his weight gain and growth in height, as well as fluctuations in energy level and his tendency to catch colds and develop ear infections.

After taking copious notes, Kelly recommended that we begin with a basic daily regimen of vitamins and minerals.

"I'll need time to investigate the specific nutritional challenges of CF," she said, "after which I'll probably suggest additional items."

Kelly advised me to increase the vitamin E dosage that the CF doctor had recommended and to add a small dose of selenium to help Russell absorb vitamin E.

"Let's also start him on a probiotic supplement right away," she added. "You can mix powdered *bifidobacteria* into his food," she said. "This will help to counter the deleterious side effects of repeated stints on antibiotics."[2]

She launched into a modest tirade about the overuse of antibiotics, and how this overuse was creating drug-resistant strains of bacteria. Her stance on antibiotics is considered quite mainstream today, but back in 1993 when we were having this conversation, what she believed was considered heresy. Proponents of a more conservative attitude toward prescribing antibiotics were scoffed at by the conventional medical establishment. Kelly shared several examples of experts who had been publicly shunned due to their controversial views, which made it impossible for them to publish or present their findings.[3] It took less than two decades for the general view on antibiotics to circle back 180 degrees to the heretics' viewpoint, but not until the U.S. was challenged by near epidemic levels of virulent drug-resistant bacteria, such as *methicillin-resistant Staphylococcus aureus* (MRSA) and *Clostridium difficile* (C. diff). Recent studies suggest that there may be a link between the overuse of antibiotics in children and obesity as well as food allergies. We pay a hefty price when doctors are stubbornly closed to new theories or a suggestion that they question old habits.

I had a lot to learn about antibiotics. Kelly explained that not all antibiotics have the capacity to kill a broad spectrum of bacteria (as the "big gun" antibiotics that Russell had been prescribed did). By the same token, antibiotics are not well-honed weapons that seek out only the targeted (bad) bacteria either.

"Most antibiotics kill bacteria indiscriminately," she warned, "doing enormous harm at the same time that they are doing enormous good. It is a bacterial balance that we need to achieve."

This antibiotic dance started to look like a crap shoot in which a good outcome was not all good. The CF specialist's ability to carefully select the most effective antibiotic regimen for Russell was crucial, especially given the likely exacerbated need for antibiotics down the road. The whole idea of antibiotic resistance was terrifying to me. One day, Russell's very survival might depend on an antibiotic's capacity to squelch infections. The subject of resistance made me want to learn how to ward off the infections in the first place—how to keep bad bacteria from taking up permanent residence in Russell's lungs and colonizing. Prevention was an even more complicated subject, however. The normal flora (healthy bacteria) in the lungs, such as *Staphylococcus*, were unavoidable, although they needed to be kept in check. But the *dangerous* bacteria, such as *Pseudomonas aeruginosa* or *Burkholderia cepacia*, both of which are drug-resistant and quite common to our environment, needed to be avoided at all costs. (Shortly after Russell's diagnosis, the CF specialist had told me that once a child is infected with *B. cepacia*, he or she is likely to die within 12 months.)

Before meeting with Kelly, I had been staunchly opposed to the increasingly popular fad of cutting dairy products out of the diet. I had serious concerns about Russell's need for calcium—he was still a baby, with a lot more bone growth ahead. My concerns were also compounded by worries about how such a drastic dietary change would complicate our already complicated household by necessitating different meals for each of the boys. I anticipated that she might suggest cutting dairy out of his diet and was determined to say no if she did. By the end of our first meeting, however, Kelly had me completely convinced that, while cows' milk is perfectly suited to calves (with their four stomachs), it is poorly suited to humans.

"Milk almost always causes additional mucus production," she said, "especially in people with a tendency toward allergies. In Russell's case, we obviously want to reduce mucus build-up—not make it worse."

Kelly added that when milk is pasteurized, much of its nutritional value is eliminated along with the harmful bacteria. She encouraged me to stop giving Russell all dairy products, including the yogurt and cheese that he loved, and assured me that there were plenty of other equally efficient, if not preferable, sources of calcium, such as broccoli and supplementation.[4] I was still nursing Russell in between his meals of solid food and also at bedtime, and I hadn't yet given him bottles of anything but water. Kelly encouraged me to consider giving him calcium-enriched rice milk once he was weaned off breast milk.

"Rice milk is full of nutrients," she said, "but it doesn't tend to cause mucus production the way cow's milk or even soy milk does. Rice milk is very easy to digest."

Kelly didn't seem the least bit daunted by Russell's symptoms, nor did she suggest that I scale back my ambition to fully restore his health. I thanked her and left our appointment feeling relieved and uplifted. I also left bewildered by a wealth of new information. I had no reason to doubt Kelly's credentials or breadth of knowledge; she was a Licensed Nutritionist and Dietician with a master's degree in Nutritional Science. But I thought back to my own questionable dabbling with nutritional supplements as a young adult and worried about experimenting with my son's nutrition, wondering what harm could be done. It was one thing to experiment on myself; it was quite another to experiment on a baby. Further, as the general public became increasingly interested in vitamin and mineral supplements, there had been a rash of media reports about the dangers of toxic dosages of vitamins. Yet we had so much to gain if this helped, and far too much to lose if we didn't even try. I was confident that Kelly would select beneficial vitamins and prescribe safe dosages, and I decided to take the plunge. When our visit ended, I drove directly from her house to the store to purchase the recommended supplements so that Russell could start his new nutritional regimen right away.

Kelly sent me to the Apothecary—a small pharmacy tucked away in a wooded area on the fringes of NIH's sprawling campus in Bethesda, Maryland (the same pharmacy that occasionally supplied us with Dr. Razi's homeopathic remedies). Irv Rosenberg and Mickey Weinstein, the pharmacists who founded the store, provided advice and humor-infused comfort to a multitude of pilgrims brave and/or desperate enough to seek their counsel about alternative medicine. Doctors Irv and Mickey, as they liked to be called, opened the store in 1965 as a regular pharmacy. After listening to customer after customer complain about the side effects of prescription medication, they began to stock an array of alternative remedies, eventually dubbing themselves "nutritional pharmacists."[5] Thus, in addition to filling conventional pharmaceutical prescriptions, the Apothecary had shelves crammed with all sorts of vitamins, minerals, herbal tonics, homeopathic remedies, books about alternative medicine, and other alternative healing supplies. (This would be closer to the norm in parts of Europe, but rare even today in the U.S.) Everyone working in the store was knowledgeable about the store's inventory, and staff gave customers as much time and attention as they needed. With help, I found everything on Kelly's list. When I took it all up to the cashier, I was shocked at the total cost—apparently this would be quite an expensive experiment! However, now that I had found everything Kelly had suggested, I was even more eager to give it a try despite the price tag.[6]

That evening at dinnertime, I opened up the capsules and punctured the gel caps so that I could mix the various powder and oil-based supplements directly into Russell's baby food. I could tell he wasn't thrilled with the taste but he ate it anyway. The next morning, I repeated the same dosages. Later that day, I noticed with alarm that his stools were completely different. All of a sudden, they had turned from yellowish-brown and runny to brown and firm. I called Kelly in alarm. She was thrilled and it took me a minute to realize that this was evidence that even the basic regimen that Kelly had prescribed was already taking effect.

The next day, I noticed that there was actually color in Russell's face—his skin tone had changed from a blanched white to a more acceptable pale pink. His hair color had also changed to a definitive dirty blond. As the days passed, his normal-looking stools continued, and his skin and hair color didn't vary. I also noticed that his mood lightened considerably and his energy increased. Without mentioning Russell's new nutritional regimen as a factor, I asked my husband if he detected a difference of any sort in our son; I wanted proof that I wasn't imagining things. Richard noted the same changes I had observed in both Russell's appearance and mood. I became elated. In under a week, there was concrete evidence that the nutritional supplements were working.

At our next CF clinic appointment, I shared Kelly's recommendations and the immediate positive changes in Russell's stools and energy level with Dr. Sullivan. Some of the things Kelly suggested were met with skepticism. Both Dr. Sullivan and the clinic's nutritionist doubted that Russell would be able get enough calcium without dairy products in his diet. They doubted that he would be able to absorb any more than the dosage of vitamin E they had already prescribed, and the nutritionist expressed alarm about the potential toxicity of selenium.

I was very impressed with Kelly's extensive knowledge of nutrition and by her requests for endless detail about Russell's health status and diet (far more than the CF clinic staff had ever asked about). I was especially impressed by her commitment to explore the nutritional component of CF in order to individualize Russell's nutritional regimen as much as possible. It also helped that I had such respect for Dr. Razi, and that she had spoken highly of Kelly. But now I had all these differing opinions from professionals that I respected—Dr. Razi and Kelly vs. the CF doctor and nutritionist—and I was mightily confused. Since the hospital already had a nutritionist on the CF team, I could have left it at that. But I wasn't content to simply feed Russell "everything you and I should *not* eat" (i.e., high calorie, high fat junk food) as the CF nutritionist had advised us early on. I hadn't anticipated that there would be such different viewpoints within the same specialty (nutrition), and once again found myself forced to make a choice.

When I shared Kelly's concerns about dairy products' tendency to increase mucus, Dr. Sullivan acknowledged that one of his pediatric colleagues at Johns Hopkins Hospital had recently joined the ranks of those who discourage giving dairy products to any young child, whether ill or healthy, because of the potential for clogging the digestive and respiratory systems with excess mucus. I suppose it was open-minded of Dr. Sullivan to share this with me, but he obviously disagreed with his colleague, because he went on to reiterate his concerns about Russell's calcium intake on a diet without dairy, as did the clinic nutritionist. (Several years later, Dr. Sullivan surprised me by acknowledging the mucus-producing impact of dairy products—as if our earlier exchange had never happened. I never knew if his change of heart was influenced by Russell's ability to maintain an acceptable level of calcium despite removing dairy from his diet, or the ongoing lack of mucus build-up in his lungs, or whether he was influenced by a growing number of like-minded colleagues.)

Because acupuncture, homeopathic remedies, and osteopathic treatments were considered outside of the medical realm by the conventional doctors we encountered, there was little opportunity for everyone to debate their conflicting opinions. They could more or less ignore each other. Nutrition was an entirely different matter. On the one hand, the nutritionist on the CF team had been working with children with CF for years. She had thorough conventional training and knew a lot about the specific nutritional impact of CF. On the other hand, while Kelly was on the young side and had admitted that she would have to go up a learning curve about CF, she too was very well-trained (actually, her credentials surpassed those of the hospital's nutritionist). What seemed key to me was that Kelly was open-minded, and I gleaned from her stories about other clients that she was not easily discouraged. She was keen on experimenting with dietary changes to improve Russell's ability to absorb nutrients, and she was motivated to sift through cutting-edge nutritional supplements that would alter how his body was battling CF. The conventional medical approach was to compensate and cope with the disease's impact, whereas Kelly's alternative approach was to literally alter the way the body functioned in order to help Russell surmount the disease. After several consultations with her, I decided to follow Kelly's advice about diet and nutritional supplementation. To alleviate any future confusion with contrasting opinions, I told Dr. Sullivan as diplomatically as I could at the next visit that I wouldn't need the assistance of the hospital nutritionist anymore. He accepted my decision without any fuss.

After taking several weeks to fully investigate the digestive and nutrient absorption challenges of CF, Kelly recommended a regimen for Russell that included both daily nutritional supplementation and dietary changes. His supplementation included a fairly standard spectrum of vitamins and minerals (in baby doses) but also highlighted items that were specific to him, such as folic acid (because of his spina bifida) and selenium (because it is an antioxidant and enhances the absorption of vitamin E). She added calcium to counter the removal of dairy products from his diet. His regimen also included large doses of two other antioxidants: vitamin C and vitamin A (which has strong anti-viral properties). She called Russell's nutritional "prescription" in to the Apothecary, where pharmacists prepared a composite supplement that included all of the carefully calculated dosages on Kelly's list. The composite was in powder form and packaged into small gelatin capsules, which the Apothecary then sent to us through the mail.

Russell was supposed to take three small capsules of this nutritional composite twice a day along with other supplements that were oil-based (such as vitamin E) or in a liquid form (such as tea). I also mixed powdered *bifidobacteria* (which had to be refrigerated) into his baby food at every meal. As a baby and then toddler, Russell was of course unable to swallow pills, so I emptied the powder from the capsules, squeezed the oil from the gel caps, and crushed any tablets with a mortar and pestle—mixing all of this directly into his baby food. The taste was pretty nasty and only barely disguised by the line-up of ultra-sweet, strong-flavored baby food desserts I tried. At a surprisingly young age (perhaps age three or four), Russell decided to swallow his pills instead of continuing to eat the bad-tasting mush (i.e., baby food plus supplements). Over time, he developed the Herculean ability to swallow an entire handful of pills at once; his lifetime record is something like 25 pills in one swallow. It was both amazing and a little scary to witness.

In addition to the supplementation, Kelly recommended what foods to take out of his daily diet (e.g., dairy products and junk food high in saturated or trans fats) and what foods to add into his daily diet (e.g., mango, papaya, and other fresh tropical fruit that contain natural enzymes). She encouraged me to feed him foods high in healthy fats, such as avocado, and to put plenty of butter (her one exception to the "no dairy" rule) on everything—meat, pasta, hot cereal, rice, sweet potatoes, other cooked vegetables—as an easy way to ensure that he was getting plenty of calories.

Around this time (the early 1990's), a national movement to eat organic foods was gaining a lot of traction. Health food stores were springing up everywhere and even the mainstream grocery stores were starting to sell (expensive) organic produce grown without the use of chemical pesticides and synthetic fertilizers, in addition to their regular (cheaper) line of conventionally grown produce. Kelly encouraged me to feed Russell (and the rest of our family) organic foods as much as possible. She noted that this would cut down on the unnecessary burden that the ingestion of toxic pesticides and fertilizers would place on his major organs responsible for processing and eliminating toxic residue, especially the liver and kidneys. It would also avoid burdening his immune and endocrine systems with the hormone and antibiotic residue in non-organic chicken and meat.

There was a lot of confusion in the nation's burgeoning interest in nutrition. Reporters didn't appear to have a solid grasp of the debate and often made matters worse by confusing the general public with a flood of dietary recommendations and retractions. We would be told: "Don't eat butter! It's bad for you!" A few months later, we would be told: "Do eat butter! Margarine and butter substitutes are bad for you!" "Don't eat eggs; they contribute to high cholesterol!" "Do eat eggs; they're a good source of protein!" "Don't eat fats; they lead to heart disease!" "Eat at least some fats; they're an important part of a healthy diet!" Even wine, coffee, and chocolate were declared culprits only to have their status reversed as saviors. It was pretty confusing for those of us who were trying to switch to a healthier diet. In the end, I concluded that the best approach would be for my family to eat food that was organic and real (as opposed to artificial concoctions such as butter substitutes or artificial sweeteners, or food that had been processed and stripped of its nutrients such as white flour). It simplified the guessing game.

Every few months, and eventually only once or twice a year, Kelly and I had a follow-up phone consultation in which I would update her on Russell's growth, any residual CF symptoms, and any other details that might indicate to her a need to reduce or increase a supplement or to add something new. His daily regimen was never meant to be a generic plan appropriate for anyone with CF; Kelly carefully individualized it to Russell's unique needs. This was quite an experiment and one that I would never have been able to pull off by myself without Kelly's expert guidance.

As previously noted, one of the biggest concerns following Russell's diagnosis with CF was his lack of growth. His above average size at birth (9½ pounds and 21¼ inches long) placed him in the 95th percentile for weight and the 90th for height on the pediatric growth chart. By the time he was four months old, however, he was not only no longer above average, he wasn't even average. His weight had plummeted to the 10th percentile and his height was so low that it registered below the bottom of the rankings. By April, four months after we first started seeing our pediatrician, Dr. Brynelson, she finally diagnosed Russell with failure to thrive and directed us to have him tested for CF.

At our appointments at the CF clinic, Dr. Sullivan routinely highlighted the importance of growth. He said that most children with CF who placed in the 50th percentile or higher did considerably better than smaller children in terms of long-term prognosis. His goal was to have Russell reach the 50th percentile in weight (and height too, if possible). He also emphasized the connection between weight and height, i.e., that increases in weight gain were necessary to spur subsequent growth in height.

"If Russell's growth doesn't improve soon," said Dr. Sullivan, "we can always try growth hormones."

Once Dr. Sullivan highlighted the connection between Russell's growth and an improved prognosis, I became obsessed with my son's ranking on the growth chart. When his height was measured in the CF clinic, I urged the nurse to really stretch him out while he lay on the scale, sure that she was letting him bend his knees which would cause us to lose precious percentage points on the chart. He was also measured during his less frequent check-ups at the spina bifida clinic, which were scheduled on the same day as appointments at the CF clinic. Somehow the height measurements taken in the two clinics always differed even when they were taken on the same day. It drove me crazy. His weight was different too, often as much as five percentage points lower in the CF clinic than in the spina bifida clinic, leading me to neurotically suspect that the CF scales were intentionally skewed on the low side to pressure us mothers to feed our children more. When I shared my confusion with the nurse at one of the clinics, they assured me that a technician traveled throughout the hospital every day, calibrating each clinic's scales and measurement tools to ensure that they were all accurate. Yet, Russell's records plainly showed a discrepancy between the clinics at each ensuing appointment.

Eventually Russell's weight and height began to climb back up the chart. At age one, four months after his diagnosis with CF and the initiation of supplemental pancreatic enzymes, his height was just barely above zero at the bottom of the chart, but his weight had increased to just below the 15th percentile. I felt that we were at least making progress. At the end of October (at 14 months old), Russell began the specialized nutritional regimen that Kelly prescribed after she learned more about CF. When I took him to the pediatrician three months later, when he was 17 months old, Dr. Brynelson and I were thrilled to discover that Russell's weight had jumped to just below the 50th percentile and his gains in height put him squarely back on the chart, just above the 15th percentile. Russell's father was just under six feet. But some of the men in my family were as tall as 6'5", and our older son always placed in the 90th percentile for height. I was convinced that Russell's genetic potential was well above the 50th percentile and closer to his brother's above average height.

Going forward, I continued to scrutinize his growth, but now I experienced growing excitement rather than constant worry. We were making clear progress, and although Dr. Sullivan completely ignored my tentative suggestion that the alternative healing (especially nutritional supplements and dietary changes) might be having an impact on Russell's growth, our pediatrician was confident that his growth spurt was a direct result of the nutritional supplementation. By two years and three months, after adding a lipase-only enzyme supplement to his daily regimen (I explain the enzyme issue a little later in this chapter), Russell's ranking jumped to the 75th percentile for weight and the 50th percentile for height. We had finally arrived at a plateau where there was solid evidence of restored health.[7]

Some months later, when scrutinizing his growth chart again, I realized how foolish I had been—the difference between the 50th and 60th percentile in height is less than a centimeter for babies under 36 months, and the difference in weight a mere handful of ounces! Why was I fussing over differences that were so miniscule? And why hadn't anyone pointed this out to me? I felt like a worn out soldier doing endless battle with no reinforcements in sight. I was no match for this dreaded disease, nor could I keep up with a medical system that marched onward with little concern for a mother's angst. Later in the game, when I complained to Dr. Brynelson about the difference in weight measurements taken in the two hospital clinics, she offered to measure Russell's height while he was standing up (25th percentile) and then lying down (50th percentile)—we shared a good belly laugh over the 25-point difference and I promised that I would relax about the growth rankings.

Malabsorption is a general problem with CF, but poor absorption of fat in particular is a major hindrance to weight gain. Because vitamin E is a fat soluble vitamin, it is considered to be a fairly reliable indicator of fat absorption in children with CF. Thus, Russell's vitamin E level was monitored closely as part of his routine check-ups at the CF clinic. A normal measurement for vitamin E is defined as between 5.1 and 23.2 ug/L (micrograms per liter). When he was first diagnosed with CF, Russell's vitamin E level was on the low side—only 4.0 ug/L. Dr. Sullivan anticipated this and immediately started Russell on a vitamin E supplement. One of Kelly's first recommendations was to double the daily vitamin E dosage that Dr. Sullivan had prescribed, from 50 IU per day to 100 IU per day.[8] She also noted that vitamin E is more easily absorbed by the body when taken in conjunction with the trace element selenium, so she added selenium into Russell's daily regimen. Kelly recommended a very low dose since selenium can be toxic when taken in high doses.

When Russell had a blood test three months later, it indicated a clear improvement—his vitamin E level had more than doubled, from 4.0 to 8.8 ug/L. And it kept increasing. By the time Russell was five years old, his lab result indicated an even higher level of 12.9 ug/L. When he saw that report, Dr. Sullivan exclaimed, "In my 20 years of working with children with CF, I've never seen a normal vitamin E level before!" (I sat there giddy with anticipation that he would logically follow up his exclamation with the question: "I wonder why?" It never came.) Over time, Kelly added other nutritional supplements to specifically support Russell's absorption of fat and fat-soluble vitamin E, and his lab results continued to show a normalized vitamin E level.

Vitamin E was receiving quite a bit of attention in those days as one of four known antioxidants, along with vitamin C, beta carotene (vitamin A), and selenium. Antioxidants are crucial nutrients that sustain good health. They also rid the body of "free radicals"—chemical compounds that are generated in a number of ways and which are believed to cause cancer. The body already has built-in mechanisms to cope with this ongoing process of eliminating free radicals, but the modern American diet high in saturated and trans fats creates an excess of free radicals, exacerbating the burden on the immune system. As an important antioxidant, adequate intake of vitamin E boosts the body's ability to cope with free radicals. Vitamin E is also an anticoagulant and may prevent heart disease and stroke.[9] All things considered, I was convinced that a normal vitamin E level was a crucial goal, not simply as an indication of Russell's effective fat absorption, but also because of the protection that vitamin E would afford him once a normal level was achieved. My goal was never limited to Russell's enjoying a healthy, if short life. My mind's eye pictured him in his seventies, eighties, and nineties. I wanted to ensure that his arteries and liver and lungs were all healthy enough to carry him through a perfectly normal lifespan.

As time passed, Kelly and I continued our collaborative research into the nutritional challenges of CF. She added and subtracted various supplements, tailoring Russell's regimen to CF as well as to his specific symptoms and health trends. I spent hours at the National Library of Medicine on the NIH campus in Bethesda, pouring over peer-reviewed journals and other research literature that might reveal something, anything, different to try. I looked as far afield as Japan and Australia to consider the fish oil and herbs that were being used there to treat CF. I wanted badly to sneak into the foreign journal stacks in the library's basement, but that would have required special status and I wasn't allowed. (I wouldn't have been able to understand them in their original languages anyway.) Kelly scoured nutrition journals (and eventually websites as the Internet matured) to pick up anything new that might be of value. I was thrilled that she was so open to learning more, and that she viewed me as her intellectual peer. We constantly shared new findings back and forth.

At one point, Kelly sent me a letter that had been published in the November 30, 1985 issue of the British medical journal, *The Lancet*.[10] The letter described study findings reported in 1979 about a possible connection between selenium deficiency and cystic fibrosis. The original study was attributed to someone named J.D. Wallach in a book that had been published by the University of Missouri Press in Columbia, Missouri. I began my attempts to track this person down.

My sister was a professor within the Missouri state university system, and she offered to search for the study through her university's library database. After a few weeks, she sent me an article from a 1990 publication called *Biological Trace Element Research* which described several studies.[11] The primary study had been conducted in mainland China by Dr. Joel D. Wallach and five other scientists (four of whom were Chinese physicians), and funded by an international consortium of American, Mexican, and Chinese universities and medical schools. Using autopsy reports, the researchers contemplated the common denominators of cystic fibrosis and Keshan disease—a fatal heart condition caused by a deficiency of the trace element selenium, which was first identified in 1907 in the Keshan district of northeastern

China.

The article also included background on Dr. Wallach's previous studies on cystic fibrosis and selenium deficiencies.[12] Many years earlier, while a researcher at NIH in the late 1970's, he had diagnosed CF in a rhesus monkey—a diagnosis that was subsequently confirmed by pathologists who specialized in CF at Emory University, Johns Hopkins University, and the University of Chicago. Testing his theories that a selenium deficiency might be the ultimate cause of CF, as it was in the case of Keshan disease (a disease that shared the same major organ deterioration typical of CF, and a disease that he had also been studying for some time), Dr. Wallach then successfully artificially induced CF in primates in laboratory studies by deliberately causing dietary deficiencies of selenium. Autopsy reports of liver and pancreatic lesions in deceased CF patients were found to be consistent with the lesions caused by the selenium deficiency in laboratory animals and Keshan disease in humans in China.

According to Dr. Wallach in his book *Let's Play Doctor*, for all his determination to prove what he believed to be the true cause of CF, one day, he was abruptly fired from NIH and given 24 hours' notice to pack up his things and leave. There is reference in various journal articles to the considerable confusion and mystery surrounding the reason for his dismissal. Much of his research tested the theory that the genetic transmission of cystic fibrosis had not been definitively proven and that CF might instead be the result of a selenium deficiency (in the mother). His work also explored what happens to the health of the pancreas and other organs when the selenium deficiency is corrected in various animal models. I eventually found follow-up commentaries in archived issues of *The Lancet* in which researchers from England expressed their support of Dr. Wallach's emphasis on a link between antioxidant deficiencies and CF. I found his theories intriguing but also perturbing because his conclusions conflicted with the generally accepted inherited origins of CF. My curiosity was piqued by the fact that NIH was so keen to get rid of a researcher whose experiments with CF had received such high-level confirmation.

The first CF gene was discovered in 1989, coinciding with Dr. Wallach's write-up of the Keshan disease study in China. It would be interesting to know how the subsequent discovery of over 1,000 CF mutations might influence Dr. Wallach's thinking today. I'm not at all sure that the clear evidence of a genetic basis for CF automatically discounts his theories, since much of his work called into question which comes first: the mutation or the nutritional deficiency that causes a mutation to manifest.

The article comparing CF with Keshan disease was fascinating, though completely over my head, despite the medical dictionary I kept open at my side. I yearned for a conversation with Dr. Wallach himself. The study in China came after his departure from NIH. His home institution at the time that the article was written was a medical university in Mexico. I eventually found a series of published articles between 1978 and 1993 that placed him first in Missouri, then China, NIH (Bethesda, Maryland), Mexico, and, finally, California. One brief biography stated that he had begun his career as a veterinarian (not uncommon for researchers who study human medical conditions), but that he had also gone on to obtain a degree in naturopathic medicine.[13] My desire intensified to speak directly with this man who knew so much about both CF and nutrition, and whose speculation on the cause of CF had serious implications for a cure.

It took me eight months to track him down, but I finally met Dr. Wallach in person at a talk he gave at an airport hotel just outside Baltimore in 1994. He was there to promote his line of "Total Toddies" or colloidal mineral products. I shook his hand and then burst into tears as I explained why our meeting held such meaning for me. He gave me a gentle hug and assured me that my son (who was two years old at the time) would be okay. I then took a seat and listened to his presentation on the many medical illnesses and conditions that are positively impacted by his mineral supplements. Although my respect for him was considerable, this "cure-all" seemed a bit simplistic to me, and I wondered if his upsetting experiences in the conventional medical research realm had driven him to an extreme of sorts.

The next day, I called Kelly to get her opinion. She told me that she was very familiar with Dr. Wallach's colloidal mineral products and that she often prescribed them to her geriatric patients because of their generally compromised ability to absorb nutrients. She wondered out loud why she hadn't thought of it before and suggested that we add the colloidal minerals into Russell's regimen. She too was convinced that selenium had a major role to play, but she also believed that a number of other minerals were just as critical. Together, we reviewed the extensive list and dosages of vitamins and minerals provided in the Total Toddy product, in order to recalculate Russell's other supplementation prepared by the pharmacists at the Apothecary.

Though I knew that curing CF wouldn't be as simple as adding a few key supplements into my son's diet, I was intrigued by Dr. Wallach's logical theories that began with soil depletion and mineral-depleted crops which produced the mineral-depleted food available in the grocery store, and ended with our resultant nutritional deficiencies and deficiency-induced genetic mutations and disease. His underlying theory was that a genetic blueprint does not necessarily cause or come before a problem manifests, but rather that a mutation may well be caused by the underlying problem, e.g. nutritional deficiencies.

His theories were based on sound agricultural science, i.e., that soil replenishment in the U.S. has been consistently limited to adding N-P-K (nitrogen, phosphorus, and potassium) since those three elements are all that plants require (in addition to sunlight and water) in order to grow and produce fruit, seeds, grains, or vegetables. On the other hand, we humans require modest amounts of a number of essential trace elements that are present in healthy soil and absorbed by plants grown in healthy soil (e.g., manganese, iron, copper, zinc, and selenium) and thus subsequently available to us through our food. Today, these trace elements are virtually absent in most agricultural cropland in the U.S. due to decades of overuse, poor crop rotation, and insufficient nutritional replenishment of cropland.[14, 15]

The Toddy product that Russell took cost more than one dollar per day, and I had trouble affording it in addition to all the other out-of-pocket health expenses. After a couple of years of struggling with bills, I was obliged to stop using the expensive Toddy product. It undoubtedly did Russell good during the time that it was part of his daily regimen. If health insurance had covered Russell's nutritional supplements, they would have been affordable.

Another symptom that Kelly addressed was excessive sweating, one of the less well known aspects of CF. This symptom might be dismissed as a minor nuisance, except that when we perspire or sweat, we lose sodium chloride (i.e., salt). When a person without CF sweats, he or she normally reabsorbs some of this salt back through the cells of the skin. The CF mutation, however, impedes the ability of sodium chloride to move in and out of the cell. As I noted earlier in Chapter 2, in some organs of CF patients, the sodium chloride cannot get out of the cell (e.g., the lungs). But in the case of the skin (an organ that functions differently from the internal organs impacted by CF), sodium chloride can leave the cell but cannot re-enter or be reabsorbed back into the cell as it should be. Thus, in a person with CF, the loss of sodium chloride is greater than normal, both due to excessive sweating and the skin cells' inability to reabsorb sodium chloride to offset the loss. As sodium chloride is a key electrolyte, this unnatural loss of salt in the sweat can lead to an electrolyte imbalance in individuals with CF. When Russell first entered care at the CF clinic, we learned about the grave risk of an electrolyte imbalance. When a subsequent laboratory test confirmed an imbalance, I was encouraged by the CF nutritionist to feed Russell salty foods to offset the loss of salt due to CF.

After learning about Russell's confirmed electrolyte imbalance, Kelly suggested that we add homeopathic "cell salts" to his daily regimen. Cell salts are not a homeopathic remedy as such, but are instead considered to be a homeopathic nutritional supplement. When we perspire, we excrete a number of beneficial minerals and trace metals such as sodium, chloride, iron, manganese, and copper (as well as toxic minerals and metals such as arsenic or lead that our body may have absorbed).[16] Homeopathy recognizes a total of twelve beneficial "salts" that are excreted when we perspire, not just sodium chloride. Kelly theorized that, due to his CF, Russell would be unable to re-absorb any of these salts, not simply sodium chloride, and that he would benefit from a homeopathic supplement (manufactured by Boiron) that contained all twelve salts: Calcarea Fluorica, Calcarea Phosphate, Ferrum Phosphate, Kali Muriaticum, Kali Phosphate, Kali Sulphate, Magnesia Phosphate, Natrum Muriaticum (sodium chloride), Natrum Phosphate, Natrum Sulphate, and Silicea. The "cell salt" supplement comes in the form of small round tablets that have a bland taste. Unlike homeopathic remedies that are placed under the tongue to dissolve and need to be taken either well before or well after meals, cell salts can be chewed and taken any time, even at mealtime. This was an important convenience factor, as it meant that Russell could take all of his nutritional supplements with meals. After a few months of taking the homeopathic cell salts, Russell's lab tests indicated that his electrolytes had completely normalized. He continued to take them daily and had no further indication of an imbalance.

One of the other big challenges of CF is the need to replace enzymes that are normally produced by the pancreas and transported to the duodenum (the upper part of the small intestine) where the most crucial phase of digestion and metabolism of food nutrients occurs. The pancreas produces three major enzymes needed to digest food: protease, amylase, and lipase. However, in a person with CF, the small duct that connects the pancreas to the duodenum is blocked by mucus "plugs" caused by the same chloride transport malfunction at work in the lungs. Thus, although the pancreas of a person with CF may well produce enzymes, when the body attempts to transport them to the duodenum, they cannot make their way through the plugged duct. Thus, individuals with CF take supplemental enzymes (extracted from the pancreas of pigs) with their meals and snacks to support the digestion process.

Enzyme supplementation has advanced over the years to include an "enteric coating" that prevents the enzymes from activating in the acidic stomach before they reach the alkaline duodenum where they are actually needed (and where they are normally directly deposited through the pancreatic duct). As soon as enteric-coated enzymes went on the market, life expectancy for children with CF increased markedly. The more I learned about the utterly fundamental role that enzymes play in digestion and the absorption of nutrients, the more keen I became to ensure that Russell was getting the enzyme supplementation he needed.

Each of the three major digestive enzymes is designed to break down a specific component in food: *protease* breaks down proteins (such as in meat, dairy products, and soy), *amylase* breaks down complex carbohydrates or starch (such as in fruits, grains, and some vegetables), and *lipase* breaks down fats (such as in fatty meat, butter, and desserts). But here comes the tricky part: enzymes themselves are proteins. Therefore protease—the enzyme responsible for processing proteins—will unfortunately begin to process its fellow supplemented enzymes (amylase and lipase) as soon as the enzyme product activates. The problem of protease breaking down amylase and lipase is not unique to CF, but the implications for each of those two enzymes differ.

Digestion begins in the mouth where amylase is normally present in saliva. Though CF reduces the amount of amylase released by the salivary glands, it is theorized that there is still sufficient amylase in saliva so that when protease inadvertently breaks down the supplemental amylase in the duodenum, the impact is minimized. Lipase, however, is another matter. Even in healthy people, lipase is often broken down by protease that is sent to the duodenum before the lipase is able to complete its task of digesting fat. To make up for this shortage, the pancreas will normally continue to produce and secrete more lipase, in vast quantities if necessary, until there is enough lipase present in the duodenum to fully break down the fat that has been ingested. But in a person with CF, additional lipase cannot get through the pancreatic duct, and the amount of lipase contained in the enteric-coated enzyme product falls dramatically short of the need.

The insufficient supply of lipase in a person with CF was at the source of Russell's inability to absorb fat and gain weight (and height). In the course of learning about enzymes, I found it challenging to decipher which "facts" were accurate. I heard from one source, for example, that it is not possible to extract adequate amounts of lipase from a pig's pancreas, without any explanation as to why this is so. I was also told that there was an optimal balance of enzymes that dictated the dosage of each of the three enzymes and limited how much lipase could be included in enzyme supplementation products. Further, I read about instances where high doses of lipase had caused life-threatening colonic strictures in infants, and that this risk had motivated manufacturers to limit the amount of lipase in their products. I found all of this confusing and somewhat contradictory. What complicates things even more is that people with CF are unable to secure sufficient lipase from enzyme supplementation products to digest a normal diet, let alone the high-fat foods that they are encouraged to eat. The problem is not solved by taking more of the prescription enzymes, as this would increase not only the lipase but also the protease, and the added protease would merely break down the added lipase, preventing the added lipase from being of any benefit.

Insufficient lipase not only leads to poor absorption of fat, it also compromises the absorption of fat-soluble nutrients, such as vitamin E. Because CF has such a deleterious effect on the lungs, the compromised ability to absorb antioxidants (such as the fat-soluble vitamins A and E) takes on even more critical significance. This was my introduction to the destructive "tail wagging the dog" nature of CF. One malfunction leads to another, which leads to another, and another, and then eventually manages to exacerbate the original malfunction, making matters even worse.

The more I learned about how CF was hindering Russell's ability to properly digest his food and the ripple effect that this had, the more motivated I became to find a solution to the original digestive problem. For the first time, I began to realize that CF was not just a respiratory disease, it was a full body assault. The cause of death is usually lung failure, but it seemed to me that there was a complex inter-relationship between all of the organs and functions impacted by CF. By undoing the malfunctions that CF caused in the digestive and immune systems, I wondered if it were possible to prevent or at least appreciably slow the downward spiral toward respiratory disease. There was little talk about any such inter-relationship during our appointments at the CF clinic. The focus was either on the lungs *or* the pancreas, never both at the same time. And there was no conversation about what effect one organ's function or malfunction might be having on another organ's function.

Until around 1940, modern medicine considered CF to be the same thing as "celiac disease" because they shared the same digestive and immune system symptoms. Any concurrent respiratory symptoms were attributed to some other cause. The problems of the pancreas and the lungs were finally linked together as the same disease by Dr. Dorothy Hansine Andersen in 1938.[17] But it was only with the advent of enteric-coated pancreatic enzymes, which enabled children to survive the compromised function of the pancreas, that the primary focus of CF care shifted from the pancreas to controlling the disease's deadly impact on the lungs. I'm not questioning whether the lung disease caused by CF is important—of course it is, because it usually ends up being the cause of death. But CF also seriously compromises other major systems, including the digestive and immune systems, which may well facilitate an escalation of the deadly lung disease. From the first manifestation of the disease, digestion and metabolism of critical nutrients is compromised, causing weakness and debility throughout the body and, in particular, compromising the immune system, which is so fundamental to healing the lungs as well as the rest of the body.

Today, CF patients continue to be monitored and treated primarily by pulmonologists and other specialists in respiratory disease. I fear that this intense focus on the respiratory aspect of CF has distracted us from giving sufficient attention to the compromised digestive system, which is why nutrition is such an important topic. Further, in 1996, CF researchers discovered that the protein in the lung (the CFTR described in Chapter 2) that causes the problematic mucous plugs in the lungs is also responsible for fighting infection. The lung defect caused by CF was thus compromising the function of the respiratory system and the immune system at the same time. Good nutrition is also critical to a healthy immune system, among other things providing an ample supply of antioxidants.

Understanding the ripple effect of CF malfunctions inspired a new question: Why couldn't there be a similar ripple effect of recovered functions? Just as one malfunction leads to a secondary malfunction, wouldn't fixing one function (or even improving it) be likely to improve other related functions?

Although we weren't able to see inside of Russell's body to observe and measure every little positive change, that didn't mean positive changes weren't occurring. The CF doctor relied on lab results and exams to confirm his conjecture about what was going on internally. Poor weight gain confirmed his conjecture that fat was not being properly absorbed by Russell's digestive tract. Subsequent weight gains and growth spurts confirmed his conjecture that, due to enzyme supplementation, fat had begun to be successfully absorbed. This is how medicine is supposed to work. But the doctors were almost exclusively focused on the negative—which function is problematic, what trend is downward, has any red flag appeared, and so on. I was determined instead to spend more time monitoring positive changes and to figure out how to generate more positive change.

Little by little, as Russell's health rebounded and I saw concrete evidence that the alternative healing was making a difference, I grew to have faith in Russell's body's ability to change course—away from the negative and toward the positive.

Somehow we needed to explore the influence that each positive change was having on other functions, and follow and support that ripple effect. This is where the alternative healers were so vitally important to me. They didn't scoff or smirk or worry that I would end up disappointed—they jumped right into the passenger seat and shouted, "Go! Go!" They were as eager as I was to pursue positive solutions.

Once I became aware of the challenges of lipase supplementation, I began to search for a lipase supplement that Russell could take in addition to the prescribed three-enzyme products. Some of the enzyme products that I found were derived from plants instead of pigs, but I was cautioned by a naturopathic doctor (Dr. Wallach, in fact) that they wouldn't be strong enough to do the job. That was a disappointment—I would have been much happier for Russell to take a pineapple-based supplement than a product that required sacrificing a pig and which might be contaminated by whatever the pig was being fed. In the end, almost all of the products that I found provided the same combination of three enzymes that he was already taking (as well as minimal amounts of all sorts of other enzymes, such as bromelain or papain). This wouldn't help solve the lipase deficiency at all, since he didn't need additional protease. I concluded that the only solution was to find a lipase-only supplement to add to his regimen. I ran my thoughts about augmenting Russell's lipase intake with a lipase-only supplement past Dr. Sullivan.

"That would be nice but you won't find a lipase-only

supplement—it doesn't exist," he predicted with confidence. I ignored his pessimism and kept looking.

In a few months' time, with Kelly's support, I was able to track down a lipase-only supplement manufactured by a company in Idaho that was run by a naturopathic doctor. Their plant-derived lipase was extracted from the *aspergillus* mold and packaged as a powder in very small capsules. I asked Dr. Sullivan to partner with me in determining an appropriate dosage for Russell, and to rule out my concerns about the *aspergillus* source. As if things weren't already complicated enough, Dr. Sullivan had warned us that *aspergillus* is one of a number of difficult-to-treat organisms that tend to take up permanent residence in CF lungs. Further, because of the separation between the conventional pharmaceutical industry (which had the backing of the medical establishment and the FDA) and the alternative supplement industry (which had the backing of an emerging natural healing sector and growing conflicts with both the medical establishment and the FDA), the enzymes in Russell's conventional porcine-derived enzymes were measured in USP or United States Pharmacopeia Units whereas the lipase-only enzyme supplement that I found was measured in lipase units (LU). I could not find a single physician, pharmacist, nutritionist, or manufacturer anywhere (including the manufacturer of the lipase himself) who knew how to translate one of these measurements into the other. Figuring out the right dosage for my baby boy was going to be tricky.

Without question, all of the exploring that I did during

Russell's early years would have been a lot easier had the Internet been available. I think it's possible that well into the future, "ancient times" are going to be defined as LBI—*Life Before Internet*. But even the conversion tools that one finds on the Web today cannot bypass the chaos caused by a lack of standardization and cooperation between the pharmaceutical and nutritional supplement industries.[18] Alternative supplement manufacturers seem to feel that it's their inalienable right to make up whatever measurement scale or parameter they fancy for the ingredients in their products. An enzyme supplement that I examined at a local health food store recently had ingredients measured in PUs, HUTs, SAPUs, PCs, DUs, BGUs, CUs and a dozen other acronyms just on the label of one product.

When searching for the lipase-only supplement, I was still at the beginning of my experimentation with strange substances, and not yet sufficiently confident to decide on my own whether or not to give Russell the supplement that Kelly and I found. I desperately wanted Dr. Sullivan to explore it with me. We only saw him every three to four months, so I actually wrote him a letter, explaining that I had found a lipase-only supplement and asking him to contact the Idaho-based manufacturer to discuss dosages. He never placed the call and showed no interest in talking it over with me at our next appointment, forcing me to make what felt like a very risky judgment call (what with the threat of colonic strictures and concerns about *aspergillus*) without the benefit of his expert opinion. Perhaps he deemed the supplement to have no value and thought I would drop it without his help; instead I sought help elsewhere.

I was assured by both the manufacturer and Kelly that the *aspergillus* mold was completely deactivated in the extraction process, posing no risk to Russell. (I reminded myself that childhood vaccines and the *E. coli* homeopathic remedy that Dr. Razi had prescribed were based on the same principle.) I shared my concern with them that too high a dose had the potential to cause colonic strictures. Together, the three of us came up with what we felt was a reasonably cautious but helpful dose for a child of Russell's age and weight (and specific to CF), and I started giving him the lipase-only supplement with each meal along with the three-enzyme supplement prescribed by Dr. Sullivan. His weight gain accelerated as soon as he started taking additional lipase. In fact, it was Dr. Brynelson, our general pediatrician, who noticed that Russell's first major growth spurt occurred within three months of starting Kelly's individualized regimen at 14 months, and that a second major growth spurt occurred within four months of adding the lipase-only supplement to his daily regimen at 23 months.

In early 1998, I finally had an exhaustive and very satisfying discussion with a well-reputed manufacturer of nutritional supplements who answered all of my questions about measurements and enzyme activation. He agreed with the conclusions that Kelly and I, along with the lipase manufacturer, had drawn together, and also felt that the dosage we had settled on was acceptable. It was an after-the-fact confirmation, but it lessened my residual worries about our experimentation.

Kelly's knowledge even went beyond nutrition and homeopathy. After learning more about CF, she ordered a special Traditional Chinese Medicine herbal remedy for Russell called "Six Gentlemen." The remedy includes ginseng, licorice, tangerine peel, ginger, and several other herbs to improve digestion and tonify the spleen (an organ in the immune system). The remedy is also used in cases where there is excessive "phlegm" or mucus—it seemed tailor-made for CF. The first time that I prepared this herbal remedy for Russell as a brewed tea, I took a tiny sip and practically gagged due to its horribly bitter taste. After it cooled, I put it into a sippy cup and, amazingly enough, Russell drank it down without any complaint.

Following the introduction of the "Six Gentlemen" remedy, Russell's appetite improved and his stools finally completely normalized, becoming firm, brown, and regular. (Perhaps I seem just a wee bit eager to describe my child's poop, but after seven months of continuous diaper changes to cope with steatorrhea and several more months before his less severe diarrhea finally resolved, I considered this final transition to normal stools a blessing.)

One of the things that stood out throughout our exploration of alternative healing was Russell's utter lack of complaining and willingness to try something new. Sometimes I would taste a remedy deliberately (as I did with the Chinese tea). Other times, I would absentmindedly lick a spoon after mixing powder or crushed pills into his baby food. The tastes were often abhorrent, but he didn't seem to mind. It convinced me that, even as a baby and toddler, he somehow knew that these yucky-tasting supplements were good for his health. Of course I encouraged him verbally, but I never forced him to drink or eat any of his remedies or supplements. For the most part, he was a willing and even eager participant in all of the alternative healing.

Chapter 8

Herbal Medicine and Beyond

Revere the healing power of nature.

Hippocrates of Kos (460-370 B.C.)

HUMAN BEINGS HAVE BEEN USING PLANTS TO HEAL themselves for millennia. I was intrigued by how herbal medicine might benefit Russell, but they were close to pharmaceuticals in my mind. I worried about their potency and the potential to hurt my son if I gave him the wrong herb or the wrong dose of an appropriate herb. After hearing several friends repeatedly mention their use of echinacea to boost their immune systems, I purchased a couple of books on herbal medicine. These included John R. Christopher's *School of Natural Healing* and *Herbal Home Health Care* (focused on children) and Simon Mills's *Out of the Earth*. I began to learn the basics. Each of these books celebrated the diversity and wonderful qualities of herbal remedies; and both authors also cautioned against their misuse, which can be exceedingly dangerous, even deadly. Once again, I felt the need for a seasoned professional to pinpoint which herbal remedies would be helpful to Russell and especially to determine the appropriate dosage for a small child.

Several people suggested that I consult with Tom Wolfe. Tom was an herbalist and the owner of the Smile Herb Shop in College Park, Maryland, which he had founded with his wife in the 1970's. I called him one day in 1994. Russell was around two years old at the time, and I had no plan or concrete vision for the use of herbs. Though Russell was a lot healthier than he had been when he was diagnosed at eight months, he was still plagued by a number of CF-related respiratory and digestive symptoms. As soon as Tom understood that I was calling about a child with CF, he appeared to grow a little uncomfortable and suggested that I speak with a different herbalist he knew, named Sunny Mavor, who specialized in children. He gave me her phone number, and I called her later that day.

Sunny turned out to be a very interesting woman and a well-credentialed herbalist who had founded a company called *Herbs for Kids* in Bozeman, Montana. Her company produced a line of herbal remedies specifically designed for children. She, like Tom, however, was a bit guarded once she learned the seriousness of Russell's challenges. She felt that I needed to consult with someone more experienced at diagnosing and healing children, and she referred me to a woman named Tieraona Low Dog who was an experienced Native American herbalist, located in the Southwest. Sunny cautioned me that Tieraona was currently in the process of completing medical school and had also just given birth, and that she might not be so easy to track down. I was very intrigued by the thought of a Native American herbalist with conventional medical training, but not surprisingly, given how full her plate was at that time, my calls to her were not returned. All these wonderful herbalists, and yet no one could help me. I felt like a skipping stone that had been tossed into the pond without landing anywhere. I became discouraged and let the whole matter drop.

A year later, when Russell was three years old, a friend told me about a young woman, Megan Coss, who was knowledgeable about herbs. She worked at the local food co-op in Frederick. From the moment we met, Megan exuded caring and sympathy, which I really needed. I had been a single mother for a year and was overwhelmed by my work and parenting responsibilities. Russell's health was improving by then, but he still suffered from stomach aches, nasal polyps, and constant colds. Life for the three of us (me and my sons) was good for the most part, but the constant worry about Russell wore me down.

Megan was immediately intrigued by our story. She helped me step gently into the world of herbs, suggesting that I start by using echinacea and usnea to control Russell's colds and sinus infections. If effective, these herbs would reduce his frequent need for antibiotics. I found these two herbs enticing. Part of Russell's burden of CF was a compromised ability to combat bacteria, which suggested to me the need to boost his immune system and strengthen its ability to fight infections, rather than constantly suppressing it by using prophylactic antibiotics and steroids. Megan told me that these particular herbal remedies had a long tradition of use by Native Americans. Both plants grow wild: echinacea is a flowering plant in the daisy family and usnea is a lichen that grows on trees, much like Spanish moss.

I was particularly eager to try echinacea, given its growing reputation to ward off colds, and started giving Russell a modest dose every time he caught a cold. It seemed to work for him about half of the time. Echinacea works best when given as soon as any symptoms appear, but it was hard to get that timing right with a three-year-old who didn't have an adult's awareness of subtle changes in his body. When the echinacea didn't stop a cold from coming on, infections often settled in and Russell's nasal mucus would turn a telling shade of green, indicating an infection. Megan then suggested that I use usnea, which reliably turned the mucus back from green to clear overnight. I was thrilled to avoid what had become an almost constant use of antibiotics. Once I started using these two herbal remedies, Russell rarely developed a cough, even with colds.

After I became comfortable with the echinacea and usnea, Megan and I experimented with other herbal remedies. I put drops of St. John's wort in an oil base in Russell's nose to combat his nasal polyps, and I gave him wild cherry bark drops to suck on to loosen the mucus in his lungs and encourage expectoration. Megan knew of Tom Wolfe. In fact, she had moved back east from California to consult with Tom and help her father battle lung cancer, which he was apparently doing successfully with the help of herbal remedies that Tom had recommended. Once I was finally able to articulate my goal with herbs out loud, i.e., to boost Russell's immune system generally and to use herbs in the place of antibiotics, Megan urged me to contact Tom again and ask him to take Russell on as his patient. I did, and once again, Tom referred me to someone else.

To my delight, Tom's suggestion that we work with Claudia Joy Wingo, a new herbalist in his shop, worked out perfectly. Claudia was not only a registered medical herbalist originally trained in Australia, she was also a registered nurse (R.N.). When I called her and told her Russell's story, she very eagerly agreed to work with me to help Russell. In her years of in-hospital training as a nurse in Australia, she had had extensive contact with children who had CF, providing their chest therapy, giving them their medications, and so on. It felt serendipitous to find an herbalist who also had such a strong medical background and understood cystic fibrosis. She told me that, in Australia, every hospital had an assigned natural healing "liaison" or alternative practitioner to work directly with the doctors and patients. She had served in that role for several hospitals. This was 1995, and once again, I was reminded of how behind the times we were in the U.S. regarding "alternative" healing.

Our first visit with Claudia took place in the early fall of 1995 at the Smile Herb Shop. We found Claudia in the main building, an old slate-blue Victorian, but she told us to follow her into the backyard with its plentiful herb gardens and elegant two-story rabbit run. Three-year-old Russell stopped to watch the gardener feed a huge handful of clover to the rabbits. "This is their favorite," he said with a smile when he noticed Russell watching.

Once Russell had explored the rabbit run sufficiently, I coaxed him inside Claudia's beautiful cedar-paneled one-room office with a bag of toys. He soon settled down and our interview began. Claudia started by asking about Russell's medical history as well as a questions about his diet and nutritional supplements. She was especially keen on hearing about the herbal remedies that I had tried so far with Russell and what their effect had been. Claudia's voice retained a subtle and delightful hint of Australia. It turned out that she was American, but had spent some 20 years in Australia, completing her entire medical training there.

Claudia's knowledge of western *and* eastern herbal remedies, as well as nutrition, soon became apparent. By the time our appointment ended, I was ready to begin Russell on a new daily regimen of garlic which has strong anti-viral properties and is excreted through the lungs, chlorophyll to strengthen his immune system, and nettle tea with honey to strengthen his resistance to allergies prior to pollen season. Claudia recommended that I look for local un-doctored (raw) honey to use in his tea. She said that there was growing evidence that eating honey produced by local bees who gather the pollen from trees and flowers from the local habitat can reduce or even prevent people from having allergic reactions to the pollen surges in spring and fall. I asked her if raw honey might be dangerous for Russell, given the risk of infant botulism. She assured me that, at Russell's age, raw honey would not pose a risk.

Claudia also said that she wanted to create individualized tonics for Russell to take on a daily basis but that this would take some thought. She said that she planned to create tonics that would strengthen his immune system and help to clear mucus from his lungs.

"But in times of sickness," she said, "You should stop the immune tonic and, instead, give Russell high doses of an echinacea/osha mixture that I will prepare. This will help him fight both viral and bacterial infections."[1]

Osha is another lichen that, as with usnea, strengthens the immune system. She also said that she wanted to consider the use of a mushroom product called "Power Mushrooms" that was manufactured by Health Concerns to boost Russell's immune system. I was fascinated by this new world of herbs and seemingly unlimited arsenal of healing agents. Claudia noted (as Megan had) that many of the herbs used by practitioners today have been used for thousands of years by indigenous peoples all around the globe. "They are still used," she said, "because they have a documentable impact on a number of ills that is hard to dispute." They can also be dangerous, she cautioned me, if misused or taken in inappropriately large dosages.

Many herbal remedies are available today in health food stores and even some pharmacies. I dabbled in herbal remedies as a young adult, but I was never comfortable trying something new or unknown with Russell without Claudia's guidance. The more reputable manufacturers of herbal or other plant remedies (lichens or mushrooms, for example) are very careful about how they distribute their products. Health Concerns, for example, does not sell its products over the counter, but will only sell them to a licensed practitioner.

Claudia's interest in herbs started early, with a grandmother who was an herbalist in the Ozark Mountains in Missouri and a father who was a botanist. She studied herbal medicine in Israel and then Australia, where she received her formal training and diplomas in Botanical Medicine, Nutrition, and Remedial Massage. She went to nursing school and worked as an R.N. in hospitals in Australia, completed field assignments in Central America and Bangladesh, and eventually obtained a master's degree in Tropical Disease. After she moved back to the U.S. in 2013, she resumed her teaching positions at the University of Maryland Medical School's Center for Integrative Medicine and at the Tai Sophia Institute in Columbia, Maryland (now the Maryland University of Integrative Health). She is also an Examiner on the Board of the Natural Herbalists Association of Australia.

Claudia's background in healing had such breadth and depth to it that I lost all of my prior anxiety about using herbs with Russell. One of the books I had been reading, *Beyond Antibiotics: 50 (or so) Ways to Boost Immunity and Avoid Antibiotics*, stated:

> Seventy-five percent of drugs are based on knowledge of plant substances. One-fourth of all prescription drugs contain one or more plant-derived ingredients. For instance, childhood leukemia once had a mortality rate of 80 percent. Today there is an 80 percent survival rate thanks to the drug *Vincristine*, derived from the rosy periwinkle.[2]

Claudia confirmed that herbs are indeed the inspiration for and close cousins of most of the medications manufactured by pharmaceutical companies and prescribed by conventional western doctors. Unlike medications, however, Claudia noted that the special capacity of herbal remedies is due to using all of the herb's innate ingredients. Using the whole herb as a remedy strengthens the effectiveness of herbs—unlike manufactured medications that tend to extract only one active ingredient or component from a plant. Herbal remedies that are holistic and include all components of a plant also decrease the likelihood that there will be any side effects.

I was so intrigued by Claudia's faith in herbs that I decided to use them myself. One day, I experienced the onset of a minor cold. Because I was normally quite healthy, I didn't take much notice (and didn't think to use echinacea), but as the day wore on, my head began to throb with a sinus headache. By late afternoon, I was forced into bed, grateful to relinquish my children to the evil clutches of TV (something I was dead set against most other times). I suddenly remembered that I was scheduled to facilitate all-day workshops the following two days, but I was reluctant to cancel since they would earn me good money.

It was too late in the game to use echinacea to fight the cold. I finally thought to place a call to Claudia, this time on my behalf, with the hope that she could suggest an herbal remedy. She told me to hang my head over a bowl of steaming water with one drop each of the essential oils of thyme (an anti-viral herb) and peppermint (a relaxant). Only one drop, she cautioned. In my own questionable wisdom, I decided that one drop would hardly be enough, and I put a good five drops of each oil into a large bowl of very hot water. I then settled onto a stool at the kitchen counter, positioned a towel over both my head and the bowl, and proceeded to draw the steam in through my nose. I immediately lurched back, almost falling off the stool, feeling as if I'd just breathed in ammonia. I felt pretty foolish; five drops was obviously too much. Why on earth was I consulting with experts, if I was going to ignore their advice? Fortunately, I never played around with Russell's dosages.

I didn't repeat the bowl and steam exercise with a lower dose, but instead switched to the bath which Claudia had also recommended. I filled the bath by running a very hot shower with the curtain closed, in order to maximize the steam. I put several drops of both the thyme and peppermint oils into the shower as the bath filled (yes, I am stubborn *and* slow to learn... one drop just didn't seem like enough). The smell was delicious. When it was filled, I got into the bathtub and lay back, breathing in the herb-filled steam until the water became uncomfortably cool. Once out of the bath, I was amazed at how much better I felt. By the next morning, I felt absolutely fine.

In the first few years after finding Claudia, she prescribed a number of different herbal remedies for Russell. Even though I am quite matter-of-fact about it now after so many years, just writing about meeting Claudia makes me cry. The fear of having a small child destined to die from this awful disease, CF, was terrifying. Despite the hints of improvement in Russell's health, the dragon had clearly sunk its long sharp claws into both his and my body, and was carrying us away high in the sky. I couldn't predict where we were headed or whether the place where we would ultimately land would turn out to be a happy place or a place of horrible grief. Every day was a new adventure with Russell. Some days were a good adventure, with my realizing that the latest remedy worked so well that we could avoid antibiotics. Other days were not so good, with my concluding that a remedy was not reducing his cough and we would have to, once again, resort to antibiotics. Every time I put him back on antibiotics, I was forced to confront his CF head-on, this monster of a disease that might steal away my little boy at any moment. Fear was a constant state of mind.

Claudia's knowledge of herbal medicine and faith in Russell's ability to gain strength brought me great relief (thus, my "happy" tears). She not only knew about herbal medicine, she also had treated children with CF during her nursing career. This gave her the unique ability to create individualized herbal tonics that went to the core of Russell's challenge, primarily his immune system and the mucus in his lungs. But she viewed his immune system as strong and intact, despite the discovery that the CF mutation undermined the immune function of lung cells. Claudia's focus on bolstering Russell's immune and respiratory systems, and her positive approach to building up his general health, was the opposite of the conventional doctors' fixation on his lungs and treatment of negative symptoms.

Over time, Claudia sought to build up his immune system using plants such as usnea, osha (an antimicrobial), and peach to combat viruses he was exposed to in daily life and bacteria that may have taken up residence in his lungs. She suggested chlorophyll and nettle, especially during high pollen times, to help curb Russell's allergies. She also created a special respiratory tonic to help break up the mucus in his lungs and make it easier for him to cough it up, which resulted in a lung environment less conducive for bacteria to reproduce. Claudia alternated which herbs she put into his respiratory tonic depending on his current state of health. The tonic might include four or five herbs, such as elecampagne, grindelia, thyme, boneset, licorice, milk thistle, wild indigo, sage, or elderberry. Each time Russell developed a cough, the respiratory tonic took it away within a day or so. The herbs had a strong smell and taste, but Russell never complained when I mixed herbal drops into a small glass of juice.

In addition, Claudia created an individualized immune tonic for Russell that she updated regularly as well. The immune tonic included some combination of reishi (mushrooms), astragalus, thyme, schizandra, milk thistle, ginger, or cinnamon. Russell took this immune tonic every day, and rarely caught colds even after he started to attend nursery school and then kindergarten—germ havens of the world! Claudia also prepared drops for his nose to treat his nasal polyps. These drops contained several herbs, such as fenugreek, thuja occidentalis (a type of cypress tree), thyme, golden seal, cranesbill (geranium), bayberry, witch hazel, or horse chestnut. Finally, she suggested that I add a drop or two of eucalyptus or peppermint oil into the humidifier in the boys' bedroom at night to help Russell de-congest and sleep more soundly. Her positive attitude and faith in his body's ability to recuperate and strengthen, her encyclopedic knowledge of the many different herbs we could try, and her enormous compassion toward both Russell and me every time we interacted with her was extremely reassuring.

Claudia's knowledge was not limited to herbs. Most of our alternative healing practitioners had been cross-trained in more than one healing approach, and Claudia had also been trained in nutrition. From time to time, she advised me to add a nutritional supplement to Russell's regimen, such as chewable papaya with meals because the added enzymes (papain, amylase, and protease) would support his digestion. Any time he had a stomach ache, especially after a big meal, chewing a couple of these papaya tablets would usually do the trick. She also suggested *Cholacol* (manufactured by Standard Process), which contained a mixture of collisonia root and bovine bile salts to stimulate proper bile production in Russell's liver, and *Transfer Factor* (manufactured by 4Life), which contained elements of cow colostrum that would further strengthen Russell's immune system. I worried that the animal-based products might be contaminated in some way, but Claudia assured me that she was very picky about which manufacturers were trustworthy. I valued her expertise since I didn't know one company from the next.

Claudia also recommended a number of plant-based supplements to decrease inflammation, including quercitin, pycnogenol, flax seed, and turmeric. Inflammation is a systemic (or body-wide) problem with CF, as it is with a number of diseases, but it wasn't getting much attention back when Russell was a little boy. I was lucky to have a well-informed practitioner who understood its importance long before it was mainstream knowledge.

Claudia was always alert to new discoveries in the herbal medicine realm. Sometimes she found products with multiple ingredients made by nutritional, herbal, or Chinese medicine manufacturers that she liked, such as *Zyflamend* to reduce inflammation (its ingredients include rosemary, turmeric, ginger, holy basil, and green tea) or *Breathe* to promote normal lung function (its ingredients include mushrooms, such as cordyceps, reishi, and chaga). Both of these products were manufactured by New Chapter. She also suggested that we try *Nasal Tabs*, a Chinese medicine product manufactured by Health Concerns that contained a variety of herbs such as cinnamon twig, eucalyptus leaf, thyme leaf, and licorice root, to reduce his constantly runny nose.

Sometimes a manufacturer would stop producing one of Russell's supplements, (such as when New Chapter's new owner stopped manufacturing *Breathe*) and Claudia and I would have to scurry around to find a replacement. Product changes were a source of anxiety for me over the years. Small alternative companies originally founded several decades ago by an individual or couple were being sold to larger corporations as the founders wearied of the work or retired. Tom's of Maine, for example, was sold to Colgate-Palmolive and Burt's Bees was sold to Clorox. I wondered if these massive multi-national corporations would be as dedicated to keeping a line of natural products as natural as the original owners.

Products come and go all the time in the U.S., and it's often a sign of progress. But there was a higher stake if we lost access to one of Russell's supplements. Herbal remedies and nutritional supplements had many powerful detractors, including Congress and the FDA, not to mention the doctors themselves. One of the younger doctors at the CF clinic goaded me into an argument one time, citing an article published in a major American medical journal that likened alternative medicine to snake oil, and that called for greater regulation and stiffer penalties for the sale of unproven remedies and supplements as well as for the administration of unproven alternative treatments. I knew that this conventional doctor had been trained to trust only empirical evidence. But his casual dismissal of alternative healing made me angry. I thought it unlikely that either this doctor or the author of the article had experienced the fear that I experienced daily at the thought of losing my son to a vicious disease. But, once again, doctors were dismissing the value of something that they hadn't even attempted to understand or investigate. The snake oil that they both dismissed so casually was saving my son's life.

Herbal remedies were particularly powerful for Russell. I am, of course, condensing what Claudia tried with Russell over the years. She usually suggested that we try an herbal remedy for a period of months to see if it made a difference. When it worked, I kept giving it to Russell; but if I saw no appreciable difference, Claudia recommended that we try something else. It was a remarkable experience, having her pull from an almost unlimited cornucopia of herbal remedies in order to find just the right combination for Russell.

In 2004, someone sent me an article about a study at Yale University in which mice and hamsters with artificially induced CF were given high doses of curcumin.[3] Curcumin is an active component of turmeric, the bright orange spice commonly used in Indian dishes. The article included lots of mathematical equations, but I was able to glean the gist of the study. The researchers were testing the capacity of curcumin to correct the defective cellular-level protein (CFTR) that causes the lung, digestion, and other malfunctions associated with cystic fibrosis. All of the study animals had the same DeltaF508 mutation that Russell had inherited from me. In the study, the curcumin had resulted in a positive impact on the nasal cells of the mice as well as the cells in a baby hamster's kidneys. I could barely contain my excitement.

By that time, we had been working with Claudia for close to 10 years. She had long since incorporated a modest dose of turmeric into Russell's daily regimen to reduce inflammation in his lungs and throughout his body. I sent her an email telling her about the study and asking her about the value (and risk) of giving Russell a much higher daily dose of turmeric. Claudia moved back and forth between Australia (where her in-laws lived) and the U.S., and I didn't always get a quick response from her. When she finally called me, she too was very excited about the study's findings.

"Let me do some exploring to see if there is any mention of

side effects with turmeric before we increase his dose," she advised. "I've never heard of any, but let me check first."

While I waited to hear back from Claudia, I grew impatient and sent an email to the person at Yale noted as the contact person for the study. Dr. Caplan emailed me back so quickly I almost fell off my chair. I emailed him again and asked him to call me so that I could ask him about the study. He called me later that same day. He explained that the results of the study were unexpected and that, originally, the study had had a different hypothesis and goal. He emphasized the need for further research but agreed that the results were very interesting.

"How much curcumin did you give to the mice?" I asked. "And how would this translate into a human dosage?"

"I'm not sure," Dr. Caplan responded. "We're not there yet."

"Well, I can't wait," I said, and proceeded to recap all that we had been through with Russell's spina bifida and CF diagnosis, as well as the alternative healing and its positive impact. He was both impressed and sympathetic with my impatience. Research usually takes years to come to fruition. I had no intention of waiting, not if Claudia reported back that we didn't need to worry about side effects. Dr. Caplan and I played around with dosage ideas, based on Russell's weight.

I came away from our conversation on fire with excitement. A scientist based at one of the most prestigious research universities in the country was sharing a discovery that mirrored what our herbalist already believed. He had confirmed his theory about curcumin using the conventional western scientific process, while her information was based on centuries of Ayurvedic herbal medicine practice in India about the healing properties of turmeric. This is a great example of the potential for open-minded people on both fronts to collectively investigate and apply new approaches.

Claudia got back to me within the week. She could find absolutely no mention of a toxicity level or side effects from turmeric, the spice that contained curcumin. I shared the preliminary dosage that Dr. Caplan and I had calculated; Claudia was in full agreement to go ahead. The next morning, I went to Whole Foods to purchase our first big bottle of turmeric manufactured by Nature's Way and added turmeric tablets into Russell's daily regimen. He has taken this large dosage ever since.

Herbs were the fifth and final alternative healing modality that I added into Russell's daily regimen. His regimen of acupuncture, osteopathic treatments, homeopathic remedies, nutritional supplements, and now herbal tonics was expensive and a very full plate, both for him and for me. But it was worth it. Day by day, my little boy grew stronger and healthier right before my eyes. He suffered less and less from stomach aches and diarrhea; he rarely caught colds or developed a cough; he only needed antibiotics once or twice a year; and he was filled with energy and joy from sunup to sundown every day. It was as if a miracle had happened. But this miracle would never have transpired without the wisdom and dedication of our alternative healing practitioners.

In addition to the herbs and nutritional supplements, there

were a number of other products and activities that helped Russell. I used warm castor oil packs on his chest when he was little and still catching bad colds. I would also add herbal drops into the shower or humidifier. I fed my sons organic food, installed a water filter at the kitchen sink, and used only natural non-toxic cleaners throughout our home (including our body soap, toothpaste, and shampoo). Over time, I also found products such as the Steam Inhaler, to help get the herbal remedies directly into Russell's sinuses and lungs.

In addition to the five modalities I have described in detail, I also experimented with other types of healing. Some of it was pretty unusual. When Russell was still a baby, a cousin of Richard's who lived in England (and whom I had never met) wrote me a letter offering to use *radionics*, a form of energy healing, from afar. She needed to know Russell's date and time of birth, and she asked me to send her a lock of his hair. The request for hair struck me as a little odd, but the tone of her long sympathetic letter was sweet, and I trusted her intention. I sent her the information with a lock of his hair in the mail the next day. We corresponded a few times after that, but have still never actually met. There have been compelling research findings about the power of prayer and other types of distance healing, but I have no idea whether or not this woman's efforts had an impact on Russell.

When Russell was around three, we had another experience that made me realize that the world of alternative healing held endless new possibilities, especially outside of the U.S. An

American friend of mine and her British husband frequently spent time in England. During one of her stays there, she received training in *brushing therapy*, a "sensory integration" technique that was said to enhance communication between the brain and other parts of the body. This therapy was (and still is) quite popular in England. After she returned home, my friend offered to try out her newly acquired skills on Russell without charging me anything. I couldn't see that it would do him any harm.

During the "brushing" treatments, my friend stroked upwards along the length of Russell's spine using a soft baby hairbrush. She did this very gently, over and over, without any complaint from Russell. At three years old, he was walking and running but he had never jumped. Though children normally start jumping well before the age of two, none of the doctors seemed anxious about his delayed development. A few weeks after starting the brushing therapy, Russell suddenly began to jump up and down all the time, as if he had been able to do it all along. I have no idea if there was any connection between the brushing and his new ability to jump; perhaps it was just a wonderful coincidence.

We were exposed to a third unusual healing experience a year or so after the boys and I moved to Frederick. One day, my friend Teresa and I decided to take all four of our sons (we each had two boys around the same age) to see a shaman named Running Deer who worked out of a Native American crafts store just across the Maryland line in Shepherdstown, West Virginia. Teresa hoped that Running Deer would ease her dyslexic boys' mounting frustration with schoolwork, and I hoped that he would help Russell with his medical challenges. While the boys wandered around the store fingering the enticing totems and feathered trinkets, Teresa and I sat next to Running Deer as he placed a gentle hand on top of each boy's head in turn. He then chanted several healing blessings. His quiet and calm manner was soothing and Russell smiled during his turn.

The boys eventually started to fuss that they were hungry. As Teresa and I stood up and prepared to leave, Running Deer observed out loud that he was more concerned about the potential harm that my anxiety level would have on me than my son's disease would have on him. I had barely said a word during the whole time that we were in the store, but the years of intense worry must have been plain as day on my face. I sat back down and he gently placed his hand on my head and began a quiet chant. I closed my eyes and felt a deep sadness followed by a great calm—a rather strange mix of emotions. Running Deer barely charged us for the healings, so we bought a few items before we left to express our gratitude.

In the early years, I was quite willing to explore anything so long as it didn't pose a risk to my son. I remained committed, however, to the five modalities described in the previous chapters because of their concrete positive impact over a period of years. Coupled with the conventional medical care that Russell continued to receive from Dr. Brynelson, this formed the basis of Russell's treatment plan.

We've known all of our healers now for many years. Claudia,

in particular, has been treating Russell for almost two decades. They are a stunning group of healers at the vanguard of alternative health. Several of them practice ancient traditions that conventional western medicine has managed to eclipse through political maneuvers by the American Medical Association (some of which took place over 100 years ago). Conventional medicine and its technological bravado impress us, but their greatest value is in the context of emergency and acute situations. The fact is that conventional medicine has limited success with chronic conditions, such as diabetes or hypertension, and it wasn't going to help my son beyond a slowing down of a deadly progression toward premature death. The alternative healing approaches, however, did help him heal and both regain and sustain his strength and growth.

The impact that turmeric alone has had on Russell's health is not yet possible to measure, although Dr. Caplan's study is a good start. The impact of the alternative healing that Russell received is challenging for me to measure or prove, although I have tried to include as much documentation of his rebound in this book as I thought my readers could bear. What I (and everyone else, including the doctors) can see and even measure is the lack of the expected decline. I know what turned his health around, and I know what has sustained his good health over time. Every one of the five modalities contributed something different to Russell's ability to fight off the dragon. And as our practitioners healed him, they healed me as well.

Chapter 9

The Blending of Two Worlds

Some men see things as they are, and ask why.
I dream of things that never were, and ask why not.
Robert F. Kennedy (1925-1968)

A FRIEND CALLED ME EARLY ONE MORNING IN SEPTEMBER 1996, brimming with excitement.

"Lindsay! There's a story in today's *Washington Post* about a child whose cancer was cured with herbal therapies!" she said. "Go get the paper! And call me as soon as you get back home!"

Another family was using alternative healing *with a child*? I couldn't wait to read the article. It was late morning, so both boys were already at school (Russell was in nursery school, Gus was in the third grade). I stopped what I was doing, jumped into my car, and sped to the local bookstore. After paying for the paper and returning to my car, I tore through the *Post* until I found the article: *'Miracle Child' Beating the Odds.*[1]

A little girl had been diagnosed with a brain tumor at age two, the story began, and given little chance of survival. Her parents were devastated, but because they were unwilling to admit defeat, they had turned to alternative healing. The article noted their use of *Essiac* tea and other herbal remedies, in addition to conventional surgery and chemotherapy. The article ended with an update that, contrary to all predictions, this little girl had sailed through all of her treatments, regained weight, and was now, several years later, in complete remission and attending kindergarten. The man getting into the car parked next to mine gave me an odd look as I shouted *Hurrah!* out loud for this family's victory.

The child in the story was the daughter of Virginia Congressman James Moran and his wife, Mary. As soon as I got back home, I ran to the phone. Instead of calling my friend back, however, I called "Information" and requested the Morans' home phone number. I was worried about invading their privacy, especially since the father was a well-known politician, but I couldn't help myself. In today's world, I wouldn't dream of calling a member of Congress at his home, given everyone's heightened concerns about privacy and security. Nor would I so easily obtain a home phone number, since most of us now rely on cell phones. However, this was 1996.

The Congressman's wife, Mary, answered the phone. I immediately apologized for intruding and calling her at her home. I explained that I was desperate to speak with another parent who had been through what I was experiencing with my son. She was very kind and we spoke at length, two mothers bonding over the threats that their respective children faced. The Morans' story was uplifting, and Mary encouraged me to keep experimenting with Russell's alternative treatment.

Before we hung up, Mary said, "Why don't you write to Dr. Wayne Jonas, the director of the Office of Alternative Medicine at NIH, and tell him about your son?"

The Office of Alternative Medicine or OAM, as it was called back then, was a relatively new division of the National Institutes of Health. It was founded in 1991 and has since been re-named the National Center of Complementary and Integrative Medicine or NCCIM. Mary was certain that Dr. Jonas would be intrigued by our story. She and her husband knew him personally, and she invited me to use her name. As soon as we said our goodbyes, I ran upstairs to my office to write a letter to Dr. Jonas and mailed it later that day. In the evening, when I finally had a moment to call my friend back, she was thrilled to hear how my day had unfolded.

Over the next few weeks, I called Dr. Jonas's office sporadically to follow-up on my letter, but he was never available. I didn't receive a written response in the mail either. Finally, after several months of waiting, I called the Baltimore office of Senator Barbara Mikulski to ask for her help. The Senator had a strong reputation for coming to the aid of her constituents, and I hoped that her social work background might make her extra sensitive to my plea. After chatting with one of her staff members, I was surprised to learn that the Senator herself received regular acupuncture treatments. The staffer suggested that I mail the Senator a copy of my original letter to Dr. Jonas with a request that she contact him on my behalf.

It worked! Within days of calling Senator Mikulski's office, I received a call from Dr. Jonas. Our conversation didn't start off well. I suspected from his gruff undertone that he was peeved that I'd used congressional clout to reach him. He was also on his way home from work and speaking on his car phone, which gave us a shaky connection with intermittent static. Fortunately, he turned out to be a very good listener. Once he understood why I had pursued him, he was eager to hear all about our use of alternative approaches.

Dr. Jonas shared with me that his original training as a family physician had been quite conventional, but that, over the years, he had become intrigued with alternative healing, especially homeopathy and acupuncture. He confirmed that he knew about the Morans' use of herbs to successfully combat their daughter's cancer. We talked for over an hour. He grew more and more excited as the story of Russell's health rebound unfolded, especially given the context of CF.

"Your son's outcomes are very intriguing," he said.

"Yes, well, the doctors don't show any interest in the alternative healing," I said. "So I've started writing a book—to share my experience with other parents."

"Hmmm," Dr. Jonas said. "I think that writing a book is a good idea. But readers are likely to either believe you or not, based on their own beliefs about healing. A book is unlikely to change anyone's mind." He paused for a moment. "The only way to reach members of the medical establishment is through a formal research study."

Reaching the doctors, of course, was a goal we shared. But

how could we do a study at this point, I wondered? We were years into the alternative healing.

"It's too late for a controlled study, isn't it?" I asked, not knowing exactly what a controlled study was.[2] I also fretted aloud that Russell was just one child, a "sample of one," and an anecdotal sample at that.

"We could conduct what's called a case study," Dr. Jonas responded. "A case study would enable us to trace the pattern of your son's alternative care against his lab work and test results that document his improvement. This wouldn't provide us with irrefutable proof that the source of his rebound was the alternative healing. But if the findings suggested a solid enough connection, it could spur further research that would be designed to test and potentially prove cause and effect with other children with CF."

He paused. There was a caveat. "In order for this study to be viewed as legitimate," he said, "we'll have to have the doctors on board. Do you think you can convince them to do that?"

"Which doctors?" I asked, dreading his response.

"His CF specialist, for one," he said.

Here we go again, I thought to myself.

"Oh, Dr. Jonas," I lamented, "if only I had the enthusiastic support of the CF specialist. My son's rebound has been happening right under his nose, but he doesn't seem the least bit curious as to why Russell's health has improved."

"I see," Dr. Jonas said.

"I have the enthusiastic support of my son's pediatrician

though," I continued, thinking out loud, "and she knows the CF specialist well enough to perhaps twist his arm. Would you be willing to speak with her first?"

Dr. Jonas readily agreed, and I gave him Dr. Brynelson's contact information. As soon as we hung up, I suddenly realized that I hadn't mentioned anything to our pediatrician about trying to contact Dr. Jonas in the first place. I needed to alert her that he might be calling her. By then it was early evening, but I suspected that Dr. Brynelson might still be at her office, returning parents' phone calls. If not, I could leave her a message, and try to catch her in the morning. To my surprise, when I called, the receptionist told me that Dr. Brynelson was indeed still there but unavailable, because she was on the phone with Dr. Jonas. Wow, I thought, that was quick. I was delighted with Dr. Jonas's immediate follow-through.

Dr. Brynelson called me the next day. She agreed that Dr. Jonas' proposed case study was exciting. But she cautioned me that she had also spoken with Dr. Sullivan, the CF specialist at the hospital, earlier that morning and was not at all hopeful that he would agree to participate. Since Dr. Jonas had emphasized the need for the CF specialist in particular to cooperate in the study, Dr. Brynelson urged me to call Dr. Sullivan myself to try to convince him.

I was still filled with naïve excitement when I called Dr. Sullivan later that day. Even though he had never expressed interest in the alternative healing, I couldn't imagine that he would be anything but eager to cooperate with an NIH-sponsored study. When he came to the phone, I told him all about Dr. Jonas's invitation to conduct a case study at NIH. Always polite, he said that he would be glad to consider it. I gave him Dr. Jonas's phone number so that they could speak directly doctor to doctor.

I let a week go by and then called Dr. Sullivan to see if he had been able to reach Dr. Jonas.

"I haven't had the time to call him yet, but I will," Dr. Sullivan assured me.

I called Dr. Sullivan again a week later, but he still hadn't found the time to call Dr. Jonas. In the months that followed, I repeatedly reminded, cajoled, and eventually pleaded with Dr. Sullivan to make that call. I wondered what might threaten him so much that he would choose not to pursue an offer from the highest research institution in the country to test my hypotheses. At first, I rationalized that his not calling was due to his over-busy schedule at the hospital. But as more and more time passed, I was forced to accept that he had little interest in participating in a study that, in his mind, was very likely to prove what he already believed to be true: that alternative healing was utter nonsense.

Once Russell's health had fully rebounded by age four, I often pressed Dr. Sullivan for a "read" on Russell's status. Whenever I asked, he confirmed that Russell's good health was atypical and that my son was unexpectedly healthy. He admitted repeatedly that he didn't know why, and that in his 20 years of practice, he had never seen the same normalization of electrolytes or vitamin

E level or growth chart ranking or a lack of decline in his other patients. I found his stubborn lack of curiosity about why Russell was doing so well baffling. What if a scientifically grounded case study found that all of this alternative healing was the likely reason for Russell's unusual turnaround? Surely Dr. Sullivan's other patients with CF stood to gain from such a study, not to mention the 30,000 children and young adults across the country who had CF. It was a scenario that Dr. Sullivan apparently couldn't conceive of, let alone pledge scant free time to (dis)prove. He never did place a call to NIH, and when Dr. Jonas left his position as OAM director two years later, the opportunity to conduct a case study at NIH was lost. It was a huge disappointment.

After the case study idea went nowhere, much of the drama surrounding Russell's two diagnoses and my experimentation with alternative healing settled down into a routine. I had assembled a fabulous team of alternative practitioners and was leaning heavily on our pediatrician, Dr. Brynelson, in intermittent phone consultations. After years of taking Russell to the spina bifida clinic for quarterly check-ups, it became clear that the doctors were now simply following my son statistically. There was the generic threat of a hip anomaly associated with spina bifida and the increasingly remote possibility that his spinal cord would re-tether, but his check-ups at the clinic consistently reassured me that all was fine. I began to seriously question the need for the battery of examinations, sonograms, and x-rays that the doctors ordered based on a generic protocol for all children with spina bifida versus a protocol that specifically addressed my son's unique health status. When Russell turned five, I finally decided to stop going to the spina bifida clinic altogether. Our pediatrician supported my decision, albeit reluctantly.

A few months after I accepted that the CF specialist was never going to acquiesce to a case study, I started to question whether we needed to keep going to the hospital's CF clinic. As with the spina bifida clinic, I didn't see much value in continuing a generic monitoring of Russell's CF that included routine chest x-rays and other tests when he was doing so well. I was worried about the cumulative harm that all the radiation might have down the road, and I was also worried about Russell's repeated exposure to nasty germs in the hospital setting.

No one at the CF clinic viewed Russell as a unique child with unique strengths and needs. The whole team seemed only to be preparing for a negative outcome that was statistically likely, rather than acknowledging Russell's positive health status and considering the possibility that his rebound would last. The alternative healing was so outside of their conventional medical playbook that they couldn't even see it. In hindsight, I suspect that my rejection of CF specialty care was partially a reaction to Dr. Sullivan's conviction that Russell's rebound was only temporary. I was frustrated that he and I were on such different wave lengths.

In contrast, our pediatrician, Dr. Brynelson, seemed thoroughly convinced that Russell's upswing was due to the alternative healing. "There's no other way to explain it," she insisted. She understood why I was put off by the CF team's assumption that a decline in Russell's health was inevitable as well as Dr. Sullivan's repudiation of anything outside of the conventional Western approach. Dr. Brynelson was supportive, but her optimism about what Russell's strong health in early childhood might mean for him in the long-term did not match my own. In the back of her mind, she too worried about the inevitability of his decline.

I decided to stop taking Russell to the hospital's CF clinic around age six. Dr. Brynelson urged me to select one of several local pulmonary specialists who saw patients in a private practice setting to replace the specialty CF care that we had been receiving at the hospital clinic. I suspected that their attitudes toward alternative healing would be no different from Dr. Sullivan's, but out of respect for her, I took Russell to see several of them. I was sensitive to the unusual burden she had acquired, once I stopped taking him to the two hospital clinics. Furthermore, she had become my medical "rock," and I needed to respect her judgment and recommendations.

As I had anticipated, the pulmonary specialists that Dr. Brynelson referred us to had little knowledge of or interest in alternative healing. Just as the CF specialist at the hospital clinic did, they viewed CF through a generic lens and required the same battery of tests to document the expected decline. They acknowledged Russell's good health, but were unimpressed since they assumed it was only temporary.

Except for Dr. Brynelson, none of the doctors had respect for the alternative healing. It was hard to tolerate their dismissal of something they knew so little about, especially doctors who knew next to nothing of Russell's history and major health rebound. They were obliged to acknowledge Russell's good health status but, as with Dr. Sullivan, they assumed that my son's decline was only a matter of time. In fact, Russell's amazing good health continued, and we went for almost ten years (from age six to age fifteen) without consulting a CF specialist. I kept hoping to find a doctor with expertise in CF who would not only have Dr. Brynelson's open-mindedness, but also the capacity and motivation to supervise both the conventional care and the alternative healing tracks. Unfortunately, I never found anyone. During the 10 years that Russell went without CF specialty care, he remained under Dr. Brynelson's pediatric care. She was a very solid support throughout his childhood and early teen years.

Year after year, Russell did not go downhill, but instead grew in height, weight, and overall vitality. He hardly ever caught a cold, let alone developed the predicted bronchitis or pneumonia. Some days it felt like a dream. The CF specialist had declared that Russell was destined to grow sickly and die. Instead, my son was growing markedly healthier—progress that was documented in Dr. Brynelson's medical notes and occasional lab tests to confirm proper vitamin levels. We rarely saw her outside of the normal pediatric schedule of routine exams and required immunizations. She and I would chuckle when we realized that she hadn't seen Russell in a full year.

Despite Russell's undeniable rebound, I was still vulnerable to the weight of this awful disease and the firm predictions that my son's demise was just a matter of time. Even a mild and brief cold or stomach bug could send me downhill. At those times I perversely wanted to give in to the horror in store and just be done with it. I would catch myself stuck in place, staring out the window at nothing or growing uncomfortably cold in front of an open refrigerator, morose and weepy, veering toward a decision to end all of this silly experimentation with herbs and needles and hands-on healing.

One day when I was feeling low, Russell came tearing into the room, still guffawing at some silly joke he had just told his friends. He grabbed something to eat, stopped for two seconds to plant a quick kiss on my cheek, yelled "Bye, mom!" and tore back out of the room. The contrast between what the doctors insisted was unavoidable and the normal child I saw before me was perpetually confusing. This time it led to a long-distance phone call to my sister in Missouri as soon as Russell was out of the room. I burst out crying the minute she answered the phone.

"What happened?" my sister gasped, overcome with worry.

"Nothing," I responded, sniffling loudly and wiping away my tears. "I'm just so confused, Faithy. The doctors are so damned sure that Russell's decline will begin any minute now. But he seems just fine. I can't make sense of it."

I started to cry all over again. Meanwhile Russell was still running around the house with his friends trailing behind, giggling and yelling so loudly that my sister could hear them through the phone. She lowered her voice and became stern.

"Listen to me, Lindsay," she said, practically growling through the phone. "You have to look at your son. Take in how strong he is, how healthy and vibrant he is. He's fine, he's absolutely fine! Just look at what you've done! My God, it's a miracle!"

Little by little, Faithy made me accept what I saw too—that Russell *was* fine. Hope slowly seeped back in through the cracks in my heart, and I started to breathe again. Maybe he really was OK, maybe he really was fine, maybe... maybe...

On the afternoon of his sixth birthday, Russell was jumping around the kitchen, singing loudly and acting goofy in anticipation of the special birthday dinner I was preparing. His exuberance suddenly brought to mind a conversation I had had with Dr. Sullivan that took place shortly after Russell's CF diagnosis as a baby. Still learning about the progression of this horrid disease, I had asked the doctor how quickly Russell's decline would set in. "Let me put this way," he said, "By age five, he won't be 'healthy as a horse'." In other words, I thought grimly at the time, we had no good years to look forward to.

Then I remembered a related conversation with Dr. Sullivan that occurred just after Russell's fifth birthday. Once the doctor finished listening to Russell's lungs, I asked him for his impression of how Russell was doing.

"Oh, I think he's doing quite well," he said. "I'd have to classify him as having 'mild' disease."

"Do you think he's been getting healthier?" I asked.

"He does seem to be getting healthier," Dr. Sullivan

acknowledged.

"Is this what you'd expect, given how sick he was as a baby?" I asked.

"Not normally, no," he said.

By that time, Russell's alternative regimen included daily nutritional supplements, monthly acupuncture treatments, osteopathic treatments every two or three months, and customized herbal tonics and homeopathic remedies as needed. I was dying to ask him if he'd classify him as 'healthy as a horse,' but I had a more pressing and less confrontational line of questioning in mind.

"Do you think it's possible that the alternative healing might be helping?" I asked nervously. I wondered why I kept knocking my head against this same brick wall. The year before, the doctor had dismissed the invitation to conduct a case study in collaboration with NIH; he certainly wasn't going to have a change of mind now. But I just couldn't resist asking the question.

Dr. Sullivan shrugged his shoulders and said, "It's hard to know why Russell is doing so well."

Oh for crying out loud, I thought, well *I* know: Russell's oxygen intake and ability to inhale normally was due to osteopathic manipulation and the gentle therapy I did at home to keep his ribcage open. His electrolytes re-balanced as soon as he began taking homeopathic cell salts. His vitamin E level normalized as soon we increased his vitamin E dosage and added in selenium and other antioxidants necessary for the proper absorption of vitamin E. Dramatic gains in weight and height occurred within a month of starting him on nutritional supplements and again after we added a lipase-only enzyme supplement at mealtime. These gains indicated his successful absorption of fat. Both his weight and height rankings on the pediatrician's growth chart had risen from dangerously low at diagnosis to average in a couple of years. And now, at age five, his weight ranking was inching its way toward above-average. I knew that Russell's overall lack of CF symptoms, his amazing rebound in health, and his failure to decline was due to all five types of alternative healing. I had personally observed the "before" and "after" day-in and day-out, and I knew that many of the improvements documented in Dr. Sullivan's own notes as well as in lab reports were a result of alternative healing, even though I couldn't prove it.

Russell continued to cavort about noisily in the kitchen, dragging me out of my negative reverie and bringing me back to the present time. Ha! I thought to myself, embracing Russell's unmistakable glorious health. We did it! We proved them wrong! All of them! My confidence was renewed, for the time being at least.

My persistent faith in alternative healing in the face of such casual dismissal by the CF specialist surprises me in retrospect, but it shocks others even more. During the final stages of editing this book, I took a week off to stay with my friend, Jeanne, at her home in North Carolina. During our visit, I asked Jeanne, a published writer, to read an excerpt from my manuscript and give me feedback through her writer's lens, not simply as my friend. After she finished reading the section describing Russell's first year of acupuncture treatments, she turned to me with a look of astonishment and asked, "How on earth did you have the faith to experiment with this alternative healing? Your son was just a baby!"

I thought for a moment and then felt a sudden surge of emotion. Jeanne was a lifelong academic, and I knew from previous conversations that she was also a skeptic when it came to alternative healing. I resented the implication that trusting conventional doctors had required any less faith on my part than turning to an acupuncturist.

"Faith?" I responded. "You want to know what took *faith*? Handing my newborn over to a team of strangers who planned to take a very sharp instrument, cut into his back, saw off the tips of several vertebrae, and then dig through multiple layers of tissue until they found his spinal cord so that they could take that very same sharp instrument and cut off the tip of his spinal cord in order to correct his birth defect. That took faith!" When I finished, I was practically out of breath. Tears were streaming down my face.

Her eyes opened wide. "Oh my goodness," she said. "I never even thought of that." To be honest, until that moment, neither had I.

I hoped that my friend, who was a mother as well as a clinical psychologist, would understand my outburst as pent-up emotion and not take it personally. It had indeed taken enormous faith to hand my newborn over to the surgical team. Just before our newborn's surgery, my husband and I were obliged to confront the litany of risks that we were taking and then sign a waiver that should our baby be injured, paralyzed, or die as a result of the anesthesia or invasive surgery, we agreed not to hold any of them or the hospital responsible.

Later, when I began to explore alternative healing, I didn't start out with a lot of faith either. No one sat me down after we were faced with his CF diagnosis and said, "Here's what you need to do to neutralize the CF. This will work wonders..." In fact, the complete opposite happened. The CF doctor said point blank that he could not cure CF and that my son would die young. When I raised the topic of alternative healing, it struck him as so outlandish that he burst out laughing. Even once we started down the alternative road with Russell's acupuncture treatments, I didn't have faith that it would help, so much as I was desperate to get away as fast and as far as I could from the doctor's terrifying prediction.

If necessity is the mother of invention, perhaps desperation is the mother of risk-taking. And I was nothing if not desperate. Desperate enough to try things that doctors deemed without value or even risky. Desperate enough to question treatments that doctors deemed standard for CF and vitally important. The way forward might have been unknown, but immersing myself in the doctors' pessimism would have killed me.

I had no carefully laid out plan, backed by science or testimony or faith, before embarking on an exploration of alternative healing. One thing simply led to another. Searching for information, any kind of information, in those days was a very different adventure than it is today. When the "World Wide Web" was publicly launched in the mid-1990's, it was nowhere near as broad-reaching as it is today, and connecting a computer to the Internet was agonizingly slow. I spent hours at the National Library of Medicine on the NIH campus instead, pouring through journal articles to see what I could glean. I was eager to find studies conducted outside of the U.S., hoping that I would learn something new that the CF specialist hadn't yet considered.

I felt certain that there must be other parents experimenting with alternative healing, but I had no efficient way to search for them. All of our alternative practitioners treated children as well as adults, but none of their current patients had CF or an equally cataclysmic diagnosis. At one point, when Russell was still a baby, a friend connected me with a young mother in Tennessee whose baby also had CF. She was using nutritional supplementation with her son, giving him massive amounts of probiotics to prevent infection instead of resorting to antibiotics once an infection set in. Her son was the same age as Russell, and she was on the same steep learning curve that I was, both about CF and about alternative healing.

Talking with another mother who shared the same fears about this awful disease, as well as the same desire to draw outside conventional medical lines, was reassuring. We exchanged long letters, since long-distance phone conversations between

Maryland and Tennessee were expensive back then. After a few years, we each became consumed with our busy lives and respective sons' care, and we lost touch. Two decades later, I reconnected with this mother and learned that her son had required a double lung and liver transplant, not unusual for a young person with CF by age 20.

Russell's alternative healing odyssey might not have happened without my husband Richard's serendipitous act of bringing home a flyer about acupuncture and Mary White's subsequent offer to treat Russell for free. At the time, I had no idea that acupuncture would be a starting point for a much broader exploration. Once Russell's treatments with Mary began, I hoped that his sinus and lung symptoms would decrease, just as Richard's allergy symptoms had disappeared. My optimism that acupuncture would help wasn't enough, though, given the dire predictions we were facing. Connecting with the other four alternative healers happened in quick succession.

Some of the people in our lives wondered why all of this alternative healing was necessary. Why not try the acupuncture alone first, to see if it even worked? Wouldn't it be possible to confuse Russell's little body with all of these different approaches? How would I be able to tell which one worked and which one didn't, they asked? Family members, including Richard, worried about the out-of-pocket cost of all these appointments and remedies. My mother worried about the amount of time it took out of our lives.

It is much easier to respond to these questions now, in

retrospect. Each approach offered Russell something different. I didn't view it as running from pillar to post, but rather a layering of vital support. Acupuncture strengthened his underlying basic constitution and the functioning of major organs; it also corrected blockages to the flow of *chi* or life force throughout his body. Osteopathy realigned his bone structure and the tissues that connected his bones, allowing his cranio-spinal fluid to flow freely and unlocking his ribcage so that he could inhale more deeply. Nutritional supplementation enhanced his body's ability to metabolize and absorb essential nutrients that would fuel his growth and build his resistance to germs. Homeopathic remedies supported his body's capacity to correct the underlying causes of diarrhea, electrolyte imbalance, and excessive catarrh (mucus) in his lungs. Herbal tonics stimulated expectoration of mucus from his lungs, strengthened his immune system, and reduced inflammation in his sinuses and elsewhere in his body.

If a positive change was clearly noticeable, I considered any new remedy or supplement that had recently been introduced. Sometimes I jotted down my observations in preparation for whichever appointment was next on the calendar. I was always eager to share my observations and have someone more objective than I was confirm that what I was observing was real and not just wishful thinking. Obviously, I wasn't engaged in any kind of study, and nothing about our experience was "controlled," as it would have been had Russell been involved in a rigorous clinical trial. Nonetheless, observation after observation confirmed for me that the alternative healing was having a profoundly positive impact. The doctors and alternative healers all confirmed these positive improvements, though they may have disagreed as to the reason.

In the early years, Russell and I spent a lot of time together traveling from our home in Frederick to four different cities spread across central Maryland and Washington D.C. to attend appointments with eleven different practitioners who were based in two hospital clinics, one HMO clinic, and five private practices. I was lucky that my consulting business enabled me to cram work into whatever time slots were leftover—often evenings and weekends. At this point, my life was totally consumed with parenting and working. Luckily I found great satisfaction in both, because I didn't have the time or energy for much else. It was also lucky that I had plenty of paid work, because none of the expensive alternative treatments, herbal remedies, or nutritional supplements were covered by insurance. I was also fortunate that two generous women, an aunt and a family friend, took it upon themselves to help me pay for Russell's alternative care.

When Russell was a baby, I'd nurse him if he became hungry during the long waits before appointments, using one of his little blankets for privacy. Once Russell was weaned, I'd pull endless juice boxes or crackers or bananas out of the diaper bag. If he became cranky, I'd pull out his favorite stuffed blue hippo or storybooks to entertain him. Laptops and iPhones hadn't been invented yet, so I was free to serve as Russell's personal circus ringleader, solely focused on him. When he was a little boy, I preferred that he play with me and his own toys while at the hospital, rather than get close to the other (sick) children or play with the toy-sized vehicles and buildings that were bolted down to the floor in the clinic waiting areas and likely coated with germs. He was amazingly good-natured and, unlike me, only rarely reached the end of his rope.

The spina bifida clinic was the hardest stretch for both of us—we'd typically wait 20 minutes or more in between visits with each of four doctors (plus each doctor's entourage of residents) who came to examine Russell. Each doctor's exam would last 10 to 15 minutes, but there was always a wait in between. One time, the wait between registering for our clinic appointment and the appearance of any of the doctors in the exam room inched up toward an hour. Russell was a toddler. He had been perfectly content for a while, seated up on the examination table, already stripped down to his diapers and playing with the collection of toys I set aside for these longer appointments. But, after an hour of waiting, he had no more patience to give. "Down, down, down!" he begged, wanting desperately to get down off the exam table and play with his toys on the floor—a surface that didn't appear to be all that clean.

I finally lost all patience myself and stepped out into the hall holding my cranky child to see if anyone was on their way. Seeing no one, I called out in a loud voice, "Russell has waited patiently for the doctor for almost an hour. If no one comes to examine him in the next two minutes, we're leaving!" I didn't start out motherhood as a pushy you-know-what, but after two years of appointments and countless hours of waiting, I had *had* it.

Miraculously, one of the doctors appeared within seconds and proceeded with his examination. All in all, Russell was a much better sport about the endless appointments than I was.

Russell's team of practitioners consisted of a CF specialist, the pediatrician who coordinated the spina bifida clinic, an orthopedist, a urologist, a neurosurgeon, an acupuncturist, a homeopath, an osteopath, an herbalist, a nutritionist, and our general pediatrician. I insisted that Russell be seen by the same doctors at both the spina bifida and CF clinics at the hospital at every appointment, and I made a fuss whenever they tried to substitute someone else. There were already too many professionals in Russell's life, and I wanted the doctors who treated him to at least know him.

In addition to the doctors, both clinics at the hospital had an array of nurses, medical residents and fellows, social workers, and other clinical support staff—but they tended to be a constantly changing crowd, so even though Russell and I got to know some of them well (the nurses, in particular), I didn't consider them to be part of Russell's core group of practitioners. Besides visits to the hospital clinics and our pediatrician, Russell had treatments with the acupuncturist every three weeks, treatments with the osteopath every two to three months, and occasional visits to the homeopath, nutritionist, and herbalist. On top of all of these appointments, we were sent to multiple labs and radiology suites for testing, regular pharmacies for prescription medicine, and special pharmacies or health food stores for nutritional supplements.

It was difficult for me to keep straight all of the different providers and appointments and physical locations. I used our land line, an answering machine, and a paper calendar to keep myself organized, as people did back then. If I became forgetful, the brightly colored post-its that were stuck all over the refrigerator, my desk surface, and the front door helped to keep me on track. (An iPhone calendar and reminder system would have been enormously helpful.) Somehow, we hardly ever missed an appointment and I didn't lose my mind—achievements in and of themselves.

Not only did our eclectic group of practitioners take up considerable time and money, they also represented drastically diverging points of view regarding not only the medications or treatments they prescribed, but also the basics of disease and healing—not to mention how differently they viewed *Russell*. Six of our practitioners were conventionally trained physicians, and all but our pediatrician were also specialists (neurology, pulmonology, urology, etc.). The other five practitioners were alternative healing practitioners, although three of them (the osteopath, homeopath, and herbalist) had been trained in both conventional medicine and alternative healing.

One practitioner's counsel rarely contradicted another's, and they were all committed to keeping Russell as healthy as possible. But their approaches were very different, as if they were each driving oddly contrasting vehicles—a sports car, a glider plane, a rickshaw, a submersible—vehicles that traveled at different speeds using very different means of locomotion. Each practitioner's focus also differed. The CF specialist focused only on Russell's CF symptoms, looking for negative signposts of decline within the framework of a progressive disease. The spina bifida specialists kept watch for complications that might occur despite the surgical correction of Russell's birth defect. Dr. Brynelson, Russell's pediatrician, did what all pediatricians do—she measured his growth, gave him vaccinations, and monitored his physical and cognitive development, anticipating a positive trend while keeping her eyes open for anything that seemed amiss. Dr. Brynelson left the CF and spina bifida care to the experts (until I stopped taking Russell to the hospital clinics), but often underscored the seriousness of his birth defect and, despite her growing faith in alternative healing, repeated her concern that his CF would ultimately result in debilitating sickness. Like me, she had difficulty straddling the line between hopefulness and realistic caution. I tried to keep my growing optimism to myself, but occasionally it leaked out. That worried her too—an indication that I was in denial about Russell's challenging future.

In contrast, the alternative healing practitioners were only concerned with bolstering Russell's innate constitutional strengths. Their focus was solely on the positive, with an expectation of a positive turnaround in Russell's health and, eventually, normal growth and development. Symptoms didn't worry them, and the hypothetical threat of decline held no more than their fleeting attention. To them, Russell's symptoms were not a sign of decline, instead they were indications of the opportunity to strengthen what was strong, good, and foundational. Further decline wasn't expected—positive improvement was. The alternative practitioners were fundamentally committed to a positive end goal of strong health and normal life expectancy, and nothing derailed them from this vision, not even a prognosis as deadly and immutable as CF.

It wasn't easy to share my confusion with family or close friends in order to get their support. They all wanted to feel hopeful, and once my reports about the alternative healing and Russell's rebound began to infuse them with optimism, they were reluctant to join me in my continuing interludes of anxiety. I was a buffer for Russell too, modeling a positive attitude and optimistic outlook whenever I could pull it off. If I couldn't muster anything positive, as soon as we got home from an appointment, I would go up to my office on the third floor to weep or fume in private.

I took the advice of all of our doctors and alternative practitioners seriously. Every one of them impressed me in terms of their solid training and knowledge, their many years of practice with hundreds if not thousands of patients, and their seasoned judgment. The conventional doctors saw things very differently from the alternative practitioners, but because I respected all of them, both perspectives drew me in like a magnet. I was petrified of the CF prognosis and paid close attention to the doctors' interpretation of each lab result or x-ray, any change in Russell's ranking on the growth chart, and every pulmonary function test. The CF specialist had spent two decades watching children with CF decline and die (although over time, a growing number of his patients reached young adulthood). Who was I to question his judgment and belief in an unavoidable outcome? I resented his negative-oriented scrutiny of Russell, but I was hyper-alert to it just the same.

I assure you that there was nothing "airy-fairy" about any of Russell's alternative practitioners. Our homeopath was a conventionally trained Board-certified pediatrician; the osteopaths (D.O.s) we saw were doctors who were licensed to do everything that medical doctors (M.D.s) are licensed to do; our herbalist was a registered nurse (R.N.) who had worked with children with CF that were sick enough to be hospitalized during her years spent in Australia; both of our acupuncturists had completed hundreds of hours of training in Traditional Chinese Medicine; and our nutritionist had more licensing credentials than the nutritionists at either Children's Hospital or Johns Hopkins CF clinics.

Further, each of the alternative practitioners had witnessed firsthand the complete reversal of disease in children, some diagnosed with CF. They were equally adamant that there was absolutely no reason for pessimism—they didn't fear CF and they trusted Russell's body. Each of them held the belief that healing is always possible, and I found their let's-dig-in-and-get-to-work attitude addictive. Their optimism saved me from constant anxiety that could easily have turned into paralyzing despair.

While writing this book, I became aware of my tendency to use the possessive form when referring to the alternative health practitioners—*our* acupuncturist, Russell's herbalist—and my habit of speaking in a more formal and distancing way of *the* CF doctor or the orthopedic specialist (with the sole exception of *our* pediatrician). I think my use of the possessive is extremely revealing, not only of the way I felt toward our alternative practitioners, but also of the way they felt toward us. There wasn't just faith or respect at work in our interactions with them, there was also love. I will be eternally grateful to the neurosurgical team that corrected Russell's spina bifida as well as to the CF specialists that continue to keep such careful watch for any symptoms, offering medication as needed. I am not ungrateful, but I would be hard-pressed to refer to the care Russell received from the conventional doctors as having anything to do with love.

Drawing from the best of both worlds to tackle a health-related issue is the core concept of "integrative medicine," a field that was only just emerging when Russell was young. It still has a long way to go in order to receive general acceptance.[3] In the early 1990's when our exploration first began, there was only fledgling interest in alternative healing. Today, nearly three decades later, there are hundreds, if not thousands, of books on alternative and integrative approaches to health and healing. They run the gamut from promoting regular exercise and a healthy diet to more esoteric topics such as the benefits of prayer or Traditional Chinese Medicine. The books and innumerable online videos may well be informative and even useful guides to making changes in one's daily routine. But none of the multitude I've poured through would have given me the detailed guidance that I needed to design a treatment plan for my child that integrated the best of conventional medicine with the best of alternative healing.

None of these books would have told me whether to use antibiotics or *Osha* to treat my son's cough. None of them would have cautioned me that the chest therapy that helped Russell to clear his lungs of deadly mucous might also cause his ribs to literally lock into position and restrict his breathing, nor that osteopathic treatment could help unlock his ribcage and permit deeper breathing. None of them would have suggested that Ayurvedic nose drops or supplementation with Turmeric might reduce inflammation and help curb his nasal polyps, instead of turning to steroids. None of them would have explained to me how to reconcile a practice in which the experts dictated the course of treatment (and saw patient and parental compliance as a key element in healing) with a philosophy that was almost completely dependent upon self-observations, self-directed healing, and self-discipline.

The constant back and forth between pessimistic and optimistic absolutes made me feel like a ping-pong ball. Each appointment with the CF specialist rekindled my fear that Russell's deadly prognosis was unshakeable, while each appointment with our acupuncturist rejuvenated my complete faith in Russell's inevitable rebound and ability to live out a normal lifespan. The conventional medical view of CF made the alternative healers' optimism look just plain silly, while the alternative healers' profound respect for the body's innate capacity to heal itself made conventional medicine's bar look obscenely low.

By the time Russell reached the age of five, and before we stopped going to the hospital clinics, his complex treatment plan was a routine part of our life. I finally felt that we had arrived at an acceptable plateau of truly comprehensive care. I decided that it was time to bring all of his practitioners together, conventional and alternative alike, to discuss his case. An appealing vision came to me of all five alternative practitioners—the acupuncturist, homeopath, osteopath, nutritionist, and herbalist—presenting information about their respective methodologies to the conventional physicians. I wondered how they would react to one another and became convinced that it could be a seriously productive meeting. I was particularly tickled at the thought of the acupuncturist, who had an attorney's capacity for persuasion, describing to the CF specialist how acupuncture helped to rebalance Russell's five elements (water, wood, fire, earth, and metal) and remove obstructions to the flow of *chi*.

I mentioned my idea of a team meeting to our pediatrician, the CF specialist, and each of our alternative practitioners. The alternative practitioners were largely enthusiastic, but both of the conventional doctors asked me why such a group meeting was necessary. It seemed obvious to me what could be gained from their discussing Russell's case altogether as a team. I was discouraged to learn that this team concept was foreign to them, especially given the "teams" we saw at the hospital's specialty clinics. Our pediatrician suggested that I draft a formal agenda.

She also requested that the five alternative practitioners begin to forward appointment notes to her, in order to nurture a sense of "team."

Unfortunately, a team meeting never transpired. I was quickly worn out by the conventional doctors' resistance to the idea; my drafts (and re-drafts) of agendas were never acceptable. I fear that there may have been as much concern over how to fit such a meeting into a busy workday (and, no doubt, how to bill for it), as there was concern over the purpose and content of the meeting. Over time, even some of the alternative practitioners became leery of an in-person confrontation, discouraged by my repeated complaints that the conventional doctors weren't taking the alternative treatments seriously. I remain stubbornly hopeful that, one day, this type of team approach will be routine, and that there will be mutual respect and cooperation among a multitude of healing modalities.

I didn't know anyone who could have straddled these two worlds with me and given me guidance. The only way to prevent parents from carrying the burden of such a complicated exploration alone is to expose all physicians to all practices, conventional and alternative alike, during their basic medical training. This would better enable them all to give well-rounded advice and perhaps even inspire them to work together to design integrative, individualized treatment plans for each of their patients.

We desperately need more physicians with open minds. Both homeopathy and osteopathy sprang up as a result of physicians questioning the fundamentals of nineteenth century medicine—blood-letting as a treatment for hemorrhage, ingesting mercury as a remedy for minor ailments, cutting off appendages to prevent gangrene, and lobotomies or extracting teeth as a treatment for "hysteria" in women. Thank goodness that physicians like Dr. Still (the father of Osteopathy) and Dr. Hahnemann (the father of Homeopathy) had such open minds, not to mention the *chutzpa* to promote a new approach to healing, even when they found themselves under attack by their fellow physicians.

In the end, politics was the reason that conventional Western medicine, or what is known as allopathy, flourished in the U.S., while both homeopathy and osteopathy were side-lined. Today, acupuncture, herbal medicine, nutrition, homeopathy, and osteopathy are finally gaining popularity as more people dissatisfied with conventional medicine's limited capacity to heal them seek out alternative approaches. This includes a growing number of open-minded physicians.

One of the most challenging days in terms of blending these worlds occurred just after we returned from Ohio, where Russell had been treated by the revered osteopath, Dr. Fulford. I took Russell to Children's Hospital for his scheduled check-ups with both the CF doctor and the spina bifida team—another marathon of poking and prodding in both clinics on the same day. Russell was just shy of five years old. On the heels of our trip to Ohio, I dreaded making a transition from Dr. Fulford's questioning of whether or not Russell even had CF to the pessimistic lens of the CF team. Further, my ex-husband had asked to go to the appointments with us, which was unusual. I implored Richard not to undermine me in front of the doctors, a habit of his that was intensely annoying and motivated me not to alert him to upcoming visits.

I was in considerable turmoil internally, as I tried to make sense of what had happened in Ohio. I had already shared our experience with Dr. Fulford with Richard, but I didn't plan to say anything during our hospital appointments. I asked Richard not to refer to it either. I anticipated that our CF doctor would be incredulous at best, and before putting it out for general comment (or, rather, what I feared would be potshots), I wanted to sufficiently process the information by myself to know where I stood. In fact, I planned to keep quiet and get the appointments over with as quickly as possible. Keeping quiet would be unusual for me, but I was determined to make an effort.

We started off in the CF clinic. As usual, Russell was a good sport about the whole thing. I, on the other hand, was both on the defensive and in limbo, not knowing what or whom to believe. Having just witnessed Dr. Fulford's understated questioning of whether Russell even had this disease, I feared that I was about to be rudely brought back down to earth by a reality framed by seasoned specialists who viewed CF as an incurable disease. Despite my intention not to ask any questions, toward the end of our appointment with Dr. Sullivan, I felt compelled to speak up.

"So," I asked him, trying to feign an offhand manner, "where exactly does Russell stand? Is he typical or atypical or...?"

"Oh, I think Russell is doing extremely well," Dr. Sullivan responded cheerfully.

You mean, given that he has a deadly disease and is eventually going to go downhill, I thought bitterly to myself, aware that I was headed downhill emotionally. Frustration always bubbled just beneath the surface when I had this same conversation with Dr. Sullivan.

"Are you still classifying mutations according to severity?" I then asked.

"Yes," he replied, "and given Russell's particular mutations, I would expect to see moderate to severe symptoms. But his symptoms are definitely mild."[4]

Mild? I thought angrily, *MILD?* My God, the only symptom he has are nasal polyps, and those usually shrink when I treat them homeopathically. I clamped my mouth shut and kept my thoughts to myself. I didn't want to give the doctor or Richard an opportunity to ruin my day further. We collected our coats. As he walked with us down the corridor to the clinic exit, Dr. Sullivan reached into a cabinet and grabbed a medication sample.

"Here's the Flonase nasal spray I mentioned," he said, handing me the box. "Let's see if it helps to shrink Russell's polyps."

Dr. Sullivan noticed and correctly interpreted my hesitation. "Don't worry," he said. "The steroids aren't absorbed into the system. The particles of this product are too big to go through the mucous membranes of the nose."

"Are there any side effects?" I asked.

"No," he said, "none at all." Goodness, I thought to myself with a good dose of sarcasm, a pharmaceutical that is risk-free.

We went to the cafeteria to grab a quick bite before making our way upstairs to the spina bifida clinic. Russell was acting unusually goofy in his joy at being with both parents at the same time. I focused on him, not wanting to discuss anything serious with Richard, especially the visit with Dr. Fulford. I desperately wanted to cling to Dr. Fulford's questioning the validity of Russell's diagnosis and the possibility that the doctors were wrong about his life expectancy. After our visit to Ohio, I had become buoyed again by a belief that, with the help of so many highly trained practitioners, my son would not succumb. I had become momentarily convinced that he would be fine, and I dared to consider the impossible—that perhaps he was even cured. I wanted to hold on to Dr. Fulford's stories about other kids with CF whom he had treated who had gone on to have children of their own and no disease complications. I wanted to hide my new dreams away in a safe place, protected from the doctors who I imagined would be quick to trample them and destroy my hope that Russell would be okay.

Somehow we muddled through the ensuing appointments with the spina bifida team, which continued well into the afternoon. Back home that evening, after reading the boys a chapter from *Winnie-the-Pooh*, I fished around in my bag for the Flonase sample and pulled the manufacturer's insert out of the box to read about any warnings or side effects.

Not been tested on children under 12… When the same ingredients are taken orally, the absorption is clear... Can cause retardation of growth in children... Persons taking the medication should avoid anyone with measles or chicken pox...

Wow, I contemplated out loud, that's certainly an interesting list of cautions for a 'risk-free' medication.

The next afternoon, I set off for the Frederick food co-op, determined to find an herbal substitute for Flonase with the help of Megan, the herbalist who worked there. Megan was satisfyingly disgusted at my rendition of the conversation with Russell's doctor and she chuckled when she read the warnings on the manufacturer's insert that I had brought along to show her. She offered to bring in a tincture of St. John's wort in an oil base to help reduce the inflammation in Russell's nose. Later that day, I also consulted with our homeopath over the phone. She recommended increasing Russell's homeopathic remedy instead of giving him the Flonase. With Megan and Dr. Razi's help to identify less risky alternatives, I figuratively snubbed my nose at the medical establishment. Within two days, Russell's polyps were much smaller and he was breathing through his nose again.

By the time the weekend arrived, I felt even more anxious than I had on the day at the hospital clinics. In addition to being worn out from being around so many frail children and tortured parents at the hospital, I was agitated by the unspoken conflict of opinion between Dr. Fulford and the CF specialist. I didn't have the slightest idea how to reconcile these two vastly different perspectives. It was hard to dispute either man. In his 93rd year, the white-haired, hunched-over Dr. Fulford had been practicing medicine for the better part of a century. Legend had it that he had cured any number of cases for which conventional doctors had lost all hope, including CF. On the other hand, Dr. Sullivan was a pulmonologist and department chief at a renowned children's hospital. He was a well-known expert in cystic fibrosis with more than 20 years of specialization. Plus, his Mickey Mouse ties and gentle treatment of Russell were endearing.

There have been many occasions over the years, as with the overlapping visits to the CF specialist and Dr. Fulford, when I've lost all ability to decipher the truth. Did Dr. Fulford really fix a dislocated hip that would otherwise have resulted in surgery? Did he really unblock the path of the "life force" and allow for a complete re-programming of Russell's physical being? And was the CF truly and (gulp) permanently at bay? Or was this alternative healing complete nonsense or perhaps only modestly helpful and merely postponing the inevitable? I had no idea how to blend these two worlds. How could I choose the prevailing status quo backed by the monolithic medical establishment when the alternative approaches were working? And why did the conventional doctors scoff at alternative healing and dismiss it as quackery when they too could see that it was working? Was it really easier to believe in miracles or luck rather than consider the effectiveness of a different approach?

A final example reveals why I remain convinced of the effectiveness of "alternative" healing despite its lack of credibility among conventional doctors. In 2007, at age 15, Russell suddenly developed severe trembling fits. These fits were short-lived, lasting only a few minutes, but they were extremely unpleasant. He and I were unable to figure out what was triggering the trembling, and nothing seemed to help but waiting it out. Luckily the fits were only intermittent—coming on out of the blue once every three or four months. Everyone was stymied: our new HMO pediatrician, the urgent care clinic we visited if a fit occurred on the weekend, and the hospital ER staff where we eventually landed. The fits didn't square with a profile of more serious problems such as epilepsy, brain tumors, or other nervous system malfunctions. Thankfully no one recommended further testing because it would have been difficult to turn down.

Ironically, Russell's trembling is what brought us back into CF care, this time to the CF Center at Johns Hopkins Hospital in Baltimore. A trembling fit had brought us to the Hopkins ER one evening and, once the ER physician learned about Russell's CF diagnosis and the almost 10-year lapse in CF specialty care, he insisted that we schedule a follow-up appointment with the hospital's CF Center. I, too, was worried that the trembling was somehow related to the CF, so I agreed to make an appointment.

Because we had been out of CF care for so long, we were able to get a new patient appointment relatively quickly. The Hopkins CF specialist had no idea what might be causing Russell's repeated bouts of trembling, but he reassured us that it had nothing to do with CF. The doctors never figured out what caused the fits, and apparently concluded that they posed no serious danger to Russell.

The fits continued. A year later, in 2008, my sons and I

planned to celebrate the Thanksgiving holiday in Missouri with my sister and her family. Just as we were about to leave for the airport to fly out of Baltimore, Russell had another bout of trembling. He couldn't control the shivering, and the bodily "clenching" that the shivering caused eventually made him vomit, after which he became uncomfortably cold. We had to leave home if we were going to make our flight, so I wrapped him up in several blankets in the car, hoping that the trembling would stop before we boarded the plane. At the airport, Gus found a wheelchair for Russell, which helped us get through security more quickly than usual. The trembling slowly dissipated and Russell was able to endure the flight.

By the time we landed in St. Louis, the trembling had stopped as mysteriously as it had started. I rented a car at the airport, and we arrived at my sister's home in the northeastern corner of Missouri a few hours later. Even though it was Thanksgiving Eve, as soon as my sister heard about the trembling, she called her osteopath to see if he would treat Russell. Dr. Lockwood kindly fit us into his scaled-back holiday schedule on Friday, two days later. When he examined Russell, he found a misalignment in Russell's spinal column and corrected it using gentle osteopathic manipulation. He then explained to us that the trembling had resulted from an intermittent blockage to the flow of cerebrospinal fluid which was caused by the misalignment. By that time, Russell had not had osteopathic treatments for a number of years. In the many years since that one treatment with Dr. Lockwood, Russell hasn't re-experienced any trembling whatsoever.

The contrast between what our conventional doctors know and do versus what our alternative practitioners know and do is never-ending. But despite the barriers that persist between the two camps, I am determined to blend the best of conventional medicine with the best of alternative healing in my own health care and that of my family. Each time a need arises, I am very grateful to have access to both.

Chapter 10

Where's the Proof?

The more facts you have, the better the truth you have.

Dr. Jonathan Leaky, Sr. (1940 -)

NONE OF RUSSELL'S ALTERNATIVE HEALING WAS COVERED BY health insurance. For years, the ongoing costs included monthly osteopathic treatments; occasional phone consultations with the homeopath, nutritionist, and herbalist; and the array of nutritional supplements, herbal tonics, and homeopathic remedies that comprised Russell's daily regimen. (Mary's acupuncture treatments were free.) Of course, these costs were on top of our monthly health insurance premium, co-pays, and deductibles. Some years, I claimed as much as $10,000 in unreimbursed health-related expenses on Schedule A of my tax return. The resultant lower tax liability was fleeting comfort in the face of strained finances, and the fact that insurance didn't cover the alternative care led to a continuous juggling act with other bills. Luckily I didn't lose our home as so many families with costly health issues have, but the only way for me to manage the added costs was to re-finance repeatedly to consolidate debts. That practice led to significant mortgage debt and scant savings, but prioritizing my son's well-being over financial comfort was non-negotiable.

One weekend, while the boys were at their father's house, I drafted an appeal letter to the insurance company asking them to cover Russell's alternative healing treatments. I had already submitted numerous written requests, all of which were denied, but the most recent denial letter noted that I could appeal their decision. I decided to make a formal request for an appeal hearing. My letter began with a brief description of the symptoms and medical regimen that was typical for a child with CF, including annual inpatient "tune-ups" at the hospital (usually lasting two weeks), expensive specialty medications such as *Pulmozyme*, and CF clinic check-ups at 2-month intervals. I compared the typical annual cost of this care—somewhere between $25,000 and $40,000 according to the CF specialist—with the actual costs that the HMO had incurred for Russell's CF clinic visits, enzyme prescription, and sporadic antibiotic use in the previous year: a grand total of $2,100. Given the insurance company's focus on the bottom line, I assumed that even a cursory cost benefit analysis—$2,100 versus the potential of $40,000 or more if a child is terribly ill—would be a compelling argument in favor of their supporting a continuation of Russell's alternative care, not to mention the impact that inflation would have on these medical costs over time. (By 2016, the retail cost of *Pulmozyme* alone was $36,000 per year.)[1]

According to a 1993 issue of the *New England Journal of Medicine*, Americans spend billions of dollars on alternative treatments each year. The journal article even claimed that people visited their alternative healing practitioners more often than their primary care physicians. That certainly was the case with my family. If such widespread use of alternative healing was happening more than 20 years ago, how is it that health insurance companies and conventional doctors (CF specialists in particular) continue to be so close-minded?

While finishing this book, I visited the Cystic Fibrosis Foundation's website to see if there were any references to alternative healing (www.cff.org). The Foundation was created in 1955 by a small group of parents of children with CF. In those days, children with CF rarely made it past toddlerhood. One has to admire the vision and generosity that these parents had toward the other families who would be burdened with this awful disease. Now almost 60 years later, the Foundation they started continues to be a major force, promoting and sponsoring research related to CF.

On the foundation's website, I found a "Consensus Report on Nutrition," which cautioned parents against doing anything that the doctors didn't themselves recommend. I also found an "Herbal Products Fact Sheet," which made assertions about all of the "quackery" involved in herbal healing. The herbal fact sheet noted "little research," "mixed results," and "claim not supported" next to notations on various herbs (some of the herbs I was familiar with, some I was not). "To learn more about herbal products," the fact sheet suggested several resources, including the National Center on Complementary and Alternative

Medicine (now called the "Center on Complementary and Integrative Medicine") at NIH. The resource listing also included an obscure website managed by a self-described psychiatrist who has apparently made it his business to alert the general public to all of the "quackery" involved in alternative healing. His comments were not limited to herbal medicine. If this is the extent of most CF doctors' formal exposure to alternative healing, it's no wonder they're skeptical. The quackwatch website made me hungry for intelligent science-based commentary.

An abundance of verifiable, rigorous scientific studies on alternative healing have been conducted in Europe and elsewhere, and yet success stories about alternative approaches are summarily dismissed by conventional doctors in this country as anecdotal. The dismissal of anecdotal evidence is monstrously cavalier. I mentioned to a pediatrician acquaintance one day that my son was receiving acupuncture treatments to help with his cystic fibrosis. I had enjoyed wonderful conversations with this individual in the past and had mistaken his progressive social and political views for an overall open mind. "Oh, that's just anecdotal evidence," he said. No questions: "Does it help? How is your son? Do you think it has had an impact?" Nothing. My son's atypical health may well constitute a mere sample of one, but it ought to be impressive enough or at least puzzling enough to get someone's attention. If doctors require studies and FDA approval to be convinced of anything, then by all means, bring on the researchers. I find their unwillingness to explore and scrutinize alternative healing unacceptable.

I was raised to have the utmost respect for medical doctors. Everyone refers to doctors as the "best and brightest" among us. Unfortunately, this respect can make us reluctant to question someone with such highly specialized knowledge and elevated social stature. When sick, patients who haven't undergone rigorous medical training themselves depend on the doctor to pinpoint what's wrong and decide which treatments might help. We non-physicians are literally at the mercy of whatever our doctor knows or doesn't know, and whether he or she has a discerning and open mind.

Perhaps it is our collective admiration that has pressured conventional doctors to think (or at least to act as if) they do know exactly what to do. Many of them seem to believe they can do no wrong. This is obviously not the attitude of every doctor. But many conventional doctors seem to have concluded that even if their perfect knowledge isn't perfectly complete, only they can add to that knowledge base, because all other paths are inferior and unfounded, and thus misguided. This perspective is not only flawed, it creates a reality in which any number of conditions, diseases, and states of poor health go uncorrected or even untreated altogether. Individuals unfortunate enough to have one of these "untreatable" conditions are often discouraged from bothering with unconventional (i.e., "alternative") approaches. They may even receive criticism or discouragement from their doctor and surely will receive no financial assistance from their health insurance company. This is precisely what I experienced.

At a lecture at the hospital for parents of CF patients one evening in the mid-1990's, Dr. Sullivan presented the latest update about the impact of experimental gene therapy on the lungs (administered using an inhalant up the nose). This was considered the light at the end of the tunnel for children with CF, and all of the parents at the lecture were eager to hear about its progress. In my own explorations of CF, I had begun to suspect that the disease's pancreatic insufficiency and resultant nutritional deficiencies were not just a problem in and of themselves, but were possibly an underlying contributor to the eventual lung disease. It led me to wonder if enhanced nutrition might thus be a key preventive approach.

Because the respiratory complications of CF are ultimately the cause of death, the disease is primarily treated by pulmonologists. There is a nutritionist on each hospital's CF Center team, but the nutritional advice I was given was simplistic and woefully outdated. I was increasingly puzzled by how extraneous nutrition seemed to be in my discussions with the CF specialist.

As easily as I questioned Dr. Sullivan in private during Russell's appointments, it made me uncomfortable to question him in front of other parents. I didn't want to appear disrespectful, nor did I want to put the doctor on the spot. But my eagerness to know got the better of me, so I went ahead and raised my hand.

"Why is gene therapy totally focused on bringing about DNA changes to the lung area?" I asked Dr. Sullivan. "Even if the lungs were no longer an issue, the pancreas would still be a major problem."

"I can't wait for the pancreas to *be* the main problem," the doctor responded cheerfully.

I found his fixation on "late stage" lung disease, essentially symptoms caused by the much broader exocrine debilitation, frustrating. He went on to explain that, because the lungs are easily accessed (gene therapy is administered by having the patient inhale a substance through the nose or mouth), they present a more "valued venue" for treatment. The almost exclusive focus of research on the, albeit deadly, lung symptoms, rather than on the underlying nutrition-related causes, seemed to me to be a really good example of too little, too late. Furthermore, given my son's diagnosis with "failure to thrive" as a baby, which was caused by his CF-related pancreatic insufficiencies, I knew firsthand the threat posed by a compromised pancreas.

My frustration mounted weeks later when I read about an experiment in England in which healthy DNA was administered via intravenous lipids (i.e., injected into the bloodstream) with the hope that the DNA would eventually make its way to the lungs rather than inhaling a retrovirus carrying healthy DNA directly into the lungs—the mode of transportation being studied in the U.S. By some fluke that the scientists conducting the lipid study later admitted was happenstance, not only had the DNA in the lung area changed (the intended goal of the experiment), but the DNA in the liver and small intestine had changed as well. This was a major revelation to me, and seemed to bode extremely well for eventually inserting healthy DNA into the pancreas, where it is so crucially needed. Yet, to this day, most of the research in the U.S. continues to focus on the lungs as does most of the treatment.

This lack of curiosity about or imaginative probing into underlying contributors or root causes is clearly not the result of limited intellect. Completing medical school is nothing if not a Herculean task. But there are many different manifestations of intelligence. In the late 1990's, I heard a National Public Radio interview with Ikujiro Nonaka, a Japanese academic who specializes in corporate innovation and workers' "intellectual capital." He was the newly appointed "Professor of Knowledge" at the University of California at Berkeley—a pretty cool title! In his interview, the professor maintained that all knowledge falls into one of two categories: **explicit** or accumulated factual knowledge (the kind that computers are used for storing), and **tacit** or empirical knowledge (the know-how that grows out of direct observation and experience).

What these two categories don't appear to include is the unique knowledge that grows out of a person's curiosity and eagerness to solve problems, as well as the drive to go beyond what is already known and find threads of meaning in seemingly unrelated events. I would posit that there is a third category of knowledge that is based, not so much on what is, but on what could be. So many important scientific discoveries were made by individuals who were curious or who paid attention to an unpredicted occurrence and subsequently sought meaning or connections: Newton's apple, Benjamin Franklin's kite, penicillin growing in a dirty petri dish, to name a few. Even Einstein, one of the greatest minds of our time, maintained that "imagination is much more valuable than knowledge." This inspirational drive to think outside the box could be called **inventive** or abstract knowledge—something that would seem to be absolutely fundamental to scientific and medical discovery.

I wrongly assumed that the conventional doctors would display all manner of creative and critical thinking. It gave me a jolt to realize that many of the doctors and even some of the researchers I came into contact with did not possess the same curiosity and drive that, for me, was relentless. The specialists, with their highly sophisticated explicit and tacit knowledge, more often than not seemed to be reductionists with no interest in outside conjecture or invention. This narrow approach leaves little room for cross-fertilization or serendipitous discovery of new ideas.

Further, I had wrongly expected that Dr. Sullivan's professional motivation to cure this horrible disease would equal, if not exceed, my own personal drive, and that this would motivate him to consider the new and unknown approaches that I was bringing to his doorstep. Instead, he accepted Russell's fatal prognosis, leaving all hope of a cure to the promise of medical research. My perspective changed entirely when I recognized that, as Russell's mother, I had a motivation that went far beyond that of any of the professionals to find a solution. This is not a criticism so much as an acknowledgment of the difference between professional and personal motivations. Parents of children with fatal diagnoses are often the ones to explore other options, given their driving force. There is a world of difference between a doctor's motivation that says, "Let's do the best we can, given the child's diagnosis and our (limited) capacity to influence disease progression," and a parent's motivation that says, "If I don't do something else, my child will die."

Even though the CF specialists at both Children's Hospital and Johns Hopkins Hospital would be the first to admit that they don't know how to cure CF or guarantee a long and healthy life for my son, to this day, none of them has shown any interest in how alternative healing approaches may have contributed to Russell's exceptional health rebound as a little boy or his undisputed good health as a young adult. They admit that they cannot explain why he is so healthy where most young people his age with CF are not. Yet they have no inclination whatsoever to ask the all-important question why. They chalk his good health up to the broad spectrum of severity in the realm of CF and are content to stick with their best practices. What makes this situation so unacceptable is the fact that other best practices do, in fact, exist, and many of them have been shown to have quite a significant and positive impact on supposedly untreatable conditions. My beautiful healthy son, who started out life as a sickly baby failing to thrive, is living proof.

The bias against alternative modalities is so entrenched among medical doctors in the U.S. that it is next to impossible for patients to receive any guidance, let alone support, in their exploration of alternative care. Much of this bias stems from the fact that some forms of alternative healing are based on completely different scientific theories and assumptions about how the human body works.

Acupuncture, for example, is based on the belief that a fundamental and universal source of energy follows a system of pathways throughout the body, called meridians, and that this energy can be directly stimulated (to either increase or decrease energy flow, as needed, to achieve a healthy balance) with the use of pressure exerted by fingers or needles at meridian entry or exit points. Conventional doctors seem to find it impossible to conceive of another system at work in the body that has yet to be conventionally vetted and confirmed by their Western peers.

In August 2014, I attended a symposium sponsored by the Maryland-based Life Is Yoga Institute at which a South Korean physicist named Dr. Kwang-Sup Soh presented compelling evidence that a "primo vascular system" comprised of vessels and nodes does indeed exist in the body. He showed us videos of "primo vessels" (or meridians) that had absorbed a blue dye inside the body of live animals. In some parts of the body, these tiny primo vessels traveled along the same pathways as the much larger blood and lymph vessels; in other parts, they traveled in a different direction. Several organs, such as the heart and liver, appeared to be covered with primo nodes accepting the blue dye. Dr. Soh explained that this line of research first began in North Korea in the 1960's, by a scientist who vanished following his outspoken criticism of the North Korean government, which abruptly interrupted his research. Eventually, however, his findings made their way to South Korea (the back story would make a great Hollywood spy tale), and the research was renewed by South Korean scientists.

The video that Dr. Soh presented showed a clear electromagnetic pulsation that was not the stationary "echo" of the animal's steady heartbeat, but instead was an irregular but ongoing and visible pulse that traveled along the primo vessel. He suggested that this physical evidence of a Primo Vascular System comprising "primo vessels" and "primo nodes" was the ultimate proof of the existence of the acupuncture meridians and points as defined by Traditional Chinese Medicine. (The Indian doctors present at our session confirmed that similar pathways and points, referred to as *nadis* and *nodes*, are also recognized by the traditional Ayurvedic medicine and Yoga practices of India.)

As an aside, Dr. Kwang-Sup Soh told us he was a physicist and not an acupuncturist or clinician of any kind. In fact, when asked about his background, he acknowledged that he was only superficially familiar with the practice of acupuncture, having never personally received or witnessed an acupuncture treatment. He was brought onto the research team because of his specialization in optical imaging and access to the original research from North Korea. These now completed findings are being shared across the globe.[2]

A conventionally trained medical doctor from the U.S. has no framework within which to even conceptualize, let alone believe in, *chi* or universal energy. This limitation is ironic given that the theoretical basis of a universal energy system is supported by commonly held electro-magnetic theories that a western-trained scientist would easily support.

Acupuncture is a very sophisticated medical practice that billions of Chinese (and other Asians) have utilized to good effect for thousands of years. It's tempting to make the argument that acupuncture must be a best practice simply by virtue of its extraordinarily long-standing tradition. Surely, if Traditional Chinese Medicine did not have healing properties, the Chinese population would not have successfully grown to the current 1.4 billion people. Herbal medicine's roots also go back at least a couple of thousand years to Hippocrates and Greece (and China), or probably more accurately back quite a bit further to Imhotep in Egypt. By comparison, allopathic or conventional Western medicine as we know it has been around for less than 200 years.

Interestingly, the effectiveness of acupuncture has been valued in the drug treatment field in the U.S. for years as an adjunct to treatment for opioid addiction and is the only known treatment that effectively quells the craving for crack cocaine, according to numerous studies sponsored by the National Institute on Drug Abuse at NIH, starting with research in the 1970's at the Lincoln Medical and Mental Health Center in the South Bronx neighborhood of New York City.[3] Acupuncture treatment of addicts usually consists of stimulating five "auricular" points on the ear to treat the kidney, liver, and lungs (the major organs responsible for clearing toxins from the body), and to alleviate stress and induce calmness.

In my own work in Baltimore's drug treatment realm, I have witnessed many a roomful of addicts sitting calmly with eyes closed, listening to quiet new age music in a darkened room with needles sticking out of their ears at odd angles. In this unusual setting, addicts learn that acupuncture can help them to achieve an enduring inner peace versus the fleeting "feel good" moment offered by illicit addictive drugs. Our own acupuncturist provides acupuncture to male and female inmates experiencing drug withdrawal in the Baltimore City jail, an old and foreboding stone fortress located in downtown Baltimore. If acupuncture were integrated into drug treatment programs and prisons across the country, it would undoubtedly have a broadly-felt positive impact.

As with acupuncture, the other so-called "alternative" modalities of homeopathy, osteopathy, nutrition, and herbal medicine that I used with my son, endure similarly uninformed biases. Medical doctors spend anywhere from six to twelve *years* receiving highly sophisticated training in a specialized technology couched in an ancient language (Latin). The extensive training and long hours of medical school, the need to have visible or at least palpable evidence of illness, the need to have medication-based treatments pass the clinical trial standard—it's all too much to give up.

But how many mothers and grandmothers have insisted over the centuries that chicken soup helps children get over a cold or the flu? "Wives tales" such as this are consistently ignored because there's no "proof." As soon as a study came out declaring chicken soup a winner (confirming what millions of mothers already knew, apart from any precise knowledge of white blood cell migration), doctors were quick to demonstrate their homey wisdom by advising mothers to serve chicken soup to their sick children!

How many mothers have rocked a sick child through the night, only to find the illness gone by morning? How many surgical patients have recovered more quickly under the care of a compassionate, supportive nurse holding one's hand? Yet, it takes a formalized field called Therapeutic Touch, performed mainly by licensed nurses, to legitimize the notion that touching each other is a powerful form of healing. What else heals? Laughter, love, prayer, watching children play, looking at the full moon, hearing babies giggle, swimming in the ocean, walking in the forest in the early spring, the thrill of the Northern Lights, puppies, smelling flowers, holding hands with someone you love, music, unrestrained tears, compassion. The list goes on.

Though I do believe that love and laughter heal like nothing else, I am not suggesting that this list of "lite" healing options should be equated to alternative healing modalities such as acupuncture, osteopathic manipulation, nutrition, or homeopathic and herbal remedies. But this is precisely what the American medical establishment *has* done, giving doctors permission to look down on exquisitely powerful healing modalities with scornful condescension. It's discouraging to watch undeniably intelligent people remain uninformed and respond in such a narrow-minded way.

Doctors' closed minds are also unfair to the millions of Americans who suffer from conditions that cannot be cured or effectively managed by conventional medicine. And if those individuals haven't had an opportunity or the motivation to educate themselves on alternative healing, as I did in my desperation to save my son, they continue to suffer when their pain might be alleviated. The list of prevalent ailments in the U.S. that often don't respond to conventional treatment—arthritis, cancer, and immunodeficiency conditions among them—is endless. Growing numbers of individuals suffering from just these conditions are seeking out different modes of alternative healing and discovering that they help.

None of the hospital-based CF doctors warned against the alternative healing—but they clearly didn't take it seriously. It wasn't just Dr. Sullivan, the CF specialist at Children's Hospital, who scoffed at Russell's alternative healing. Once we started going to Johns Hopkins Hospital's CF clinic in 2008, my beliefs came under more direct attack. Russell was assigned to the director of the CF clinic as his personal doctor, which I appreciated given this doctor's top-notch level of expertise. This doctor was not only a specialist in CF, he was apparently the Michael Jordan of pediatric lung transplants. He had my utmost respect.

Because Russell was age 16 and able to drive himself to appointments on his own, he and the doctor sometimes had conversations without me. This was all part of the plan—that, little by little, my son would take over his own care. After returning home from one of the first appointments that Russell attended alone, he shared that he had asked the doctor about the value of the acupuncture, herbal tonics, and other aspects of his alternative regimen. I was taken aback by this first indication that Russell doubted its value and wished that he had been open with me before consulting with the doctor. Perhaps my fervent belief in alternative healing had convinced him that I wouldn't be open to his questions.

In Russell's conversation with the doctor, the doctor said that he doubted that the alternative healing was of much value, but that it probably wasn't doing Russell any harm. I was furious. How dare the doctor be so cavalier about something he knew so little about? And how dare he undermine our approach so thoroughly?

In order to calm down, I waited until the next day to call the doctor. Russell was at school, and I was at home alone. As soon as the doctor got on the phone, I launched into a tirade (so much for being calm...). I said that his response to Russell's question risked undermining me as Russell's parent and was disrespectfully dismissive of a regimen that I had spent years crafting, with the help of top-notch alternative healing experts. I also underscored that Russell was in very good health as a result.

I asked the doctor, who was still listening politely, if he thought that our collaborative care of Russell, the doctor's and mine, would continue to work if I undermined him in the same way that he had undermined me. I pointed out that, as a teenager, Russell's compliance with the doctor's orders were still dependent on my own faith in the doctor's expertise as well as my respect for his conventional medical recommendations. How would he feel if I casually dismissed the value of antibiotics or enzymes or nebulizer treatments? I ended by stating that either we needed to treat each other with mutual respect or I would be obliged to find another doctor. I added that he needed to make amends in his next conversation with Russell.

When I finished, the doctor apologized. He said that he agreed that we needed to be mutually respectful. He assured me that he would correct his casual dismissal of alternative healing with Russell, and that he would be more careful with his responses in the future. I was stunned by his lack of defensiveness and readily accepted his apology. It had taken me 15 years to get to the point where I had the guts to confront and essentially dress down such a highly respected physician.

In 2012, when Russell turned 20, he transitioned from the pediatric CF clinic to the adult CF clinic, also at Hopkins. His new doctor was the director of the adult clinic, so once again, Russell was lucky to be under the care of a renowned CF expert. However, we were again burdened with a physician who happily acknowledged Russell's excellent health but, at the same time, was not at all interested in contemplating why. I tried approaching the Hopkins doctors one last time following a presentation to parents on current CF research and anticipated medical advances. There was zero interest and, despite all that I had learned, once again, I felt as if I were a sidelined Little League mother speaking with the Baltimore Orioles coach. If it had been up to me at this point in Russell's life, I might have stopped his going to Hopkins altogether. But Russell was a teenager and old enough to take the threat of a CF diagnosis seriously, and he had every intention of being responsible for his own well-being. He wanted to keep going, so I supported his wishes.

Is my story repeatedly dismissed by the doctors because I am "just a mother"? Or is it dismissed because the theoretical underpinnings of acupuncture and energy medicine and other types of alternative healing are simply too big a stretch for a conventionally-trained physician? There are undoubtedly multiple factors. Surely there is a terrible racial and cultural bias in the continued doubting of acupuncture, with its age-old history and continued widespread use in the East. Herbal remedies, documented in the Bible and other ancient scriptures, have also been used to good effect since time immemorial, and yet they continue to be viewed as ineffectual compared to pharmaceuticals—even when those pharmaceuticals are often artificially-contrived siblings of herbs. Homeopathy (in Germany) and osteopathy (in the U.S.) evolved alongside "allopathy" in the late 1800's, and they were both extremely popular in this country until they were outmaneuvered by economically-motivated campaigns sponsored by powerful groups of allopathic physicians. The fact that allopathic medicine "won" that battle does not justify or fully explain the complete dismissal of these strikingly different and promising modes of healing. Has everyone forgotten that both homeopathy and osteopathy were invented by conventionally-trained physicians?

Nutrition, at least, seems to be gaining a small foothold in doctors' minds, as studies are proving the connection between high fat diets and resultant obesity with heart disease and diabetes. How many Americans are helped by alternative healing practices each and every day? Whether it's using Echinacea or vitamin C to ward off an impending cold, therapeutic touch or Reiki to speed up the recovery of post-surgical cardiac patients, and mistletoe extract or *Essiac* tea or more recently Cannabis to treat cancer—alternative practices are gaining popularity because they work.

Despite mounting consumer pressure to integrate alternative healing modalities into the medical mainstream in the U.S., doctors' utter lack of intellectual curiosity is puzzling considering the wealth of knowledge they do possess and their commitment and unique position to help those who are sick. Whatever is behind their close-mindedness, their unwillingness to consider all best practices has been supported by the conservative mainstream medical and academic institutions. Further, this close-mindedness is no doubt abetted in a landscape where any variance from the standard treatment risks an accusation of malpractice. Doctors are also required to limit the services that they will provide to their patients in order to satisfy insurance companies' cost-saving (read: profit-making) mandates.

The parting shot in many of my one-on-one conversations with doctors about alternative care over the years has amounted to "Where's the proof?" Their unwillingness to even investigate other forms of healing is akin to a closed court approach which refuses to recognize any new witnesses. This happens despite the fact that their patient, Russell, is standing right before their eyes, demonstrating the very proof that they claim to need. Furthermore, Russell's dramatic health improvements were supported by physicians' examinations, lab reports, documented growth spurts, and pulmonary function tests over time—documentation that is not considered anecdotal evidence. My son was not simply an outlier, a well child at the far end of the spectrum of CF. He had been a very sick baby, burdened with all the classic symptoms of CF, including steatorrhea, constant sinus and ear infections, chronic cough, projectile vomiting, colic, and lethargy—not to mention the dreaded "failure to thrive." The fact that he went from such poor health to excellent health in a few years' time and has stayed in good health for over two decades should pique any doctor's curiosity.

Admittedly, most of the research on alternative modalities does not follow the research model so highly regarded by Western scientists, and some of the findings have been based on anecdotal evidence. None of this explains, however, why there are so few initiatives to conduct research on the efficacy of alternative healing according to American standards. The most obvious explanation is money. Research requires funding, and much of the funding for research lies in the hands of multi-national pharmaceutical corporations and the National Institutes of Health. Further, research topics are controlled by medically conservative groups such as the American Medical Association and the chiefs of medicine at top-funded university-based health systems.

No doubt the pharmaceutical giants correctly surmise that their financial interests would not be furthered by research into alternative healing. Drug companies have little incentive to back research that might prove, for example, that an inexpensive over-the-counter herbal remedy such as St. John's Wort is both a safer and more effective treatment for mild depression than pharmaceutical drugs requiring an expensive and often lifelong prescription.

Money and bias also explain the paucity of research on alternative healing in the broader scientific community. Even private foundations and government offices that have a mission (or congressional directive) to study new treatments, such as the Cystic Fibrosis Foundation or the National Center for Complementary and Integrative Health at NIH, are at the mercy of those with the fiscal or scholarly muscle to sponsor research.[4] Unfortunately, neither the small alternative remedy manufacturers nor the fledgling professional associations of alternative practitioners in the U.S. are yet in a position to fund high level research.

Consider the Genentech Corporation, which manufactures the CF "specialty" medication, *Pulmozyme.* The cost of one year's worth of this medicine is $36,000 (2015 dollars). A little math gives us a prime example of the unholy intersection of health and money: $36,000 a year multiplied by the approximate 30,000 people in the U.S. with CF, all of whom are now encouraged to use *Pulmozyme* even if (as with my son) their symptoms are not severe—we're talking about a potential of $1.4 billion a year in gross revenue from just one medication. If you have a decent health insurance policy, most of this is paid for by the insurance company. And over time, Genentech has been pressured to subsidize patients' costs. But as a hypothetical, this medication represents quite a hefty return on a pharmaceutical company's original investment in research and development, especially when that R&D was likely sponsored by NIH and the American taxpayer in the first place.

Without question, there has been insufficient research on alternative healing in the U.S. What is sorely needed is research conducted by professionals who have been properly trained in the areas that they are researching instead of superficial judgments and unscientific claims of quackery. We wouldn't give much weight to opinions about organic farming offered by farmers who have only ever farmed using manmade pesticides and chemical fertilizers; so why should we give weight to opinions about alternative healing that are offered by professionals whose training and practice has been limited to conventional Western medicine? To put it another way, we wouldn't expect pulmonologists to study the reproductive system, or dentists to study mood disorders. The researchers of alternative healing need to have at least a basic understanding of what it is they're studying.

Further, the double-blind, placebo-based, randomized, control group "gold standard" clinical trial model of research that was primarily designed to test pharmaceutical products and medication dosages may need to be set aside in favor of more appropriate research models that can measure changes in energy flow, vitality, immune response, cellular-level changes, and so on. European institutions have already been conducting high quality, rigorous research on alternative healing for some time. American researchers need to suppress their "only American" bias for a moment and consider these findings.

Frankly, we need to be more open to everything. In his book, *Spontaneous Healing*, Dr. Weil steps well outside the norm by hailing "the placebo effect" or power of suggestion. What difference does it make, Dr. Weil poses, whether the effect is real by some sort of rigid scientific standard or whether it works because the patient believes it does? In the end, it works, therefore it *is* real. This fascinating mind-body connection needs much more investigation.

In Russell's case, at least during his babyhood and childhood, the mind-body connection or placebo effect cannot be given any credit for his rebound. At that young age, he didn't grasp what his alternative treatments were nor could he articulate (to himself or to me) the changes that were taking place inside of his body. And it didn't matter what I thought about the value of his alternative healing either; he was far too young to be influenced by my hopes or conclusions about its value. What is indisputable is that his body responded and his health rebounded, both of which were thoroughly documented by conventional Western physicians. We already know the less-than-adequate outcome of sticking to conventional medical care alone to treat CF. Though there has been significant progress over the years in terms of extending life expectancy, the typical quality of life and prognosis still aren't great.

If only we had been able to participate in the case study offered by Dr. Jonas under the auspices of NIH to test the hypothesis that alternative healing in combination with conventional medical care is what produced such unusual outcomes in Russell. Unbiased, transparent, and rigorous scientific research, conducted by a cooperative team of seasoned conventional and alternative practitioners, is long overdue.

Chapter 11

The Whole Family

Nothing that is worth doing can be achieved in our lifetime;

therefore we must be saved by Hope.

Nothing we do, however virtuous, can be accomplished alone;

therefore we must be saved by Love.

Reinhold Niebuhr (1892-1971)

"I'M WRITING A BOOK ABOUT RUSSELL, MOM!" I ANNOUNCED in one of the many long distance phone conversations with my mother. "I want to share our success with other parents facing the same kind of thing." I said. Russell was about four years old at the time and in amazing health.

"What about Gus?" she interrupted.

"*What?*" I asked, confused.

"What about Gus?" she repeated. "What about a book or a chapter on him, on what this whole ordeal has been like for him?" I felt a quick pang of guilt—had I managed to neglect my beloved firstborn?

I paused for a second and said, "I'll give it some thought."

My mother wasn't trying to make me feel guilty, she was simply pointing out that Russell's challenges had had a significant impact on all of us, especially Gus. Her comment heightened my sensitivity to the ripple effect, and I decided to include a chapter describing some of the ways in which Russell's diagnosis affected his brother and our whole family.

I stood at the changing table in our bedroom one day, changing Russell's diapers. It had been several months since his surgery. Before putting a clean diaper on, I rolled him over onto his stomach for a quick glance at his lower back. He giggled; he wasn't rolling over on his own yet and enjoyed this new game. As Gus (age five) looked on, I remarked out loud how well his little brother's back was healing and announced confidently that now we could all move forward into a happy (read: carefree) future. Gus hopped onto the bed and started jumping up and down precariously close to the edge so that he could keep an eye on Russell's scar.

"What did they use to cut into his back?" Gus asked with a child's curiosity.

I stifled a cringe at his innocent question, and said, "I'm not sure, probably a scalpel." He immediately stopped jumping and looked at me with a perplexed expression.

"How come you don't know," he demanded, "when you were with him?"

"Dad and I weren't in the operating room during Russell's surgery. We weren't allowed to be there."

His eyes opened wide in shock as he blurted out, "You let them do this to him without even being there?"

"I know," I said quietly, remembering my whispered plea to

the anesthesiologist not to let my son die before handing him over to her just before surgery. "That was hard for me too." It was only then that I realized just how scared and confused Gus must be, given the mix of both too much and too little information.

It's easy to recognize the burden on the child who has the illness and to also assume that the burden extends to the child's parents. But as a healthy sibling, Gus too received a very profound lesson in life's curve balls, as well as our limited ability to protect the ones we love. He knew that he was completely powerless to do anything to "fix" Russell, but it must have been scary for him to learn that we parents were also powerless.

Gus's needs and wants were not merely mildly de-prioritized with the addition of a new baby the way they would be for any older sibling. Because of Russell's medical traumas, the birth of his baby brother turned Gus's whole world upside down. He went from being doted on as the apple of his mother's and father's eyes, to being expected to sustain himself in a semi-independent state while his parents struggled to cope and care for his sick brother. His father and I were often distracted, trying to make sense of the confusing mix of real and imagined threats to our new baby—a baby that was not Gus's to play with or cuddle for long periods, particularly following the back surgery.

I will leave a more accurate analysis to the child development experts, but Gus definitely experienced a broad array of contradictory emotions and psychological twists as a result of being the older and healthy sibling. At times, he was clearly envious of all the attention that Russell received. He might try to distract me when I was giving Russell his medicine or nutritional supplements, or when I was consoling Russell during the long bouts of colic before his CF diagnosis. At other times, Gus was very loving and protective of his baby brother. Photo after photo of them as young boys reveals a big boy with his arm wrapped around his younger brother, the two of them watching a movie or reading a book together, the little one curled up in a cozy safe place.

One time, Gus leaned in close as Russell lay gurgling in his baby slingback chair. When Gus started to tickle Russell's face with his nose, Russell suddenly clamped down on Gus's nose with his sharp baby teeth. Gus yelped with pain! Luckily I was able to come to the rescue within seconds. To Gus's credit, his five-year-old reaction was not to hit his brother or even to yell at him. In fact, once his nose was safely removed from Russell's mouth, and Gus realized he was out of danger, they both found it hilariously funny. This incident, of course, became a part of our family lore—both Russell's biting Gus's nose and Gus's self-restraint!

When I noticed Gus's normally happy demeanor turn cloudy for no apparent reason, I suspected he was feeling neglected and tried to increase the time I spent with him one-on-one. To be honest, I missed him as much as he missed me. He had been a happy-go-lucky little boy before Russell was born. His best friend lived next door on the farm within easy access—I wasn't used to worrying about his happiness. I didn't have the hindsight that I do now, or I might have worried more. But frankly, even if I had been more alert to Gus's burden, I couldn't have done things differently given the overwhelming demands of Russell's healthcare, the day-in and day-out of normal parenting, a faltering marriage, and the feast-or-famine flow of my consulting work.

I distinctly remember thinking how old Gus was at the time of Russell's birth. I felt grateful that he was such a grown-up boy—so helpful, so mature. It took me years to confront the truth that Gus had been a tender, vulnerable, little boy of four when his brother was born, and it only hit me years later when I noticed just how young a neighbor's four-year-old child appeared. The reality is that from the moment of his brother's birth and throughout the ensuing ordeals surrounding Russell's diagnoses with serious medical conditions, Gus had to face issues of life and death that required sacrifice at a very young age. It traumatized him and placed an undeniably heavy burden of worry on him as a child and adolescent that have carried into adulthood.

If Russell's medical appointments were scheduled outside of the school day, Gus came with us. But because of his good health, Gus took a back seat with all of the doctors and alternative healing practitioners except our pediatrician who was, of course, his doctor as well as Russell's. Occasionally, Gus's frustration at being viewed as "low interest" would surface. When the boys and I traveled to Ohio to visit Dr. Fulford, for example, Gus, then age eight, knew this was a momentous occasion. After all, we had flown on a plane and were staying at a hotel just to see this special doctor. Once we landed on the doctor's doorstep, Gus immediately pointed to the long since healed-over scar above his eye caused by a stray ball in Little League, and the resultant stitches.

This backseat status continued until Mary White suggested that Gus begin his own acupuncture treatments at age 11. It was important for him to experience a healer's attentive gaze. He was generally in very good health, but the acupuncture treatments helped him to overcome his lifelong peculiar sleep habits. Even as an infant, he had been a very restless sleeper. The night following his first acupuncture treatment, he slept *just like a baby*—possibly for the first time in his life. In the years that followed, I also took Gus to see several of our other alternative healing practitioners to explore whether he might benefit from their support as well. Some of them were puzzled by these visits since Gus was in such good health, but from my point of view, it was well worth the time and expense. The gesture showed Gus that he too deserved the concern of his mother and the care of our special group of practitioners.

Of course, healthy competition between my sons flared from time to time, as one would expect between brothers. Who could run the fastest (Gus), who could eat the most (Russell), who could do math the quickest in his head (Gus), who could finish reading the longest book first (both of them). They both excelled at checkers, and then at cards, and finally at chess. I stopped letting them win very early on and, once Gus learned to beat me at chess in three moves, I became a bit of a poor sport and stopped playing altogether.

Sometimes, my having doted on Gus as an only child before

Russell was born, gave Gus the clear advantage—he always won the "I'm thinking of an animal..." game. I never quite found the time to teach Russell about the diverse genera of crocodilians or the huge rodents of South America and Australia. (Such important information!) Gus had surely gotten the best of me for the first four years of his life during which he hadn't had to share me at all.

As a little boy, Russell sometimes displayed a careless bravado that was challenging for his older brother to top. The house I bought, after leaving the farm and my marriage, was 100 years old. Because of its age, the boys and I were obliged to get blood tests to check if we had absorbed any lead from the "dust" flaking off painted surfaces. Once at the clinic, eight-year-old Gus balked at the thought of getting a needle stuck into his arm and, frankly, I wasn't thrilled with the idea myself. Russell turned to us with a grin on his face and volunteered to go first. Without so much as a whimper, he climbed into the chair, pulled up his sleeve, and watched with curiosity as the nurse proceeded. He was only three years old. The nurse was shocked. "We just had a child in here that took four of us to hold down while he kicked and tried to bite us. Your kid is amazing!" Russell didn't need kudos; he seemed to know that life will dish out the good and the bad, and he was determined to take it all in stride.

For the most part, our daily lives were decidedly normal when the boys were young. But as they grew older, Gus grew more and more protective, expressing worry about his brother every time Russell advanced to the next phase of boyhood. By ninth grade,

Gus was an emerging athlete. As a young boy, Russell wasn't nearly as tough and muscular as Gus, nor as athletic, and Gus continually worried that Russell could be hurt in sports or bullied by kids on the playground. We were all overly protective of Russell, despite his regained good health.

Even if Gus didn't accompany us to an appointment, as soon as Russell and I returned, Gus would greet us at the door, asking me how it went, what the doctor said, how I interpreted what the doctor said. The lurking dragon of CF was a thoroughly shared burden. As a young child, Russell seemed to be blissfully unaware of his medical issues, even though he was the one with the disease. But Gus would overhear me complain about an appointment on the phone to my sister in Missouri or my mother in Massachusetts, or he would hear me report something new back to Richard, and he would come to me afterwards wanting more detail. Unfortunately, the scant details I was willing to share tended to exacerbate rather than quell his fears. The truth is, Russell's health was the most compelling topic of conversation in our home for many years, with a lingering backdrop of fear.

In some ways, Gus probably needed me even more than Russell did. But I never seemed to have enough time, and neglect of my children was a running theme throughout their childhood. Most of the mothers I knew felt continually torn between job and motherhood, guilty that they could never do enough in either direction. When my marriage ended, I had more time to spend with my kids, but I also had to shoulder the entire burden of day-to-day parenting and the running of a household as well as bringing home the bacon. I wanted to have a career *and* children. It was not an easy balancing act.

By the summer of 2000, Russell (age eight) was reliably healthy, and he was doing well in school. Gus (age twelve), however, had entered the turbulent fast-forward of puberty and adolescence. He and I found ourselves at loggerheads much of the time, over things large and small.

For three years, I had had a terrific consulting gig that was all-consuming, and I rarely took time off just to be with my boys. I was vaguely aware that I was "losing" Gus, but I was too pressured by the constant demands of my job to give it adequate thought. My constantly prioritizing work over my own children's needs must have sent a thoroughly distasteful message to my children. For Gus, this time period undoubtedly revived an imprint from years before, when his needs always came second to his brother's. Luckily for me, he was not willing to lose this fight. He complained bitterly that I was never there, never available just to talk or play games.

In June of that year, the job suddenly ended. Instead of jumping into a search for more work right away, I decided to take time off with my children. I finally faced up to Gus's anger and resentment toward his mother's neglect—neglect that had really started years before, with the loss of his father in his day-to-day life and my need to give Russell a disproportionate share of my attention. For most of that summer, I spent every day with my children. Gus desperately needed me and took to my undivided attention like a duck to water. I knew my children would stop needing me this intensely all too soon and, in retrospect, it was an invaluable opportunity for us to regroup as a family.

Neglect was not the only hardship for Gus; he had to weather constant fears about his brother's well-being and long term prognosis. Russell's sinus surgery at age 12 to remove overgrown nasal polyps was a particularly hellish experience.[1] My sister flew east from Missouri and my brother drove down from Massachusetts. This effort on the part of my siblings may sound a bit excessive for a "simple" surgery, but with Russell's medical history, nothing was ever viewed as simple. The day before Russell's surgery, when I asked Gus, age 16, if he wanted to come with us to the hospital, he turned to me with a hurt look on his face. "Of course I do!" he said, offended that I had even asked.

Russell's surgery went on for hours, much longer than predicted. Around the 4-hour mark, a surgical nurse came out to tell us that there had been a complication. Russell was experiencing intermittent spasms of the lungs and seemed to be having trouble breathing. They didn't know why. The surgeon had had to stop the surgery repeatedly to ensure Russell's safety.

"This is why it's taking so long," she added nervously.

The nurse gave me the number of the telephone inside the operating room and invited me to call at any point to speak with the surgeon. Her suggestion to phone the surgeon in the middle of an operation seemed odd—surely the surgeon didn't need any more distraction. But an hour later I did call to get additional reassurance that Russell was okay. Dr. Peña, the lead surgeon, got on the phone and assured me that he was just fine and that the surgery was going well.

Two more hours passed. By that time, despite the surgeon's reassurance, all of us were a nervous wreck. I suddenly noticed that Gus was missing. He had gone off to the hospital's cafeteria in search of food a while before and still hadn't returned. When I went to look for him, I found him vomiting in the hallway just outside the door of the waiting area. He was a mass of nerves and didn't know what to do with his tension. Then he expressed worry about who would clean it up. I hugged him, took him back to the waiting area, and went off to find someone from housekeeping.

Russell's surgery finally ended after nine long hours. While still in a drugged stupor, he spoke rather unkindly to the surgeon in the recovery unit. Dr. Peña took it in stride. Days later, we learned that the breathing tube had become twisted inside of Russell's trachea, making it difficult for him to breathe properly while under anesthesia. This is what caused him to have spasms during the operation, in turn forcing the surgeon to stop the procedure until each spasm quieted down. It had nothing to do with his CF. This stop and go went on for hours until the hospital's head anesthesiologist joined the surgical team and finally figured out that the tube was twisted. Despite the tube-twisting and inordinate length of the operation, Russell's surgery was a success. In the recovery room, he was delighted to find himself at least temporarily polyp-free.

I relied heavily on Gus as the healthy son and older brother throughout his childhood and adolescence, but I only fully recognized his burden in retrospect. At age 18, as Gus prepared to leave home for college, he spoke of medicine and genetics, and his determination to cure his brother's disease. He didn't end up staying on that career path, but the fact that it was a serious (and breathtakingly noble) goal of his, even for a brief time, reveals how consumed we all were with Russell's well-being.

One Sunday afternoon, when the boys were much older, I found myself alone in the house. Russell, age 17, was at his father's for the weekend, and Gus, age 21, was at his job at a local pizza parlor. I finished watching another sad movie about a sick child who dies (a masochistic pastime of mine) called "I've Loved You So Long" and then found myself standing at the sink washing dishes in slow motion, tears streaming down my face. I was brooding about the depth of my mania regarding Russell's health issues and the extreme pressure it put on Gus to be as perfect and healthy and risk-free as possible. I needed Gus to be my rock. No one else in my life would be able to keep me alive should Russell die young. Only Gus could save me. I vowed to him silently that I would be his rock, if he would be mine. I realized, with considerable relief, that despite some serious adolescent shenanigans, he seemed to be headed in the direction of stable adulthood.

Fallout from his parents' divorce and a genetic predilection toward alcoholism on both sides of the family led Gus down a precarious road during adolescence. But those factors were surely compounded by the pressure, grief, fear, and neglect that he endured as a result of his brother's medical issues. Despite everything, Gus found the courage and determination to turn everything around. Now age 31, he's one of the most responsible adults and loving fathers the world has ever known!

Ironically, Russell is quite possibly the most resilient and carefree member of our family. He didn't gravitate toward teenage rebellion or the risk-taking behaviors of his brother. In fact, he seems extraordinarily grounded in who he is, given his dramatic medical history. By the time he reached high school, Russell was terribly nonchalant, even-keeled, loved to joke around, didn't fret much about life, and took challenges in stride. He knew all about his disease, its potential complications, and the predicted decline and premature death. Yet he was the one who often lightened the mood or reassured me, or his brother, or his father. Russell was just a baby when the diagnoses and spinal cord surgery happened, and he doesn't remember those events on a conscious level and wasn't able to take in how scary it all was in the same way that we three did as witnesses, even though he was the central character. Years later, the rest of us are still recuperating from having been so thoroughly traumatized.

The one time that Russell went overboard in college, he caught flack in stereo. I put him on speakerphone so that Gus and I could talk with him together. I then gave Russell hell in a way that I had never done before. I was incensed that he was putting his life at risk (the incident in question involved far too much alcohol) when I, and so many others, had struggled to keep him from dying all his life. I was both overbearing and just a little dramatic, but perhaps the parents of teens and young adults among you can understand my uncontrolled fury.

I may have been furious, but Gus was terrified. He simply couldn't accept that his little brother had behaved so badly in the context of having a serious disease. For both Gus and me it was a wake-up call. Russell was not a special child who could be insulated from the temptations or foolhardiness of adolescence. He was a regular, flesh-and-blood kid who was capable of making the same stupid mistakes as any other. For his part, Russell was furious that he wasn't allowed to make even one mistake. He stubbornly resisted accepting just how serious the event in question had been, since "nothing that bad really happened."

Russell's well-being was, of course, an inescapable topic of conversation with my closest friends and family members. However, after his diagnosis with CF, most everyone felt very pessimistic about his future, and my quest to save my son was generally frowned upon. People outside of the health professions tend to have a hard time with scary medical topics, and I know that my obsession with my son's health made others uncomfortable. In the early years, when Russell's medical history came up in conversation, acquaintances and strangers alike would become visibly alarmed and the subject would be quickly changed (by me or by them) to something less scary. Sometimes the conversation would stop altogether. These types of reactions taught me to be selective about who to share our story with.

For years following Russell's diagnosis with CF, my mother waited anxiously by the phone at her home in Massachusetts whenever Russell and I had our full-day marathons at the hospital clinics. I wanted the doctors to confirm that my child was doing better with each visit, not reconfirm that this was a temporary delay of the inevitable decline. My mother knew that I would need to call her to unload and get emotional support the minute we arrived back home. As soon as the front door closed behind me, I'd retreat up to my third floor attic office with a cup of strong tea, well out of earshot of the boys, and call her. My mother's retorts always helped me regain my footing, which kept being derailed by the doctors' all-knowing pessimistic stance. "What did they say?" "Well, that's ridiculous!" "Did you ask them *why*?" "Well, *then* what did the doctor say?" "Oh, Liz, *damnit!!*" she'd lament in frustration. Her heart broke with each of my upsetting answers; she was angry that she couldn't protect me from this medical onslaught.

Racking up huge long-distance phone bills in order to bridge the 400 miles between Massachusetts and Maryland, together, my mother and I tried to make sense of everything I was learning. She never once questioned my capacity to grasp highly technical medical topics, and she never poked holes into my sometimes quasi-reasonable contemplations. She never suggested that the alternative healing I was exploring was outlandish or cautioned me that it was unproven. She bought into my bottom line of trying to save Russell's life hook, line, and sinker, and she was a ready sounding board for unlimited conversation.

No one is prepared to suddenly add a massive logistical, financial, and emotion-laden dimension to their lives. No parent prepares for their child to become terribly ill, alerting family and close friends in advance that they will need to step up to spell the parents with respite care, nutritional meals, clean folded laundry, and help with the bills. None of the hospital staff ever asked me how I was doing as Russell's parent or how we were coping as a family. Even when there are no easy answers, questions like: *How* are *you? How are you coping? Are you getting any relief? Do you have adequate support at home? How is your family? I know this is hard...* would humanize the whole medical experience for parents who are at their wits' end.

There was a social worker on each of the specialty teams at Children's Hospital, but their role was largely limited to practical issues and discharge advice. Family counseling should probably be offered to every family with a sick child as an integral part of a patient's treatment plan. In our case, we weren't even aware that we needed professional emotional support until it was too late. Surely someone on the medical team ought to concern themselves with the caretaker's well-being as much as the child's. Their mutual well-being is, after all, thoroughly interwoven.

Our marriage suffered terribly during that first medically-encumbered year but, like many men, my husband was reluctant to go to a counselor. If parental counseling had been a routine component of a sick child's treatment plan, Richard may well have felt obligated (or, more to the point, free) to participate. By the time we met with an actual marriage counselor, it was too late to reverse direction. Intervention by hospital social workers might not have been enough to save our marriage, but it certainly would have helped to curb the stress that we both shouldered.

Fortunately, my husband and I reacted in similar ways emotionally following Russell's birth and diagnosis with spina bifida—both of us wanted to hunker down into the cocoon of our little nuclear family and ignore the rest of the world. I was relieved that we both craved isolation; it would have been a lot harder if we hadn't had the same inclination. Only Mary and Rob, our neighbors on the farm, were welcomed into our home, bringing with them gourmet vegetarian dinners, sorely needed wine, and deeply felt sympathy stemming from their own experience with their daughter's cerebral palsy.

For days, Richard and I didn't answer the phone or return the panicked messages left by distressed family members. We simply couldn't; we didn't know what to say. Plus, every time Richard and I retold any part of the spina bifida saga, we relived the trauma all over again. The birth of a child is supposed to be a time of great celebration for the whole family, and I will always regret the pain and anxiety that we caused our mothers and siblings by excluding them during that time. Graciously, not one of them ever chastised us for our temporary need to be alone. It took a number of days, but once we got over our own shock and regained some equilibrium, we were able to reach out to our family and close friends to explain medical facts and to welcome their sympathy and good wishes.

When Russell was then diagnosed with CF seven months later, Richard and I became reclusive again. Family and friends were once more placed on hold as we struggled to digest this latest threat. After a couple of weeks, when we finally had a grasp of what was going on, we emerged from our protective shell and had a lot of (technical) explaining to do. Our siblings and mothers (both of our fathers had passed away years before) all demanded to know the details surrounding Russell's diagnosis and prognosis. I needed to talk about it, and they had every right to know the facts, but once again, these conversations caused me to relive the nightmares over and over.

My sister, who had always placed such confidence in my ability to overcome odds, was fearful that this would prove to be too much for me. My brother, ever the courageous knight in shining armor, burst into tears over the phone. My grief initiated their grief which then renewed my own. I am sure that more than one family member wondered why we had been so cursed. One serious medical challenge might be explained away. After all, life deals some freakish hands. But *two*? It seemed uncanny. Even today, I feel sheepish when telling new friends about both the spina bifida and the CF. I'm afraid it will sound preposterous, as if I'm weaving a yarn of self-pitying proportions.

When the boys were ages five and nine, the three of us drove north to Massachusetts to spend two weeks on Martha's Vineyard with my sister and her husband, their children, and my brother. It was a gorgeous setting for downtime. On one of our last mornings there, my siblings and I sat together on the beach at Gay Head watching the kids play in the water. All of a sudden, tears started to roll down my cheeks.

"Why is it," I asked my brother and sister, thinking of Russell, "that the biggest tragedy of all is the one that we cannot even speak about?"

My brother leaned closer, gently wrapped his arms around me, and kissed my forehead. "I know," he said quietly.

My sister immediately launched into an aggressive campaign speech about Russell's strong constitution and good health.

"Look at him, Lindsay!" she said forcefully, "I mean, just look at him! He's fine! He's absolutely beautiful and healthy and strong and fine! I'm *sure* of it!"

It's funny how some people respond to feelings of despair. My sister was desperate to imbue me with hope. Her love-filled reassurances were well-intentioned, and her confidence in Russell's rebound was touching, but what I really needed most at that moment was my brother's arms and sympathy. I was feeling terribly sorry for myself, and cheering me up was not the answer, at least not right then.

Although they lived in Missouri and Massachusetts, my sister and brother have also borne Russell's burden through the years. When I worried and leaned on them, they worried too. Having less information than I did often made it hard for them to distinguish between my valid worries and exaggerated alarm. We had been a close-knit threesome as children and young adults, and as aunts and uncles—there are five children between us—we have shared each other's children's successes and challenges on a deep emotional level. In particular, Russell's medical challenges have been difficult all around. My experimentation with alternative healing was sometimes met with consternation by my medically conservative brother while encouraged by my more open-minded sister. As they had during childhood, my siblings continued to be my Rocks of Gibraltar—my sister taking on the role of cheerleader and ultimate judge of Russell's successful claim on life, my brother experiencing concern that was not easily quelled but which validated my own emotional storm.

Other members of our extended family were encountering serious medical challenges of their own. A couple of years after separating from my husband, a niece on Richard's side of the family was diagnosed with Hodgkin's disease. Caitlin was only a teenager. It was impossibly sad and hard on everyone in the family. Though I could easily identify with my sister-in-law's grief, I was most worried about my niece's two younger sisters as well as my aging mother-in-law, who had weathered Russell's two diagnoses and now had to also bear up under her granddaughter Caitlin's tragic illness.

Divorce made contact with my former in-laws tricky. I wanted to respect boundaries and not intrude on Richard's family but, at the same time, my heart wanted badly to reach out to my sister-in-law and my nieces. I also felt the urge to share what I knew about alternative healing, but I didn't want to impose my own beliefs at a time that was already fraught with angst and grief. In the end, because Caitlin was 17 and already making very adult decisions about her cancer treatment, I sent her a copy of *Third Opinion* (a book by John Fink about alternative treatments for cancer), several boxes of *Essiac* herbal tea, and capsules of shark cartilage. I felt compelled to do something. It was an impractical last-ditch gesture filled with love, and it did nothing to help her survive. Not long after I sent her the package, she died following an unsuccessful bone marrow transplant at the painfully young age of 18. It was a lesson for me, that grief and loss are everywhere, spread amongst all of us. As I contemplated my in-laws' tragedy, I realized how very lucky I was to have my son with me, intact, with a future.

Some of my friends were consumed by their own fears when confronted with the news of Russell's diagnoses. One, whom I considered a close friend at the time, became pregnant with her first child late in my pregnancy with Russell. After learning the news of Russell's birth defect from a mutual friend, however, she didn't even call me to congratulate me on the birth of my son. In fact, I didn't speak with her at all for six months and only then when I showed up uninvited at her hospital bedside to congratulate her on the birth of *her* child. She admitted that she had been irrationally afraid that Russell's defect would somehow harm her own child. As with other friends who were nowhere in sight when I needed them most, she is now gone from my life.

People are scared by the tragedies and hard times that others experience. Most of us don't know what to say to help make things better, so we don't say anything at all. Some might think that if they bring up the illness, the death, the hard times, that they'll only make matters worse by harping on a difficult subject. But for those of us who are experiencing a challenge this big, especially parents with a sick child, it's all we think about. We are swimming in it 24/7. You can't make it worse for us than it already is, and talking about it might be just what we need to do.

It's not always easy for the person who is having the hard time to bring it up, however. I didn't want my woes to consume every moment of social contact, and I didn't want to be constantly unloading or leaning on others.

Because of other people's obvious discomfort, and my own exaggerated need to feel that I was coping on my own, I started to clam up. I didn't know how to share my experiences without taking a week to unload, and I worried that friends would regard my sharing as negative, a downer. Plus, my friends had their own challenges—divorce, the sickness or death of elderly parents, financial strain, teenagers in trouble. Just because they saw my motherly burden as harder than theirs didn't mean that my problems always took precedence over theirs.

This clamming up led to my suppression of strong emotions, mainly fear and sadness. I desperately needed support; I desperately needed someone to pull me out of the depths and ask me about it, to really listen to me in spite of the risk that I might go on and on. I needed someone to hold me and love me and still my fears. After the divorce and my mother's death, I didn't know where to turn to get support. My need was huge and it terrified me, so I tamped the emotions down as far as I could and forged ahead, pretending not to need anyone. It was a self-destructive path that led to many years of loneliness. I knew other parents with special needs children; I even had cousins whose children had diabetes, blindness, attention deficit disorder—but I couldn't reach out to any of them. That's unfortunate, since our emotional burdens must have been similar and, undoubtedly, they needed support as much as I did. I had my siblings and a handful of close friends who were incredibly supportive, but even with them I was reluctant to let it all come out. Once I started clamming up, it became harder and harder to open up. It was only when Russell became a decidedly healthy adolescent, who no longer needed intense mothering, that I finally started leaning on others.

Most of the outside world had no idea what it was like to have a seriously ill child. Sometimes I had the patience to explain. When Russell was in nursery school, his teacher asked me if I would like to make a presentation about CF to his class, given the curiosity his schoolmates expressed about the pills he took at mealtime. I was at once both touched and horrified. Obviously well-intentioned, she probably knew very little about CF herself and, thus, couldn't have known how deeply averse I would feel about belaboring a description of this deadly disease and its horrible symptoms—even a watered-down version—to an audience of four-year-olds. My avoidance of discussions about the disease with Russell himself had been conscious and deliberate. I politely told her that I thought such a presentation might be more appropriate when Russell was a little older and more cognizant of his special challenge.

Sometimes, it took more than a simple explanation. Once during negotiations with Gus's private school regarding financial aid, I mentioned the need to keep funds set aside for Russell's potential worsening in the future. It frightened me to express these thoughts out loud, and it upset me to have to share them with someone I barely knew. I was inexcusably rude to the woman on the other end of the phone. A few minutes after I hung up in a huff, she called me back. I had calmed down by then and immediately apologized for my bad behavior. Her compassionate response, that she understood how difficult these pressures must be and that most parents don't have to even consider such a thing, brought me to tears.

Sometimes, frankly, I've been too aggravated to explain or apologize. One time when Russell was in first grade, he began a course of antibiotics to help him get over a sinus infection. I sent in a supply of pills to the school secretary so that she could give him a dosage at lunchtime. While at a work site over an hour away, I retrieved my phone messages during a lunchtime break. There was a message from the school secretary notifying me that she couldn't find a permission form on file allowing her to dispense the medication and, thus, would not be able to give him his antibiotic. I distinctly recalled getting the form in question back from the doctor and was sure that I had handed it in along with all the other start-of-the-year school forms.

When I returned her call, we went back and forth over the phone. I got more and more agitated as she insisted that she could not legally give him his medication. After I hung up (rather more forcefully than necessary), it occurred to me that perhaps she had no clue as to why this little conversation became heated so quickly. The medicine was antibiotics, which plenty of children take from time to time. She may not have known about Russell's diagnosis, or even if she did, may not have known about its serious prognosis.

One of the symptoms of my "rawness" is a knee-jerk aggressive reaction to anything else that gets in the way of my son's wellness. On my end, it was bad enough that he was on antibiotics again, causing me to fret that there was a major flaw in his treatment regimen and that this disease would march on no matter what I did. I also knew that the school secretary was simply adhering to strict legal guidelines. I decided to speak with her the following day to ask for her forgiveness as well as sympathy.

Driving home from work that evening, I vividly recalled the secretary's condescending tone and unyielding position, and became angry with her all over again. As it turned out, as soon as I got home, I found the medication permission forms on the table by the front door right where I'd left them. I turned them in to her the next morning, slinking off with a mixture of guilt and resentment rather than apologizing. Choose your battles, Lindsay, I cautioned myself.

I didn't like the ogre that surfaced so easily. But I also wished that the professionals with whom I frequently came into contact regarding my child had a better understanding of how difficult my burden was. When I was handled with even an ounce of consideration or patience by someone being empathetic, I was immediately put at ease and could return their kindness in like measure.

A few weeks after the antibiotics permission slip incident, Russell had a routine appointment at the CF clinic. Once in the exam room, I picked up a copy of the *CF Network*—a newsletter "written by and for adults with CF." The newsletter contained all kinds of technical information and heart-rending articles written by stoic young people who were determined to live a real life despite their disease. They gave advice about travelling on planes with oxygen tanks, marrying in between hospital stays, losing a dear friend while gaining others even more dear who could handle the seriousness of their condition. In essence, it began to introduce me to both the horrors and sainthood of CF. Out of curiosity, when I got home I called the editor of the newsletter, Larry Culp. He was very friendly and we talked for a long time.

Eventually, my alternative healing story spilled out and Larry noted that, coincidentally, the very next issue of the newsletter was to be devoted to alternative healing. Though I was a middle-aged parent of a little boy with CF, and the articles in the *CF Network* had only ever been written by young adults who actually had CF, he asked me to write an article telling our story. I was excited to be sharing our alternative healing successes with others facing CF, especially given the possibility that it might help someone. In April 1998, Larry honored us with the lead article on the front page, replete with a photograph of me and my grinning six-year-old boy. For weeks after its publication, I received emails from young adult readers thanking me for the story. It was gratifying to learn that some of them had themselves explored alternative healing.

The goal of every parent with a special needs child is for the child, and the whole family, to lead as bountiful and normal a life as possible. Most parents with a sick child probably learn to cope in one way or another, taking on a second job to pay the exorbitant medical bills, securing occasional respite care in order to go out on a sorely needed date with their spouse, joining a support group, or writing about their experience. The luckiest of parents eventually achieve a balance that allows them to savor the good and weather the bad.

Chapter 12

Embracing the Dragon

No matter how far we travel toward a hill,

paying attention to surrounding terrain, stone and flower,

we are unprepared

for whatever lies

waiting

on the other side.

No one will tell you this:

our bodies understand

the dreams that are truly our own.

Jack Crimmins, 1994

from *The Far Hill*

IN OUR EIGHTH YEAR TOGETHER, MY HUSBAND AND I FINALLY went to see a marriage counselor in an attempt to salvage our unhappy marriage. The boys were still very young (ages seven and two), and I was desperate to keep our little nuclear family intact. I distinctly remember one session in the therapist's office during which I sat next to my husband on an uncomfortably short couch. It was my turn to talk. I was articulating, for the first time really, the emotional cost of Russell's CF to *me*. Mixed into my anger and sorrow was tremendous guilt that I wasn't doing enough, that I could *never* do enough to help my son. My words were difficult in coming, but quite heartfelt. I didn't often entertain these types of thoughts; self-pity was an indulgence I could hardly afford, and I was scared that it might become a habit. Even as I spoke, I wondered if the therapist was going to lecture me about my husband's needing me too, but I figured that surely I could be honest *here*, in the therapist's office.

When I stopped talking, the therapist said, "You know, Lindsay, it sounds as if you're trying to slay a dragon." She went on from there, launching into the very lecture I was dreading, but without me hearing a word.

Well, of course I am! I thought bitterly. That is precisely what I'm trying to do—slay the damned dragon. What I couldn't figure out was why she thought this was a bad thing or how my perseverance could somehow be perceived as misguided. In an instant, the marriage counselor lost all credibility with me. It occurred to me, perhaps cruelly, that since she had no children of her own, she couldn't possibly understand the pressure of a child's fatal prognosis. I vowed to avoid the topic in the future.

Now, in retrospect, I do indeed understand the fatal blow that my steadfast battle against Russell's disease and resultant neglect of Richard caused our already faltering marriage. But I also know that I couldn't possibly have taken a different path. My son (both sons) needed me, and at least there were consistent returns for my efforts, in the form of endless exuberant hugs and kisses and the most extraordinary bond a woman can ever experience. Most marriages with a special needs child end in divorce. While it may be true that our marriage was already doomed for other reasons, surely my drive to fight for my son's life made matters worse. She's right, I thought morbidly in the therapist's office that day, maybe it's time to stop kidding myself that salvaging this awful marriage could ever be an equal priority. At my behest, my husband and I separated the next spring.

Years ago, when I began thinking of possible titles for this book, I shared an abbreviated version of the above marriage counseling session to Mary, our acupuncturist. Mary listened in her quiet way until I asked, "Wouldn't that be a perfect title for my book? *Slaying The Dragon...*?" After a slight pause, she said, "What an interesting choice of symbols, Lindsay. You know, in Chinese medicine, the dragon represents the positive power of healing." She thought for a moment. "What about 'harnessing' or maybe 'embracing' the dragon instead of slaying it?" I joked out loud that I liked the idea of harnessing the dragon even better than killing it, since it implied winning some sort of power struggle over such a huge and dangerous beast.

Hearing how silly I sounded, I realized soberly that it would, of course, have to be "embracing." This was my lesson—my Tao of Disease, my Zen of Healing. My challenge has been to confront my son's monstrous disease face-to-face without flinching, genuinely embracing it as part of his life—part of *our* lives. My challenge has also been to accept the power of alternative healing modalities, such as acupuncture, at the same time that I value conventional medical treatment. The support and optimism that I gained from my talks with Mary perfectly exemplify how alternative healing has helped me cope with my fears. I wish all parents confronted with such an overwhelming challenge had this kind of support. That is, in fact, precisely why I felt compelled to write this book.

Russell is now 27 years old, and the positive impact of all the conventional and alternative care he has received over the past two decades is plainly visible. At six feet tall, he's even a wee bit taller than his older brother. His weight fluctuates between 175 and 180 pounds. He keeps his hair short, but likes to grow a beard from time to time. He works out with dumbbell weights and, when motivated, goes jogging. I can hardly believe that this strong and handsome young man is the grown-up version of the sickly little baby who was destined to die young. He is, by all accounts, in very good health and as likely as anyone else to live to a ripe old age. Everyone in our family is hopeful that alternative healing has changed the outcome of his life. Only time will tell.

In 2014, Russell graduated with a political science degree from Dickinson College, a small liberal arts college in central Pennsylvania. Following graduation, his friends scattered to new jobs all around the country, and he suddenly found himself back home, living with his mother, missing his friends, with no clearly articulated career path. This was not a young man's life dream, but instead of complaining, he secured work at a local restaurant and began to save his hard-earned pennies. The following spring, he joined up with his girlfriend who was completing a semester abroad in Italy, and they spent a couple of weeks traveling around Italy and Greece.

When Russell returned home, he wasted no time planning his next excursion—this time a solo trip to South America. He ended up bumming around Argentina and Uruguay for a month, staying at Airbnb instead of expensive hotels, speaking Spanish, being chased by wild dogs, and contemplating the universe. It was a proverbial coming-of-age adventure. When he came home, Russell was a completely different person—a full-grown, independent, mature man with a plan. He moved into his own apartment, went back to working nights at the restaurant, and spent his days writing short stories. A subsequent year of AmeriCorps in California coupled with voracious reading of philosophy books led to graduate school. What he has accomplished and who he has become has made me a proud (and boastful) mother.

Embracing the dragon has not always been easy. Even though Russell's health continued to improve for most of his childhood, the pressure I felt surrounding the threat of his illness was often too much for me—as if a 300-pound gorilla were sitting on my chest, not allowing me to breathe. I was so afraid of the suffering that CF portended—for him, for me, for Gus. The dragon was a pressure I could not have imagined without firsthand experience. For the most part, the fear was sublimated, but it still reared its ugly head from time to time.

Writing this book took every ounce of energy I could muster. It was cathartic at times and delightful fun at others, but overall, reliving all that we went through was quite a challenge. I cried as much as I wrote, sometimes needing to take a break in the middle of a section when the weeping got the better of me. Sharing our story has obliged me to contemplate why I went in the direction of alternative healing. The fact that the conventional doctors accepted the lethal prognosis of CF and dismissed any possibility of hope surely provoked the rebel in me.

But the more important and compelling reason I kept searching for solutions was that I could not bear the thought of losing my son. In the end, it was not courage that drove me to seek alternative solutions to Russell's challenge, it was utter cowardice at the thought of losing him. Love mixed with curiosity and determination drove me to search for additional healers. And once I found them, they convinced me that healing is always possible. They enabled me to reclaim hope.

I used to envy parents with a devout faith in God. I envied the ultimate security that comes with an unquestioning belief that there is a method to the madness which allows children to suffer from genocidal warfare in Sudan or unbearable poverty in Bangladesh or cystic fibrosis in America. I still envy the courage and dignity with which so many parents face their children's progressive CF symptoms. Even now, the fact that Russell has been so healthy—defying all odds—only adds to the tension of waiting for the other earth-shattering shoe to drop.

A number of years ago, I met Andrew Weil, the integrative medicine expert and author, at a book signing. Dr. Fulford, the renowned osteopath I described in Chapter 6, was one of Dr. Weil's heroes. When I whipped out a photograph of Dr. Fulford with his arm around Russell, and told Dr. Weil that I was writing a book about our use of alternative healing, he quickly jotted down the name and phone number of his New York City agent. It took me several days to muster the courage to make the call but I finally did. However, as soon as the agent confirmed that I was not a physician and hadn't discovered the cure to CF, he abruptly concluded that he wouldn't be able to find a willing publisher. My half-baked manuscript went onto the shelf for years and didn't come back down again until Russell left for college, when I had the time to dust it off and complete our story.

Sadly, I have not discovered the cure to CF. I have also had to accept the truth that CF is truly one of the worst childhood diseases. Despite all that we have achieved, the dragon continues to make occasional visits, swooping down close enough to give Russell a little scorching and remind me of its mercurial presence. In his teen years, despite generally good health, Russell had to undergo sinus surgeries to remove nasal polyps. And in 2015, Russell experienced a mild but scary episode of "hemoptysis" when a blood vessel burst in his lungs. He didn't feel it happen, but it was evident when he started coughing up blood. The CF doctor confirmed that hemoptysis is a common enough occurrence in people with CF, even among patients as healthy as Russell. When hemoptysis is major, instead of mild, as it was this time, it is typically fatal. That was quite a scorching.

All in all, Russell leads a normal life, without being inhibited or slowed down. Other than overnights following his spina bifida corrective surgery in infancy and "outpatient" sinus surgeries in adolescence, Russell has never been hospitalized—something that children with CF typically require at least once a year for intravenous antibiotics and several sessions of rigorous chest PT each day. Russell is incredibly casual about his CF and yet admirably responsible for his health. He now schedules his own appointments with the CF Center at Johns Hopkins. He pays for his own health care and recently purchased his first individual health insurance policy. Occasionally, he goes to Melanie Birch for an acupuncture treatment, and he adheres to a daily regimen of nutritional and herbal supplements prescribed by Kelly Dorfman and Claudia Wingo.

We didn't talk about his disease much when he was a child. Instead, Russell and I had lots of talks about his staying healthy and growing up to be big and strong like his brother. Every once in a while, he'd ask why none of the other children he knew had cystic fibrosis or why he had to take so many pills each day. Occasionally, he'd ask me the name of the vitamin he was about to swallow or the purpose of the herbal swill I'd asked him to drink. These were usually casual questions that received casual answers. I hoped that the backdrop of death and dying (i.e., his learning about the more common scenario associated with CF) was way off and that, by the time he figured it out, his physical vitality and emotional confidence would outweigh any fears this information might stir up.

Around age four, Russell began to rebel against chest therapy and the daily supplements that I smothered in baby food in a futile attempt to cover their putrid taste. He must have had an inkling that he was special. For years, he had been going to the hospital clinics for regular check-ups; his friends didn't. He took enzymes with meals and snacks at nursery school, but his classmates didn't. And for a long time he endured the awful burden of conventional chest physiotherapy twice a day; something his brother never had. He began to test out hopeful new theories that "only *babies* take enzymes, only *babies* get chest PT." I had never talked to him about his disease before, but I felt obliged to finally give his specialness a name. I explained to him that he, like some other children, had a condition called cystic fibrosis that would require an extra effort to stay healthy throughout his lifetime. My brief statement satisfied his four-year-old need-to-know, and he went on to endure his treatments with stoic goodwill.

By age six, Russell was indisputably healthy, and the challenge was to keep him healthy. One evening, Gus asked to be excused from the dinner table early to do some homework. I left Russell to finish eating alone for a minute, while I went off to look for something. Before I knew it, Russell had left the table as well, claiming to be finished with his own dinner. I went back into the kitchen only to find his empty plate and pill dish on the counter right next to the trash can. Feeling a little suspicious, I opened up the top of the can and, much to my horror, saw both the uneaten remainder of his meal and all of his pills sitting atop the rest of the trash. Panicked by his self-defeating act of independence, I called Russell into the kitchen and angrily lectured him about the crucial importance of his enzymes and nutritional supplements. I told him, for the first time, that CF was a serious disease and that most kids with CF were chronically ill—even needing to spend time in the hospital. I told him that, if he didn't take his supplements, he would get sick. I said that his good health was very unusual. He sat quietly, admitting to me that he had thrown his pills out on several occasions, because he didn't think he needed them.

The challenge for most children with a disease is to weather their symptoms. In contrast, Russell's challenge was to adhere to a regimen of various treatments and daily supplements that would keep him healthy. His adherence to conventional and alternative treatments was the reason for his good health, but because he was so well, he couldn't fathom what it would be like to be ill. The key to our success was his blind faith in me and the non-conformist pathway I had devised. It was a stretch for a child who just wanted to be like everyone else and, on top of it, assert his independence from his mother. I tried to strike a balance between cooperation and self-reliance. I wanted to support his slow march toward adolescence and eventual freedom from parental rule, and I certainly didn't want him to end up overly dependent on me. But as a child, he didn't have the maturity to make a judgment about the wisdom or folly of his treatment plan. Luckily, he was young enough, and at the same time old enough, to take my admonitions seriously. After our talk he promised to take his pills.

In addition to his two serious medical conditions, Russell experienced a gamut of "normal" health crises throughout childhood and adolescence as children are wont to do. He was extremely allergic to the poison oak that grows all over the southern U.S. and, on occasion, required steroids to quell an especially bad rash. He was also hit in the face by a lacrosse ball when he was 12, while he and Gus threw a ball around at the park without wearing helmets. One of Gus's fastballs hit Russell squarely in the eye, and the force of the ball broke the eye socket bone close to the bridge of his nose and optic nerve. It was a painful injury, but fortunately didn't compromise Russell's vision. (It did complicate his later sinus surgeries, however.)

Then in high school, Russell experienced chronic pain in his ankles and knees after playing basketball. When we went to see an orthopedist, we discovered that he had bone deformities in his lower legs. We opted for no surgery given the doctor's pessimism about the corrective surgery and hoped that custom orthotics and sturdy sneakers would suffice. Later, while on summer break from college, Russell had to have his wisdom teeth removed to make room for his molars. I was always taken by surprise when a health issue unrelated to his two diagnoses claimed our attention.

Eventually, Russell shared with me that he really didn't want to talk with me about his CF anymore or even read about it. It was a depressing subject for him, and he had no intention of allowing his disease to take center stage in his life. He was quite aware of the fact that his good health was a luxury that most adolescents and young adults with CF didn't enjoy; many of them had no choice about whether or not to learn more about their disease—their very survival depended on their knowledge. Russell very reasonably wanted to shut out depressing scenarios that were less and less likely for him as his good health continued.

In 2013, Russell anticipated his first appointment with the Adult CF Clinic at Johns Hopkins Hospital. (As life expectancy has increased over the years, a whole new CF specialization evolved to treat adults.) Up to that point, I usually had asked whether or not he'd like me to go with him to an appointment. Most of the time, he didn't care either way. Since I liked to ask my own questions of the doctors, and so long as Russell didn't care, I typically went with him to his appointments. But this first appointment with the Adult Clinic felt different to him. When I asked whether or not I should go with him, he responded, "Well, that kind of defeats the purpose of the *adult* clinic, doesn't it?" Words of a wise young man. So I didn't go.

On the last day of his freshman winter break in college, Russell attended the first appointment with the adult CF clinic. I waited anxiously at home while he drove downtown to the hospital and back. The appointment took longer than we anticipated, and as soon as he returned, his brother and I jumped into the car with him to take him back to college in Pennsylvania. As soon as we got on the highway, I asked Russell to tell me about his appointment. He started by sharing his PFT scores (pulmonary function tests); they were above the 100th percentile. That was certainly good news. Then he said that the doctor had prescribed *Pulmozyme*, a still somewhat experimental inhaled medication that improves lung function.

I went on to ask other questions and he responded with even more truncated answers. I grew more and more annoyed that I hadn't been there to question the doctors' recommendations myself, and Russell became more and more annoyed with my emotion-laden questions. He finally blurted out, "I don't want to talk about it anymore!" which ended our tense back-and-forth. After a few minutes, he added diplomatically, "We can talk about all of this again when I come home from college next time." Gus then completely changed the subject with an announcement that he had been offered the new job he had been hoping to get. He had been waiting impatiently for our tense conversation to be over to share his good news. All three of us were relieved to stop talking about the CF clinic, and we turned our attention to a happier topic.

When Gus and I returned to Baltimore that evening, I dropped him off at the row house in Fells Point where he lived with friends and went home to scour the Internet for answers. I looked up *Pulmozyme* on three different websites: the National Institutes of Health, the Cystic Fibrosis Foundation, and

Genentech, the manufacturer. I knew that *Pulmozyme* was a commonly prescribed CF medication, but this was the first time anyone had suggested that Russell needed it. I was particularly keen on learning about its side effects. The details given on each of the three websites were almost identical. Side effects included a number of mild symptoms (such as rashes and runny nose) as well as three serious symptoms: loss of voice, chest pain, and difficulty breathing.

While I was reading, I was interrupted by a phone call from the pharmacy. *Pulmozyme* was a very expensive medication, and the pharmacist wanted confirmation that he should fill the prescription before ordering it. I asked the pharmacist to please keep the prescription on file but to wait to fill it until one of us called him back. Russell and I were still in a gray zone in terms of who handled these types of logistics. He carried an insurance card in his wallet and was 21 years old. Legally, he could instruct the pharmacy to fill any prescription the doctor called in. But he still relied on me to complete the footwork involved in health insurance and prescriptions and was somewhat of a procrastinator. It meant that he was unlikely to step in and fill the *Pulmozyme* prescription before I had a chance to explore the medicine's pros and cons and debate with the doctor about Russell's need to take it.

As I sat there grappling with my swirling emotions, I realized that I had come face-to-face with the next dragon: I was no longer in control of my son's health care! Russell was in great health by anyone's standards, including the CF doctor's, and yet that doctor was prescribing a medication that Russell very possibly didn't need (*Pulmozyme*) and which could cause serious side effects. I lamented that if I had been at the appointment, I would have asked the doctor these questions directly. What if Russell accepted all of the doctors' future recommendations without asking any questions? He was an adult now, which meant he was free to make decisions based on his own judgment. He was also free to simply defer to the doctors' judgment and there was precious little I could do about it. I wanted badly to have faith in my son's ability and motivation to ask questions, but I was scared.

I would hate to think that anyone might misconstrue my internal debates as proof that I don't respect conventional doctors or the medical establishment in general, for that would be far from the truth. Modern medicine recently saved my sons' father following a heart attack. It saved the lives of my daughter-in-law and two of my nieces when complications arose during childbirth. Surgery fixed torn tendons in my shoulder and arm, after I was hit by a car several years ago. As a baby, my son benefited enormously from the sophisticated approach and modern tools of pediatric neurosurgery, preventing what otherwise could have been a lifetime of disabilities. And I am grateful that Russell has been under the care of excellent CF specialists who instituted crucial interventions (including enzymes, home nebulizer treatments, and pulmonary function tests) and who continue to keep kept a close watch on him.

No doubt there are as many inept, money-hungry alternative

practitioners as there are flawed doctors in the conventional medical arena. But there do seem to be pervasive themes within each world. The many alternative practitioners we have come to know display endless curiosity about the body's capacity to heal itself. They were drawn to their practices by an open mind, faith in the body's ability to heal, and a desire to empower their patients with self-healing techniques. They have also been willing to consider *all* potential paths to improved health.

My faith in alternative healing has often put me in an awkward position. When we finally found a CF support group a couple of years after Russell's diagnosis, the other parents showed little curiosity about my explorations into alternative healing. I was careful to simply tell them my story rather than suggest that alternative healing might be applicable for their children. But my anecdotes about acidophilus preventing diarrhea while Russell was on antibiotics, or my efforts to feed him as nutritious a diet as possible in anticipation of a long life, often fell on deaf ears. At one meeting, after I complained about the hospital nutritionist's advice to feed Russell a diet high in white sugar, fats, and sodium-laced fast food, one of the fathers piped up, "What's wrong with sugar?" At another meeting, I shared how tired I was and how I felt that I could never do enough. One of the mothers cautioned me not to overdo it. "I slaved in the kitchen for years to feed my boys just the right foods. It's not worth losing yourself over," she testified. She was one of those parents I had been told about with two children with CF, a case in which the previously symptom-free older sibling was diagnosed at age two following his baby brother's diagnosis at birth.

This book is written for parents, but I don't know how many parents will be willing to consider alternative approaches if their doctors remain skeptical. My offers of anecdotal evidence are unlikely to carry sufficient weight. It is difficult for me to understand, though, how it can be less threatening to accept the course of a deadly disease, than it is to consider the possibilities posed by alternative healing. Rather than explore further what we don't understand, even when we can observe the benefits with our own eyes, some of us are content to dismiss the unknown out-of-hand and instead stick with what we know to be "true." A great example of closed minds is the history of hygiene and germ transmission. Early proponents of this theory were assiduously discredited for almost a century—one physician was literally driven mad by the rejection of his life's work. Now, a hundred years later, the use of hygiene to prevent germ transmission and infection is a cornerstone of modern medicine.

What if, when needles are inserted into certain points on my body, the "whoosh" of energy I feel is real? What if the reason that researchers can't find a molecule of the original plant or mineral source in homeopathic remedies is not because there's nothing there, but because what's left is much smaller than a molecule and we don't yet know how to measure it, let alone appreciate the power of something that small? What if what's left is more like a hint or a shadow—enough to direct the body into action, but too subtle for us to yet recognize? What if these remedies do not work in the traditionally understood ways but rather carry some sort of electro-magnetic charge?

What if it's true that had I taken Russell to an osteopath immediately following his spina bifida surgery, he would not have even manifested cystic fibrosis because his internal environment wouldn't have provided the conditions necessary for this particular genetic coding to launch? What if, as many highly reputed physicians who knew him claim, all Dr. Fulford really had to do was lay his hands on people and, using intuition and deep spiritual connections, heal them? What if herbal remedies work precisely because they are made from the whole root or leaf or even the entire plant? What if the CF specialist's reluctance to acknowledge Russell's unique rebound in health is not based on sound scientific judgment, but rather on a reluctance many doctors share to accept a change in the paradigm?

Until the 1960's, children born with CF rarely survived past infancy; most died by the age of two. Russell had a beautiful mass of blond curls at age two, and I was incapable of cutting his hair. My mother-in-law, who loved her grandsons almost as much as I did, facetiously chided me that he looked like a girl. Losing him then would have been akin to losing myself. When Russell was diagnosed in 1993, the CF specialist told me that they hadn't lost a child under the age of 12 in years. The doctor's comment conjured a picture of a long and lanky Russell at age 12, perhaps athletic like his brother, just entering the heady and chaotic phase of adolescence, testing himself in new ways (no doubt testing *me* in new ways...). Losing him then would have broken my heart. At the time of Russell's diagnosis with CF, life expectancy was 29 years, but many children with CF die long before reaching that age. Would my son die at age 15, when he should be playing sports and thinking about dating? Age 21, when he could order his first beer? Age 29, when it's time to fall in love and marry? When is it a good time to die?

Genetic research continues to hold my interest, but I doubt that it will be the key to my son's survival. Altering DNA, nature's most precious blueprint, may well cause more problems than solutions as researchers go up a steep learning curve. Medical treatment can be riskier than the very disease it's meant to treat. My brother-in-law and his wife lost their 18-year-old daughter to Hodgkin's disease, but the ultimate cause of death was not the cancer, it was her body's rejection of a bone marrow transplant. And a friend of mine lost his 34-year-old wife to breast cancer, though it was not the cancer that killed her, it was the deadly impact of chemotherapy on her heart that precipitated her passing. I know that these treatments can be an extraordinary lifeline for some. But when these treatments fail, as they often do, it seems akin to using a B-52 bomber to kill bugs in the garden.

What I most want to share with other parents is that, even in the context of a deadly diagnosis, conventional medicine may not be the only viable option. There is a huge spectrum of healing approaches to consider. Conventional medicine offered my son what it could while urging me to accept the inevitability of his early death. Adding alternative healing to the mix allowed me to reclaim hope. Not a hope stripped of its power and made fragile by caveats and cautionary words: maybe he'll live a little longer, maybe they will discover a cure in time. No. The hope I gained from alternative healing was built upon a mighty fortress of recorded success stretching back hundreds and even thousands of years.

All in all, conventional medicine takes a terribly pessimistic view, focused as it is on disease and illness, and it has left out what I believe to be the most crucial element of healing—hope. My hope was nurtured by the resolute faith our alternative health practitioners had in Russell's body's ability to recalibrate and heal itself. And the improvements they believed could happen *did* happen; the major health rebound they anticipated did slowly emerge.

There will be naysayers: "You shouldn't be making these claims! All those thousands of other parents of children with CF—you're giving them false hope!" My response is unequivocal: I don't believe that there is such a thing as false hope. There is either hope or no hope. It is indeed my wish to give parents hope. Hope is precisely what motivated me to do all that I did with my son; and he is, by all accounts, in excellent health. In fact, there are quite a few doctors who can no longer say with any certainty what my son's long-term prognosis is. Given the supposedly immutable fatal prognosis confirmed by recognizable genetic markers, their lack of clarity is extraordinary.

In my lifetime, I have witnessed many instances where cynics and even well-intentioned realists have criticized others for making predictions based on false hope. How many people anticipated our ability to put a man on the moon before the landing of Apollo 11? How many of us believed we would ever see the Berlin Wall come down? And who in their right mind expected Nelson Mandela to walk out those prison doors one day, a free (and forgiving) man, only to become the first Black African president of South Africa? Every person who imagined these things had hope. Obviously, it took more than hope to make them happen, but hope and a vision of change was at the core. It was hope and unrelenting determination that led to a vaccine for polio and a cure for childhood leukemia, just as it will one day lead to a cure for AIDS and for cancer. Hope, I believe, is *never* misplaced.

As a small boy, Russell loved babies. I don't mean the way many children tend to gravitate toward babies. I mean Russell *adored* babies and could not pass them by. On the street or in the park, he would rush to the side of a baby carriage or mother holding a small bundle of joy just to catch sight of that tiny little mouth and eyes, to toy with those tiny fingers and toes. I sometimes felt regret that he would never have a younger brother or sister to moon over, but then I remembered that he too would be a parent one day. We often talked about him and his brother having children, and I made it very clear that, while having children would be their choice, I looked forward enormously to my role as Granny.

One night, at around age four, as Russell was trying to fall asleep, he confessed to me, "You know, mom, I *love* babies."

"I know," I said.

"I think I'll *marry* a baby," he continued.

"Wow, that really *is* love," I said, stifling a giggle.

Russell is surely made for the role of father, and the dogged optimism that I have reaped from alternative healing has strengthened my vision of him in that role. Not as a new father at 29, whose life is then wickedly swept away before he has a chance to coach Little League. But as an older, more mature father, taking long walks through the woods with his adolescent son or daughter, explaining the meaning of the Universe and the appeal of the opposite sex. A father who sheds delicious tears of joy when *his* child—as an adult—hands him his first grandchild.

Alternative healing allowed me to dream again about a full and long life for my son, and to reclaim sweet Hope.

Afterword

IT TOOK ME 24 YEARS TO WRITE THIS BOOK. I STARTED writing when Russell was around three, jotting down thoughts and feelings that would otherwise have been lost. It was certainly cathartic for me to write it down. The first two chapters literally poured out of me, while I wept buckets. Once I started writing in earnest, I began to remember all sorts of incidents and details that had been stored out of view. I purchased dozens of little writing pads to keep on hand everywhere I went, should another memory suddenly surface. What began as a therapeutic exercise eventually evolved into the idea of a book. I wanted to give other parents what I wished I had had—someone else's story to motivate me, guide me, validate me during a difficult journey. It was difficult to relive the early years each time I did any editing. The truth is, had I had the slightest clue just how grueling writing this book would be (and how long it would take), I would have happily turned to pig farming instead. But now the book is finished and out of my hands. I hope that it helps someone.

The circle of life continues. In the spring of 2014, my beloved firstborn, Gus, informed me that his girlfriend, Katie, was pregnant with their first child. I have never seen him so excited about anything in his life. I too was over the moon—I was going to be a grandmother! As the pregnancy unfolded, in addition to normal prenatal concerns, Katie was tested to see if she was a genetic carrier of CF. We knew that Gus was a carrier from the testing that our family had undergone years before. If Katie was a carrier too, the doctors said that it was likely their baby would have CF. At 20 weeks, we found out with enormous relief that Katie did not have any of the most common CF mutations. We also learned that the baby she was carrying was a boy.

That December, their sweet little healthy baby boy was born. Just as a mother forgets about the pain involved in labor and birth as soon as her baby is placed into her arms, this exquisite addition to our family made all of the mothering woes I had shouldered for two decades completely disappear. Holding the precious offspring of my offspring was glorious. Gus and Katie named their baby Camden Russell, and Uncle Russell eagerly stepped into his new role. Two years later, little Cora was born—finally a baby girl. I felt as if I had died and gone to heaven.

In spite of all our challenges, I've never once doubted that I've been blessed with the most wonderful sons a mother could want. Even as children, my boys amazed me with their understanding of the world around them, constantly making me proud. There was nothing quite so sweet as watching them splash around wildly in the surf, or lean their heads together in concentration over some new Lego project or Magic game. And it nearly took my breath away to see Gus hold his little brother and whisper quiet reassurances after a fall.

Russell worshipped his older brother, imitating everything Gus said or did without the slightest hesitation. Sometimes his fantasy of growing up to be just like his brother got all mixed up with present-day reality. At age three, he suddenly announced to me from the back of the car that he too had played in a soccer game that day, and did I know that he had scored a goal? One day, Russell's adoration became too big to contain. "Gus, I want to be you," he grinned.

When he was little, there were occasional nights when Russell crawled into my bed, seeking solace from a nightmare or wet sheets. Half asleep, I would wrap myself around his warm little body, relishing the fleeting but delicious notion that I could protect my son and keep him safe. At those times, I wanted to fill his reservoir of safe haven to the brim—to protect him from whatever difficulties lay ahead. My own life before children had been incredibly rich, filled with trips to exotic places, loving friends, and a passion for music and nature. It's what I wished for my sons. And yet I knew all too well how life can broadside you when you least expect it. Just like when the bagel became stuck in his craw, I knew there would be other crises and hardships that Russell would have to endure, wholly unrelated to his medical challenges.

Russell has faced life with enviable tenacity and courage. When he was a child, people often remarked that he was an old soul. One evening on the way home, Russell interrupted my conversation with his brother to tell me, "You know, mom, all things can change." "What do you mean?" I ventured, a little taken aback by the enormity of his statement. "You know... All Things Can Change," he responded in that inimitable way of four-year-olds to emphatically repeat themselves word-for-word when you stupidly ask for clarification. I decided to go with the words themselves. It wasn't the first time that Russell sounded like a little Buddha on the mountain. His brother, then age eight, took offense at the simplicity of his statement and began to argue that, "Not everything can change, Russell," suggesting that a dead tree certainly couldn't change, and so on. But Russell stood firm in the essence of his statement, absolutely unwilling to succumb to his older brother's more advanced verbal jousting. Sometimes I wonder if he has been sent here to teach us all—by example.

In the early years, even after his health had rebounded, every time Russell coughed, every time his nose ran, every time he complained that his "waist" hurt, I spiraled downward into a momentary panic, afraid that all I had done would ultimately fail to control the evil that lurked within. Even now, when I see that the tall, strong young man before me has clearly beaten the odds, the dragon is still there, lurking over his shoulder, tugging at my sleeve—a mysterious mixture of threat and inspiration.

I am well aware of the irony that I will not live long enough to fully celebrate my victory. But I cling to a vision of Russell as an old man of 90, rocking on a porch somewhere, overlooking the mountains or maybe the sea, with his older brother at his side. I picture them reminiscing, laughing heartily about the years gone by, and speaking in soft tones about the mother who loved them so.

Chapter Notes

Chapter 1 Our Journey Begins

[1] Russell's medical records document that, as soon as he was admitted to Children's National Medical Center, he received x-rays and sonograms of his spine; sonograms of his head, kidneys, and bladder; and an x-ray video (VCUG) of his urinary tract. His records also indicate that he had received a chest x-ray at the local hospital shortly after we arrived the night before. All of these tests were conducted within 24 hours of his birth.

[2] For the most part, doctors' names throughout the book are real, but in certain cases, a pseudonym is used.

[3] Neural tube diagram retrieved from the University of Michigan Medical School website on January 20, 2014:
http://www.med.umich.edu/lrc/coursepages/m1/embryology/embryo/08nervoussystem.htm.

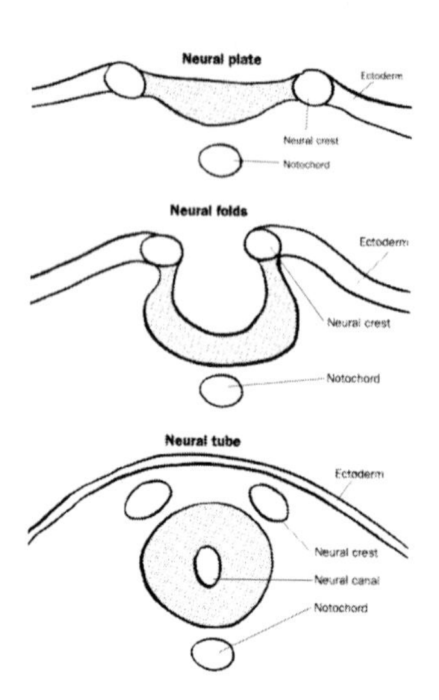

[4] See the Spina Bifida Association's website for more information: http://www.spinabifidaassociation.org/site/c.evKRI7OXIoJ8H/b.8277225/k.5A79/What_is_Spina_Bifida.htm.

[5] Tethered cord diagram, retrieved from the Spina Bifida HQ website on January 20, 2014: http://www.spinabifida.net/6-disorders-associated-with-spina-bifida.html.

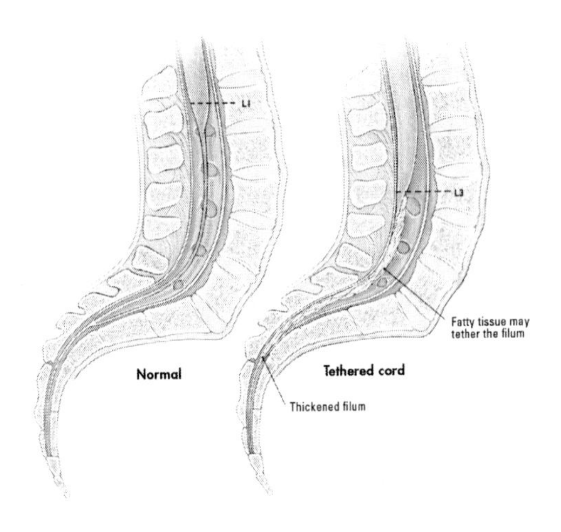

[6] For brevity's sake, Children's National Medical Center in Washington, D.C. is referred to throughout the book as "Children's Hospital."

[7] It is important to note that spina bifida occurs while the neural tube is forming, sometime during the fourth week following conception—i.e., before a woman is aware that she has missed a menstrual period or suspects that she might be pregnant. Therefore it is crucial that women of child-bearing age (and their doctors) know to start taking vitamins with folic acid pre-conception. By the time a woman realizes she's pregnant, it's already too late for nutritional supplementation to prevent this serious birth defect.

Chapter 2 The Crueler Threat

[1] COBRA stands for the Consolidated Omnibus Budget Reconciliation Act, passed by Congress in 1986. This law allows employees who lose access to group health coverage to continue the coverage under the employer's group health plan—at the (former) employee's expense, of course. Each state sets its own limit as to how long COBRA coverage can extend.

[2] HMO stands for health management organization, or a type of combination healthcare-insurance company that provides medical services to patients who are all customers of the HMO and part of the same risk pool.

[3] A normal child's sweat will contain between fifteen and thirty millimoles of chloride per liter. Concentrations of chloride greater than 60 millimoles per liter (mmol/L) indicate a diagnosis of cystic fibrosis.

[4] Cystic fibrosis is an autosomal (non sex-linked) recessive inherited disease, in which a child must inherit a mutation from each parent. Close to 2,000 CF mutations have been identified so far. The mutations inherited from each of the parents do not need to be exactly the same; in Russell's case, he inherited the F508del gene from me, and the N1303K gene from Richard. Neither of us knew anything about the disease having surfaced before in our respective family histories.

Scientists believe that the genetic mutations associated with cystic fibrosis were in existence as far back as 10,000 years ago. See: Casals, T., Vázquez, C., Lázaro, C., Girbau, E., Giménez, F.J., Estivill, X. (1992). Cystic fibrosis in the Basque country: High frequency of mutation delta F508 in patients of Basque origin. *American Journal of Human Genetics*, 50(2), pp.404-10.

[5] Diagram of organs affected by cystic fibrosis, retrieved from the University of Texas at Austin website on January 23, 2014: http://vdsstream.wikispaces.com/Cystic+Fibrosis+and+the+drug+vancomycin.

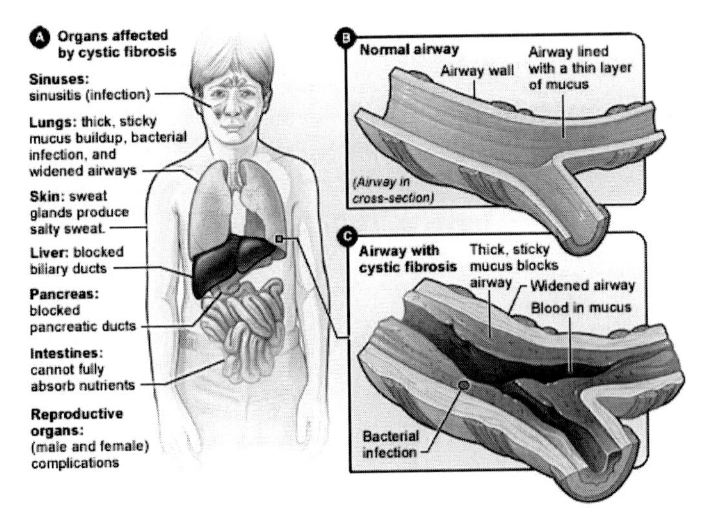

[6] See National Library of Medicine's exhibit, Celebrating America's Women Physicians on the NIH website: https://cfmedicine.nlm.nih.gov/physicians/biography_8.html.

[7] Zeitlin, P.L. (2008). Cystic fibrosis and estrogens: A perfect storm. *Journal of Clinical Investigation*, 188(12), pp. 3841-3844.

[8] Sometime later, Zymase was taken off the market because its higher doses were causing life-threatening colonic strictures in infants. Luckily, by then, Russell was able to swallow his pills whole.

[9] This life expectancy estimate can be misleading. According to the Cystic Fibrosis Foundation website: "Data show that of the babies who are born in 2017, half are predicted to live to be 46 years or older." In other words, based on his year of birth, 1992, Russell has a 50-50 chance of living beyond

29. For more information, visit the CF Foundation's website:
http://www.cff.org/AboutCF/Faqs/#Does_a_lung_transplant_cure_CF?

[10] Much later, I was to learn that life expectancy with CF varies dramatically from country to country. According to a university-based doctor whom I located on the Internet, for example, the typical life expectancy for a person with CF in Scotland around the time of Russell's diagnosis was 50 years. I was amazed to learn that, despite all of our medical sophistication, the U.S. lagged so far behind. I don't know why American doctors aren't compelled to rush right over to Scotland to understand why. Maybe Russell and I will be lucky enough to visit the land of our ancestors at some point in the future, and learn about the Scottish approach to CF for ourselves.

[11] One book I highly recommend along these lines is *When Bad Things Happen to Good People*. Although I'm not particularly religious, the author Rabbi Harold Kushner's questioning of his deep faith in the face of his own son's diagnosis with a rare disease and subsequent early death was sublimely comforting.

Chapter 3 My Transformation

[1] Harris, A. & Super, M. *Cystic Fibrosis: The Facts*, published in 1991 by Oxford University Press (NY).

[2] A routine "complete blood count" (or CBC) reveals the measurements of red and white blood cells among other things. It is a basic blood test that is given to virtually all patients to routinely screen for infections and blood anomalies.

[3] IgE, or Immunoglobulin E, is a type of immunoglobulin or glycoprotein that functions as an antibody, indicating the body's response to an allergen. Russell's level reached a high of 700 U/ml at age two. The normal range of

IgE for that age group is between 0.5 and 12 U/ml according to the lab at Children's Hospital; thus, his level was considered extremely high. His IgE ultimately went down to 160 U/ml by age three and a half (18 months later) without his receiving any allergy-related treatment. By age eight, his IgE was considered completely normal at 166 IU/ml (the normal range of IgE for this age group is 0 – 393 IU/ml, according to Quest Diagnostics Laboratory.

[4] Researchers at Harvard University have conjectured that, although inheriting two CF mutations is lethal, inheriting only one CF mutation was possibly protective against typhoid in certain parts of the world for many centuries. For more information: http://news.harvard.edu/ gazette/1998/07.09/CysticFibrosisG.html. See also: Drayna, Dennis. Founder Mutations. *Scientific American*, October 2005, pp. 78-85.

Chapter 4 Acupuncture

[1] A good resource for learning more about acupuncture is *Between Heaven and Earth: A Guide to Chinese Medicine*, by Harriet Beinfield and Efrem Korngold, published in 1991 by Ballantine Books (New York).

[2] *The Expressiveness of the Body and the Divergence of Greek and Chinese Medicine*, by Shigehisa Kuriyama, published in 1999 by Zone Books (New York), gives a fascinating comparison of these two very divergent Western and Eastern medical traditions.

[3] The Traditional Acupuncture Institute (TAI) was founded by Robert Duggan and Dianne Connelly as the "College of Chinese Acupuncture, U.S."—an offshoot of an existing acupuncture school in England. In 1985, it became the first acupuncture school in the U.S. to be accredited by the

National Accreditation Commission for Schools and Colleges of Acupuncture and Oriental Medicine. TAI later changed its name to the Tai Sophia Institute in 2000, and expanded its mission to include master's degree programs in herbal medicine and the applied healing arts, in addition to the original acupuncture and oriental medicine program. In 2013, the school became an accredited university and was renamed the Maryland University of Integrative Health.

[4] The Dalkon Shield intrauterine contraceptive device caused injuries in many of the women who had it inserted, including sterility and death. It was eventually taken off the U.S. market in 1974 after its manufacturer lost a massive class action lawsuit—one of the largest tort cases in history.

Chapter 5 Homeopathy

[1] *The Homeopathic Treatment of Children: Pediatric Constitutional Types*, by Paul Herscu, N.D., published in 1991 by North Atlantic Books (Berkeley CA).

[2] For NCCAM's perspective, visit the NIH website: http://search2.google.cit.nih.gov/search?q=cache:PkiIUhiY4G0J:nccam.nih.gov/health/homeopathy+homeopathy&site=NCCAM&client=NCCAM_frontend&proxystylesheet=NCCAM_frontend&output=xml_no_dtd&ie=UTF-8&access=p&oe=UTF-8.

[3] See *Homeopathy: Medicine of the New Man*, by George Vithoulkas, M.I.H., originally published in 1979 by Simon & Schuster (New York), for a very readable and condensed look at Dr. Hahnemann's experiments and theories.

[4] The *Materia Medica Pura* is now available in a computerized database that greatly facilitates a homeopath's search for diagnostic clarity and appropriate remedies.

[5] Homeopathic remedies come in dosages that have a number such as 6, 30, or 100 (which indicates how many times a remedy has been diluted and "succussed" or shaken hard) and a letter such as X, C, or LM (or Roman numeral which indicates the ratio of the remedy to the dilutant, usually water or alcohol). In homeopathy, the greater its dilution, the stronger the dosage; thus, 100C (a typically high dosage) is significantly stronger than 6X (the lowest dosage).

[6] See the website of Boiron, the largest manufacturer of homeopathic remedies:
http://www.boiron.com/en/content/download/1758/13415/file/COMPANY_Brochure_2006.pdf

[7] With both of my children, I waited to initiate pediatric vaccines until they were six months old—two months later than was recommended at the time. This decision was based on (1) my belief that the major adjustments that a newborn has to make to being outside of the protective and known womb environment was enough of an initial challenge, and (2) I wasn't excessively worried about their exposure to germs because we were living on a farm and my children had limited contact with the outside world in their first few months. I had to stand firm with our pediatrician, who was uncomfortable with waiting.

[8] We are constantly discovering smaller and smaller particles in our world, such as the *Higgs boson* or so-called "God particle" discovered in 2012.

Chapter 6 Osteopathy

[1] For more information about osteopathy, its origins and uses, see Dr. Fulford's Touch of Life: The Healing Power of the Natural Life Force, by Robert C. Fulford, D.O., with Gene Stone, published in 1996 by Simon

and Schuster (New York).

[2] The following information and quote are taken from Dr. Miller's article entitled "Osteopathy and Chronic Pain," which appeared in the March, 1991, issue of Lifeline, a magazine published by the National Chronic Pain Outreach Association.

[3] See Spontaneous Healing: How to Discover and Enhance Your Body's Natural Ability to Maintain and Heal Itself, by Andrew Weil, published in 1995 by Alfred A. Knopf (New York).

[4] Kemper, K.J. (1996). Separation or synthesis: A holistic approach to therapeutics. Pediatrics in Review, 17:279-283.

[5] Visit Cedars-Sinai Medical Center website: (http://www.cedars-sinai.edu/Patients/Health-Conditions/Spina-Bifida.aspx) for more information.

[6] A fascinating 30-minute video made in the 1980's of Dr. Fulford treating patients and being interviewed by Dr. Andrew Weil is available on YouTube: https://www.youtube.com/watch?v=6cSSVI1zf18.

Chapter 7 Nutrition

[1] Kelly Dorfman authored an impressively comprehensive and thoroughly researched book on children's nutritional issues called *Cure Your Child with Food: The Hidden Connection Between Nutrition and Childhood Ailments.* The book was published in 2013 by Workman Publishing Company (New York).

[2] The human body is filled with bacteria at all times. Antibiotics are prescribed to get rid of a particular bacterium that has over-colonized (such as pseudomonas) or been introduced through a wound (such as

staphylococcus). But most of them kill any and all bacteria in their path, whether good or bad, especially the Augmentin and Pediazole "big gun" antibiotics that Russell was taking. This results in a dearth of good bacteria or probiotics in the "gut" (small intestine) and upsets the normal symbiotic relationship that we have with good bacteria. For more information, see: http://www.sciencedaily.com/releases/2013/01/130109081145.htm.

[3] Kelly suggested that I read *The Antibiotic Paradox: How Miracle Drugs Are Destroying the Miracle* by Dr. Stuart Levy, published in 1992 by Plenum Press (New York).

[4] According to Linda Page, a naturopathic doctor, "Contrary to advertising, dairy products are not a very good source of calcium for people. We don't absorb calcium from dairy well because of pasteurizing and homogenizing, high protein and fat content, and an unbalanced ratio of phosphorus to magnesium. Bovine growth hormone residues, pesticides, herbicides, fertilizers, and additives used in cattle-raising also inhibit calcium and mineral absorption." For more information, see *Healthy Healing (14th Edition)* by Linda G. Page, PhD, published in 2011 by Healthy Healing Enterprises, LLC (Sonora, CA) or visit Dr. Page's website: http://www.healthyhealing.com/.

[5] Irv and Mickey retired in 2002. For the history of the Apothecary (renamed the Village Green), and its evolution into an "integrative pharmacy," see: http://www.myvillagegreen.com/about-us/.

[6] We spent a total of $13,000 on Russell's alternative healing in that first year of exploration (none of it reimbursed by insurance), and my pocketbook was in a continual state of distress.

[7] By age 21, at which point he had probably reached his full height, Russell was six feet tall, placing him in the 80th percentile for height among young men his age

(http://www.cdc.gov/growthcharts/data/set1clinical/cj41l021.pdf). He weighed in at 180 pounds (also the 80th percentile), which together with his height, nearly classified him as *overweight* according to his 24.4 Body Mass Index calculation (http://www.nhlbi.nih.gov/guidelines/obesity/BMI/bmicalc.htm).

[8] Most vitamin and mineral supplements are measured in milligrams (mg.) or micrograms (mcg.) which indicate either its weight or volume (an important distinction). Vitamins A, D, and E, however, are typically measured in International Units or IU—a measurement established by the International Conference for the Unification of Formulas.

[9] For more information about vitamin E, visit NIH's Office of Dietary Supplements website: http://ods.od.nih.gov/factsheets/VitaminE-HealthProfessional/.

[10] Braganza, J.M., Selenium deficiency, cystic fibrosis, and pancreatic cancer. *The Lancet,* Letter to the Editor, vol 326/issue 8466 (p.1238). November 30, 1985. Available from: https://doi.org/10.1016/S0140-6736(85)90761-5.

[11] Wallach, J.D., Ma Lan, Wei Han Yu, Bo-Qi Gu, Feng Teng Yu, & Goddard, R.F. (1990). Common denominators in the etiology and pathology of visceral lesions of cystic fibrosis and Keshan disease. *Biological Trace Element Research,* 24, pp. 189-205.

[12] For more information on Dr. Wallach, see his website: http://www.thewallachfiles.com.

[13] Naturopathic doctors are medical doctors who approach health and medicine from a nutritional standpoint. The Association of Accredited Naturopathic Medical College reports that naturopathic physicians (N.D.) are currently licensed in 17 states in the U.S. and that there is pending legislation to allow licensing in another seven states

(http://www.aanmc.org/careers/naturopathic-doctor-licensure.php).

[14] Fraga, C.G. (2005). Relevance, essentiality, and toxicity of trace elements in human health. *Molecular Aspects of Medicine*, 26(4-5), pp. 235-44.

[15] Li, C., et al. (2007). Selenium deficiency and endemic heart failure in China: A case study of biogeochemistry for human health. *AMBIO: A Journal of the Human Environment,* 36(1), pp. 90-93.

Interestingly enough, thanks to a number of studies that proved the connection between Keshan disease and selenium deficiency, the disease has since been eliminated in China via intensive education campaigns and mandatory selenium supplementation (of mothers and *children*) sponsored by the Chinese government. A longitudinal genetic analysis that looked at maternal selenium deficiencies and the occurrence of genetic mutations as well as CF or Keshan disease in children would be fascinating. A study of the impact of selenium supplementation on both disease and genetics in children would be even more interesting. Down the road, as genetics are better understood and as genetic analysis becomes less expensive and more widespread, perhaps Dr. Wallach will be vindicated.

[16] Cohn, J.R. & Emmett, E. A. (1978). The excretion of trace metals in human sweat. *Annals of Clinical and Laboratory Science,* 8(4), pp. 270-275.

[17] For more information about Dr. Andersen and her medical discoveries, see: http://www.nlm.nih.gov/changingthefaceofmedicine/physicians/biography_8.html.

[18] For a good example of the ongoing chaos, see footnotes on this webpage: http://rnblog.rockwellnutrition.com/2011/01/enzymes-standards-of-measurement/.

Chapter 8 Herbal Medicine and Beyond

[1] According to the March, 1995, issue of *Alternative Therapies*, an integrative medicine project at the Ludwig Maximilian University of Munich was conducting a large, randomized double-blind clinical trial on echinacea's role in the prevention of upper respiratory tract infections.

[2] See *Beyond Antibiotics: 50 (or so) Ways to Boost Immunity and Avoid Antibiotics*, by Michael A. Schmidt, Lendon H. Smith, and Keith W. Sehnert, published in 1993 by North Atlantic Books (Berkeley CA).

[3] Egan ME, Pearson M, Weiner SA, Rajendran V, Rubin D, Glockner-Pagel J, Canny S, Du K, Lukacs GL, Caplan MJ. Curcumin, a major constituent of turmeric, corrects cystic fibrosis defects. *Science.* 2004; 304(5670):600-600.

For another more recent study at Yale, see: Cartiera MS, Ferreira EC, Caputo C, Egan ME, Caplan MJ, and Saltzman WM. Partial correction of cystic fibrosis defects with PLGA nanoparticles encapsulating curcumin. *Molecular Pharmacology*, 2010 Feb 1; 7(1):86.

Chapter 9 The Blending of Two Worlds

[1] Hall, C.W. (September 11, 1996).`Miracle Child' Is Beating the Odds; Rep. Moran's Daughter Cancer-Free After Radiation, Herbal Therapies. The Washington Post: Washington, D.C.

[2] A controlled study or control group study is research which is thoroughly prepared in advance (taking a year or more to prepare) and which compares a group of individuals who receive the treatment being studied with a group of individuals who do not receive the treatment.

[3] Dr. Andrew Weil launched the Center for Integrative Medicine at the University of Arizona, the first such medical education program in the country, in 1994—two years after Russell was born.

[4] In order to manifest the symptoms of CF, and not simply be a carrier, a child must inherit a CF mutation from each parent. In the past two decades, geneticists have discovered that there are over a thousand genetic mutations associated with CF. Together with CF clinicians, they have ranked these mutations according to severity. Through DNA testing, we learned that Russell inherited the most common and one of the worst CF mutations (ΔF508 or F508del) in terms of severity of symptoms and early decline from me, and the third most common N1303K mutation from his father.

Chapter 10 Where's the Proof?

[1] For a cost analysis conducted in the U.S. in 1996, see: http://www.ncbi.nlm.nih.gov/pubmed/13129414. For a more recent cost analysis conducted in France in 2006, see: http://journals.cambridge.org/action/displayAbstract;jsessionid=F137199CB3089D157C134C8B7E609126.journals?fromPage=online&aid=472351.

[2] For anyone interested in learning more about Dr. Soh's research, his review article from 2013 is a good start. See Kwang-Sup Soh, Kyung A. Kang, and Yeon Hee Ryu; "50 Years of Bong-Han Theory and 10 Years of Primo Vascular System," printed in the *Evidence-Based Complementary and Alternative Medicine* journal (Volume 2013, Article ID 587827, 12 pages; http://dx.dol.org/10.1155/2013/587827) published by the Hindawi Publishing Corporation.

[3] See *NIDA NOTES*, Vol. 6, No. 1, Winter 1990/1991 published by the

National Institute on Drug Abuse (at NIH) for information on studies sponsored by NIDA, starting with research in the 1970s at the Lincoln Medical and Mental Health Center in the South Bronx neighborhood of New York City.

[4] See Dr. Donald Liebell's book, *Fighting Back: How to Naturally Overcome the Chronic Effects of Lyme Disease and Other Tick-Triggered Illness… After All Else Has Failed,* (self-published in 2015, available through Amazon.com) for a fascinating analysis of the political and economic strategies used to undermine the popularity of homeopathy in the U.S.

Resources

Note: There are many, *many* books written on alternative healing and on the selected topics below. This list includes some of my favorites.

Acupuncture:

Between Heaven and Earth: A Guide to Chinese Medicine by Harriet Beinfield, L.Ac., and Efrem Korngold, L.Ac., O.M.D. Published by Ballantine Books, New York NY, 1991.

The Expressiveness of the Body and the Divergence of Greek and Chinese Medicine by Shigehisa Kuriyama, Ph.D. Published by Zone Books, New York NY, 1999.

Homeopathy:

The Science of Homeopathy by George Vithoulkas, M.I.H. Published by Grove Weidenfield, New York NY, 1980.

The Homeopathic Treatment of Children—Pediatric Constitutional Types by Paul Herscu, N.D. Published by North Atlantic Books, Berkeley CA, 1991.

Homeopathic Self-Care: The Quick & Easy Guide for the Whole Family by Robert Ullman, N.D., and Judyth Reichenberg-Ullman, N.D. Published by Prima Publishing, Rocklin CA, 1997.

Nutrition:

Prescription for Nutritional Healing: A Practical A-to-Z Reference to Drug-Free Remedies Using Vitamins, Minerals, Herbs & Food Supplements (5th Edition) by Phyllis A. Balch, CNC. Published by Penguin Group, New York NY, 2010.

How To Get Well: Dr. Airola's Handbook of Natural Healing by Paavo Airola, N.D., Ph.D.
Published by Health Plus Publishers, Phoenix AZ, 1974.

Fast Food Nation: The Dark Side of the All-American Meal by Eric Schlosser. Published by Harper Collins, New York NY, 2001.

Cure Your Child With Food: The Hidden Connection Between Nutrition and Childhood Ailments by Kelly Dorfman, M.S., L.N.D. Published by Workman Publishing, New York NY, 2011.

Osteopathy:

Dr. Fulford's Touch of Life: The Healing Power of the Natural Life Force by Robert C. Fulford, D.O. Published by Pocket Books, New York NY, 1996.

Robert Fulford, D.O. and the Philosopher Physician by Zackary Comeaux, DO, FAAO. Published by Eastland Press, Seattle WA, 2002.

Herbal Medicine:

Out of the Earth: The Essential Book of Herbal Medicine by Simon Y. Mills, M.A., F.C.P.P. Published by Viking Arkana, New York NY, 1991.

School of Natural Healing by John R. Christopher. Published by BiWorld Publishers, Provo UT, 1976.

The New Holistic Herbal: A Herbal Celebrating the Wholeness of Life by David Hoffman. Published by Element, Rockport ME, 1983

Cystic Fibrosis:

Cystic Fibrosis: The Facts by Ann Harris and Maurice Super. Published by Oxford University Press, New York NY 1991.

Cystic Fibrosis Foundation

4550 Montgomery Avenue

Suite 1100 N

Bethesda MD 20814

Tel: 301-951-4422 or 800-344-4823 (toll free)

cff.org

Spina Bifida:

Spina Bifida Association
1600 Wilson Boulevard
Suite 800
Arlington VA 22209
Tel: 800-621-3141 (toll free)
spinabifidaassociation.org

General:

Spontaneous Healing: How to Discover and Enhance Your Body's Natural Ability to Maintain and Heal Itself by Andrew Weil, M.D. Published by Alfred Knopf, New York NY, 1995.

Natural Health, Natural Medicine: A Comprehensive Manual for Wellness and Self-care by Andrew Weil, M.D. Published by Houghton Mifflin, New York NY, 1995.

Manifesto for a New Medicine by James Gordon, M.D. Published by Addison-Wesley, New York NY,1996.

Women's Bodies, Women's Wisdom: Creating Physical and Emotional Health and Healing by Christiane Northrup, M.D. Published by Bantum Book, New York NY, 1994.

Third Opinion: An International Resource Guide to Alternative Therapy Centers for Treating and Preventing Cancer, Arthritis, Diabetes, HIV/AIDS, MS, CFS, and Other Diseases (4th Edition) by John M. Fink. Published by Square One Publishers, Garden City Park NY, 2005.

The Last Best Cure: My Quest to Awaken the Healing Parts of My Brain and Get back My Body, My Joy, and My Life by Donna Jackson Nakazawa. Published by Hudson Street Press, New York NY, 2013.

Healthy Healing: A Step-By-Step Guide to Healing over 400 Ailments Through Diet, Whole Herbs, Supplements and Exercise (14th Edition) by Linda Page Ph.D. and Sarah Abernathy. Published by Healthy Healing Enterprises, Minneapolis MN, 2011.

Radical Remission: Surviving Cancer Against All Odds by Kelly Turner, Ph.D. Published by HarperCollins, New York NY, 2014.

Mind Over Medicine: Scientific Proof That You Can Heal Yourself by Lissa Rankin, M.D. Published by Hay House, Carlsbad CA, 2013.

Acknowledgements

Many people encouraged me to share the story of my son's health rebound. Some of them—such as the HMO medical director who repeatedly turned down my requests to cover my son's alternative care expenses while, at the same time, acknowledging that I was saving her company tens of thousands of dollars each year—may regret their encouragement when they see their part of the story in print.

Innumerable people helped me in direct and indirect ways to write this book. I am indebted to all of the conventional doctors and alternative healing practitioners who contributed to Russell's treatment regimen. Though each one deserves recognition, I am compelled to highlight a special few: Mary White, Joel Wallach, and the late Robert Fulford for sharing your profound life-affirming and outside-the-box perspectives on both healing and the causes of disease, and for giving me hope during Russell's early years; Barbara Brynelson for keeping a close watch on both my sons, and for being an M.D. with an enthusiastically open mind; and Melanie Birch, Ioana Razi, Peter Hinderberger, Harold Goodman, Lisa Chun, Kelly Dorfman, Claudia Wingo, Tracey Elizalde, Oscar Taube, all of the doctors in the Spina Bifida Clinic and Cystic Fibrosis Center at Children's National Medical Center, and all of the doctors in the Cystic Fibrosis Center at Johns Hopkins Hospital for your superior skill and unending commitment to Russell's well-being.

Thanks also to the many physicians and healers who have inspired me indirectly through their written testimonials about the truths and mysteries of healing and whose ardent commitment to an integration of best practices from conventional and alternative spheres is bound to pay off. This list includes Andrew Weil, Christiane Northrup, Dean Ornish, the late Paavo Airola, Mehmet Oz, Tieraono Low Dog, the late John Christopher, the late Louise Hay, Patch Adams, Wayne Jonas, Carolyn Myss, Deepak Chopra, Lissa Rankin, Kelly Turner, and James Gordon.

Thanks to my friend and fellow author, Melanie Choukas-Bradley, for your example and endless encouragement. Thanks to Scott Brouard and Bobby Donovan for the ingenious tree house you built for my boys in our tree-less backyard. Thanks to Jeanne Lemkau for your beautiful prose and inspirational example of mid-life rebellion in Cuba. Thanks to David Miller for believing in me and demanding that I write. Thanks to Charlie Fenyvesi, Tim Ward, and all my other friends of the Sugarloaf Mountain Artists and Writers Group for your moral support and inside tips about the writing industry. Thanks to fellow writers Alexandra Viets, Caroline Heald, Nana Rinehart, and Julie Mangin for your insight, practical suggestions, and enthusiasm. A special thanks to Sara Mansfield Taber for generous editorial guidance and scholarly advice; without your enthusiastic support, the book would have remained in the doldrums. Thanks to the late Dick Winslow, editing advisor extraordinaire, for buoying me up with your enthusiasm and confidence in my writing abilities at the very start. Endless gratitude to the late Amy Fink for your master editing and endless support; YOU are the reason I was able to continue to move forward despite the gazillion rewrites (*and* the reason I didn't just use a hyphen!). Bounteous thanks to Sheila Peters, my best friend and cousin, for countless hours of support, shrewd edits, profound inspiration, energy medicine sessions, unwavering faith, and love. Without you, the book would never have seen the light of day. Hugs to Angelina Gallegos, Cynthia Dano, Pat Berger, Irina Bock, Kimberly Kirschner, Julianne O'Brien, Andrea Sexton, Debbie Stuckey, and Kristi Cromwell from the Radical Remission tribe of goddess warriors, who read late drafts and gave me both suggestions and invaluable encouragement. Thanks to Marta Kahn (and Ethel, Lucy, and Stinky) for your stupendous proofreading and friendship!

A huge shout-out to Gareth Bentall and Politics & Prose in DC for the beautiful front cover design and publishing support. Another huge shout-out to Benjamin Jancewicz and Zerflin for marketing, book launch, and printing support, and for being an all-around inspiring artist and entrepreneur!

Thanks to Jennifer for sharing your parallel explorations with your son. Thanks to Teresa for her inspiring parallel journey and love of my boys. Thanks to Mary and Rob for scrumptious vegetarian meals and obscenely good wine, and for the loving support you gave Gus in his early years. Thanks to Roberta and Simon for giving Gus stable ground (and baths) during a fraught time. Thanks to Sue and the crew at the Mount Washington Starbucks for their good cheer and patience with my habit of occupying a bench seat for *hours* at a time. Thanks to Michael for believing in me and helping me to believe in myself.

Thanks to the late Eleanor Beane Winthrop and the late Barbara Butz Lombardi for your open minds, love, and generosity that made my early explorations with Russell's alternative health care possible. Thanks to Ginger Joy, who helped me bring Russell into this world, and Melanie Birch, Gail Kurek, Anjali Sunita, Kristina Auth, Neal Blaxberg, Jenny Ehrhardt, Bill Hixson, Michael and Rachel Baylin, Harold Goodman, Rhonda Bebout, Bill Blaker, Jeannine Olson, and Mindy Lais—my *own* guardian angels, whose love and skill at healing have helped me face life's challenges over the past three decades.

Thanks to my dear cousin Kay Polansky for your sense of humor, astute comments on early drafts, confidence in me as a mother, and unlimited chocolate ice cream. Thanks to the late Joy and David Jenkins for your unqualified love throughout my teens and young adulthood, and your encouragement to write this story down. Thanks to my treasured siblings, Faith and Geoff, for loving my children as you do your own and for your steadfast support. Thanks to Katie for loving Gus and for boldly filling the daughterly gap in my life and for bringing my blessed grandchildren, Camden *Russell* and Cora, into the world.

Lastly, I will be forever indebted to my wondrous sons, Augustus and Russell, for teaching me about true love and healing as no one else could.

Blessings to the universe for sparing us the worst. Namaste.

About the Author

Lindsay Beane, DrPH, is a public health researcher and writer who works to improve the health of urban communities of color. Dr. Beane has helped to secure over $100 million in support of community health centers, hospitals, and social service agencies that serve the poor. She has also co-founded non-profit agencies in Boston and Baltimore to foster the cultural arts, youth filmmaking, and community revitalization. In 1999, Dr. Beane received the *Social Visionary Award* from the Hood College Bonner Scholars Program for her work in the southern Park Heights community of Baltimore, Maryland.

For more information about the author, Lindsay Beane, visit: www.LindsayBeane.com.

Also, see Lindsay and Russell's story posted on the Radical Remission Project website:
http://radicalremission.com/healing-story-of-the-month-march-2017/.

270320-500-1-60W